SO FAR, SO GOOD

Sixty years together in words and pictures

Dear Joan

with love and thanks for your interest

Peter & Susie

PENCROSS BOOKS

38/100

SO FAR, SO GOOD

Sixty years together in words and pictures

Peter and Susan Barrett

Published in 2021 by Pencross Books, Cullompton, Devon EX15 3SR

Copyright © Peter and Susan Barrett

ISBN 978-1-9996480-6-0

Designed by Peter Barrett

Printed and bound in Great Britain by Short Run Press Ltd, Exeter, Devon

INTRODUCTION

Do what you can when you can

On June 18th this year Peter and I will have been married sixty years. We'd planned to celebrate this diamond wedding anniversary with a party here, on the terrace of Little Penn where we've come to rest at this late stage of our lives. Covid 19 has arrived to impose its own rules on all of us. Today, April 29th, we have no idea what the situation will be in seven weeks' time. Although we feel we're most unlikely to catch the virus ourselves – we've been in social isolation since March 16th – no-one can be totally confident of continuing health and life, even in normal times. Lockdown may be completely lifted by June 20th, the date of the possible party. Restrictions may still be in place, or re-imposed. There's no way of forecasting. But one of our life rules has not changed: do what you can when you can.

I can write. I will write the story of the sixty years of our marriage. Peter can paint. He has begun painting the story, in a kind of Bayeux tapestry way. Words and pictures will go together: the third memoir of, and in, our life together. A diamond wedding anniversary present for each other.

View of the Upper Culm Valley from the terrace.
On a clear day, the hump of Cosdon Hill
on Dartmoor is visible on the
distant horizon, forty miles away

We met in 1959, working in the same advertising agency in London. Across the road from McCann-Erickson was the Printers' Devil, a convenient first stop for the agency's copywriters and graphic designers after work.

Work! We just had fun, well-paid fun. It took no time at all to come up with a few headlines and some text – about frozen peas, anti-dandruff shampoo, a building society, a certain make of clock – and then wander along the corridor chatting with the others in the creative department, who might be writing novels or creating fabulously complicated and clever leaving cards, in one small two-person office after another, and then into the library to catch up on the strip cartoons in the Daily Mail, Flook and Rip Kirby.

Peter, working in the large room full of graphic designers at the end of the corridor, decided that the library was the best place to find me alone. We used to say that Flook introduced us.

He'd attracted my attention before this. At the end of the copywriters' corridor there was a small room where the designers went to fill their water jars. I'd noticed a tallish, fair-haired bloke who always wore a blue sweater. (He still wears blue sweaters. It's just the hair that's gone). I was involved with an American anthropologist at the time and not on the look-out for anyone else. But I did like the look of Peter Barrett and said yes when he asked me out. We arranged to meet at 7.30 outside Holborn tube station. We would go to the cinema. We never got there. I waited and waited, for at least ten minutes, even as long as half an hour. I jumped to the conclusion that Peter had thought better of it. I'd been an idiot. Barry was sulking and alone in Hampstead. He hadn't believed my lame excuse of a work party. So I left the tube rendezvous and went to Barry in Hampstead. Peter, I learnt next day, had been on a photo shoot out of London which had gone on and on. There were no cell phones in 1959, just the frustration of missed meetings and long explanations. We fixed another date. This time we met outside Swan and Edgar's in Piccadilly Circus. After the film and a meal, we went back to the spot in Piccadilly where Peter had parked his car. It had disappeared. After some consternation, we realised we'd fallen foul of the recently introduced parking restrictions and the car had been towed away. We had to tramp around dark and deserted docklands to get it released from a pound. Neither of us minded. It was a new experience, something to remember.

Then came Christmas and I was to go home to Devon. Before I went, a large parcel arrived at number 28 Primrose Hill Road, a flat I shared with three friends, Rosie, Pam and Lucy. Under a covering of thick brown paper was a large cardboard box printed with the name of a famous store, Dickens and Jones. Inside the box under layers of tissue paper lay the most garish nightdress I had ever set eyes on. Its bright tangerine flounces were covered in filmy black material. I held it up to a chorus of shrieks. *No, it's not from Barry and no, it doesn't mean anything that this chap called Peter has given me this. I've only gone out with him once and and and …*But they were convinced Peter was serious. There was another present, too: a book called Innocents Abroad. In it the author took a disparaging look at American visitors to Europe. Barry saw a copy. The combination of the two presents signalled the end of Barry's visits to Primrose Hill Road.

Another end looked possible at this time. My mother had a stroke in early January and was in hospital for weeks. I asked for leave of absence and went home. In a way, I loved this escape from London. To have an excuse to be home – to look after my father while my mother was in hospital and then to look after my mother as well when she came home – this was an unexpected present for me. I'd longed for home during my time away at school. A gate at the top of the garden opened onto a corner of Dartmoor. From there, thirty miles or so of gorse, heather, bracken, rushing brown rivers, treacherous bogs and the granite boulders of tors stretched away to the east and the next town. Wandering alone on the open moor was my delight. In those days there were very few cars or people on the moor. I loved being alone. I loved being home. But I thought the price I would pay for this freedom might be too high – it could mean the loss of a promising new friendship. In Peter's eyes I would be off the map. I knew how easy it was when living and working in London to think that the world and life as we knew it ended at Hammersmith.

At this crucial point Peter showed his determined streak. If he wants something, he goes for it. The journey between London and south west Devon took far longer in those days. I was not at all good at answering the telephone and disliked that form of communication. I still do. I loved letter-writing. Peter was not a letter-writer but he took it up, giving it the full treatment: fountain pen, thick paper of the best quality, sheets and sheets of it. His handwriting hasn't changed. On the page it looks as though it's been drawn rather than written. Neat but inexplicable loops make chains across the page, the kind a spider might make if constrained for space. He also came down by train almost as soon as I'd departed. He drew a picture for my mother who was still in hospital, her mouth twisted, her left side paralysed. She came to the conclusion that Peter was the most promising young man I'd brought home.

In March I returned to London and copywriting. In April his sister Jennifer got married. After the reception, we were sitting in the Morris Minor parked in a Dulwich side street. "Will you marry me?" he asked. I couldn't think how to answer this baffling question. After a silence, I came up with "I *think* so." I would tell him in the morning. I was staying in Dulwich with my own sister. I tussled all night. We barely knew each other. Yet from the start it had felt right. We were friends with common interests, as well as –from early on – lovers. Peter wanted to paint. I wanted to write. We wanted the same conditions but not in competition with each other as we might have been were we both painters or both writers.

We married in June, six months after the nightie present. He was 24 and I would be 22 in less than a week. Peter developed an abscess behind a molar a few days before the wedding. He arrived at the church drugged almost to the point of incoherence with pain-killers. As we drove away from the reception, he couldn't stop talking. I sat beside him silently, thinking I'd made a dreadful mistake. Who was this person I'd just married? Half way between Godalming and Dover he admitted that he'd forgotten the car documents and we had to alter course to take in Dulwich on the way. It was a stiflingly hot June day and equally hot that night. The bed in the Dover hotel was too hard for Peter and too narrow. The pillows were wrong. He complained bitterly and slept on the floor. This made him even crosser. If

I'd known then how important a good night's sleep was, and still is, to him, I would have chosen to be the one on the floor. As it was, I was mystified that anyone could make such a fuss about toothache and a hard mattress. It took me years to realise why. He hadn't been to boarding school. And, because I'd been to boarding school, I was a most unsympathetic wife.

I'm always interested to learn how the two halves of a couple come to meet in the first place. Turning the spotlight on ourselves, what were the paths that led the two of us to meet in the library of McCann-Erickson advertising agency?

On asking that question, it becomes immediately obvious that our paths don't start at the moment of our birth. We need to look at the families that produced us. Nature and nurture are intertwined. Why were we the sort of people we were before meeting? What made us compatible? What were our differences? And what have we become, through being together?

The garden gate of Susie's childhood home opened onto a corner of Dartmoor

IN THE MAKING
PETER

Peter was born in September 1935 in Bombay, India. This has always caused a second checking glance by passport officials. He is clearly not Indian. His father, John Barrett, was the son of a Lancashire cattle dealer. John was the adventurous member of the family. He left home as a young man to go to London where he became a chartered accountant. Soon after joining the accounts department of the Army and Navy Stores he had the chance to work for them in India. He and his new wife, Florence Rose Day from Dulwich, sailed out to Bombay. They'd met playing tennis and, in India, they went on playing tennis. Florrie never took up golf and bridge; John was good at both. There was plenty of time for sport, for cocktail parties and dances. Their social life was supported by servants and a salary that met all needs, with enough left over for luxuries.

It was no wonder they talked of their years in India with nostalgia, John more so than Florrie. For him it was a new and exhilarating experience. For Florrie it was her Dulwich life translated to a foreign country, rather too hot for comfort. She talked of her pre-marriage years spent with her brother and two sisters and a large group of friends with the sparkle that John reserved for tales of their life in Bombay.

Peter's interest in wildlife had its origins in his wartime childhood in Wales, inspired most particularly by a visit to the island of Skomer when he was 12

They'd been married just 11 months when Peter was born in September 1935. If Florrie missed her family and home particularly at this time, she never said so. They belonged to a generation that didn't talk about feelings; certainly not the negative ones. Florrie had an amah to help her with the baby. I can imagine her finding it hard to let anyone else look after Peter. The biggest, if not quite the only, story from this time concerned the cobra which was found slithering its way towards the cot where the baby was sleeping under a mosquito net. The amah seized the snake, took it outside and beat it to death. Peter, had he been a few years older, would surely have made a drawing of the snake and kept the skin for future reference.

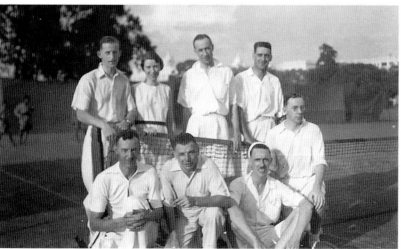

He regrets missing, through lack of memories, those early years in India. Of course, he didn't really miss them. They are part of him. Our development from the first spark of life is an ever-flowing interaction between our genetic inheritance and our environment. Peter's first experiences of the world were in a place of heat, light and colour. The sounds and the smells were Indian. I imagine this was a world of vivid intensity, however much it was filtered by his parents.

In 1938 they left, never to return. From the age of three, Peter absorbed the sounds and smells of England, muted colours, gentle light and moderation in all things. I think he carries within himself a craving for a brightly lit place, his paradise lost, that has seldom been satisfied since, except in Greece. There are places where the scenery excites him – in Africa, America, New Zealand. British landscape he found too tame. In the last ten years or so, Peter has been happily painting scenes in the British Isles – lochs and glens, moors and woods, hedgerows and rivers, trees and fields, beaches and seaside towns, and the wildlife that inhabits these places. Tameness, if that is what it is, has become the attraction.

No longer do either of us want to queue in airports, tramp through acres of transit lounges, spend nights away from our own comfortable bed, our deep bath, and our ever-nourishing view that stretches away down the valley of the river Culm towards Dartmoor. Old age now governs our tastes. It reminds me of Peter's father when we asked him where he'd like to go, now he could decide for himself, Florrie having died. "Bora Bora," he said with enthusiasm. "I've always wanted to go to Bora Bora." We took him immediately to a travel agency, but halfway towards the desk, he decided against the idea. "I'm too old," he said. We, being a generation younger, thought it a shame he hadn't a more adventurous spirit. We now understand.

Peter started recording what he saw when he was very young. Florrie kept a painting of hens he did when he was five or six which she showed me proudly. It was clear that he'd looked at the hens and painted what he saw, rather than taking the easy way out: reproducing an accepted shape, a generic symbol of Hen.

The chickens were in the garden of Nightingales, the cottage the family rented in Hever, Kent. Nearby there was a farm. There was a pond in the farmyard where ducks swam. Men came into the yard holding cocked guns and dead rabbits. Peter drew the rabbits and ducks with the same attention to detail as he drew the hens. But he never drew the men with the guns, or his mother feeding the hens. Up to the recent past, people rarely appeared in his work.

The family had moved to Kent from a flat in Beckenham where his sister Jennifer was born in January 1939. The flat was so small and their life was in such a state of upheaval – the war with Germany had begun – that the new baby was put in a drawer which was stowed out of the way on top of a wardrobe. The story has the same condensed economy as the cobra story. This is the nature of family tales. The details of an incident are trimmed away on each re-telling while the main ingredients must remain the same. The varying perceptions and experiences of different members of the family during the incident are honed to uniformity. The story takes on the quality of myth. "That was when we sheltered from the bombs under the billiard table at Granny's." Listeners are vigilant. No deviation from communal memory – of the story, not of the original incident – is tolerated. They were at Hever when they helped make hay while overhead planes seared the summer sky. The family had escaped the danger of bombs in London only to find themselves in greater danger in Kent. On the ground their life had all the charms of pastoral peacetime – fetching fresh milk from the farm, collecting eggs, packing fruit, raking hay – while above them young English and German pilots ripped the silence with attack and counter-attack. Peter's inability to tolerate the noise of light aircraft overhead dates from the Battle of Britain. Horror of fireworks comes from the bombing in London.

Then – and it was to the whole family's relief – John was seconded to the Ministry of Food which had been transferred to North Wales. After a short stay with John's parents in Poulton-le-Fylde, the family rented rooms in Eglwysbach. Peter remembers the name as the place where he saw a kingfisher flying over the river Conwy.

That first Welsh Christmas his father gave him "How to Draw Birds" by Raymond Sheppard. It is still part of his library of books. Pa Barrett's handwriting is on the fly leaf. *To* (underlined with a decisive upward-slanting slash) *Peter for Xmas 1941* (next line) *from* (next line) *Daddy* (full stop and firmly underlined, with just the hint of an upward curve. This was written in black ink, faded now to dark grey. If we can read character from handwriting, then Pa Barrett was neat and decisive. Sadness catches me. He died in 1991, a widower living in the village down the hill from us, and along the road from our daughter. When I first met him, in London in 1960, I was fascinated by the regularity of his life, epitomised for me by his bowler hat and furled umbrella. It gave me a thrill (by virtue of its unfamiliarity, I suppose) to see him leave the house at exactly the right time each morning, his bowler on his head, smartly tapping his way down Burbage Road's treelined pavement, to catch the train from Herne Hill to Victoria. In the 1960s he was the Chief Accountant and Secretary of the Army and Navy Stores. He returned, at exactly the same time each evening, to toy with the supper Ma had cooked. The boardroom lunches were generous, a far cry from the wartime days of rationing.

Working for the Ministry of Food in North Wales during the war cannot have been too arduous. There may even have been some perks. Peter talks of trips by car, unheard of in my family. After a few months spent in rented rooms in Eglwysbach, the family moved across the river Conway to a house with a big garden in Deganwy. Here Ma got going with hens and a vegetable garden. Onto the table came a relentless supply of the vegetables that can still make Peter blench – swedes, turnips, cabbage, spinach, Brussel sprouts and – a particular horror – leeks in white sauce which he always gagged on. *Eat up your greens, dear. Think of all the starving children in Africa.*

On the other hand, the imaginative way Ma added variety to the menu left Peter with a liking for the sort of food that many people run away from: sheep's eyes, brains, heart and lungs, brawn, soft and hard roe. His favourite Greek meal is spleen tied to a skewer by lengths of intestine and grilled over charcoal.

The locals talked Welsh. There were evacuees, rough kids who chased you if they saw you. It was safer to stay indoors. The rented house was well-stocked with books. He remembers shutting himself away to read tales of African explorers, Jules Vernes' extraordinary voyages and Pinocchio by Antonio Collodio, a strange and frightening story in its original version. There was Romany on Children's Hour, too. When Peter learnt, years later, that Romany was not a genuine gypsy, he felt betrayed – but not badly enough to get rid of the books. He still has two Romany books. Out with Romany Once More (to Peter from Mummy, Xmas 1942) and Out with Romany By the Sea (to Peter from Daddy, Xmas 1942). Who went to the bookshop to buy them? I guess Mummy. The odd thing is that the inscription *from Mummy* is in Daddy's handwriting, while the *from Daddy* was written by Mummy. I can hear Florrie say, in her amused, despairing tones, "Oh, you've gone and got them muddled up, John, I ask you!"

Here's an extract from *Out with Romany By the Sea*.

"After breakfast we went down to the village shop to get our groceries. As I checked off the things I noticed that Tim was eyeing the tall glass jars filled with coloured rock, barley sugar and humbugs, which lined the shelf behind that shop window. So I brought a varied assortment and enough lemonade powder to make gallons of it. Bird-watching is thirsty work. Finally everything was stowed on board the boat and we were ready to bid farewell to the Penfolds."

The author was G. Bramwell Evens, Romany of the BBC, University of London Press, war-time address St Hugh's School, Bickley, Kent. Bramwell Evans knew how to appeal to small boys. Bird-watching Peter knew about. Barley sugar, humbugs and coloured rock were tantalising figments of the imagination. Sweets didn't come off the ration until April 24th 1949 when Peter was 13.

Bird-nesting in Wales taught Peter how to identify the different species of birds. He made friends with a boy who lived nearby and who was, like him, part of the small English-speaking community, a fellow expatriate. They were both at the collecting stage of boyhood – of anything and everything from cigarette cards and stamps to shells, stones and birds' eggs. From April to June they spent as many hours of the day as they could out in the countryside, watching birds and discovering where their nests were

hidden. They would take a single egg from each nest for their collections. They quickly learnt how to distinguish one species from another. If a linnet's egg was needed, it was no good watching and following a chaffinch.

There was another neighbour who shared and encouraged Peter's interest in nature. He lived in a big house on his own and was known as Old Mr. Meacher, although he may not have been old at all. Here beside me as I write is a book that Old Mr Meacher gave Peter. It is a small, dog-eared, thin little paperback measuring four inches by just under six. Its cover announces that it is one of Gowan's Nature Books, costing sixpence, with the title Freshwater Fishes picked out in red on a background which may not have been brown in the first place but has an overall, tobacco-stain tan to it now. Between the title and the authors' names, Walford B. Johnson and Stanley C. Johnson B.A., a disgruntled-looking striped perch hangs among waving reeds. Michael Meacher wrote his name inside the front cover in April 1927. But the book, first published in 1906, has an earlier name crossed out, Evelyn Mathew, The Vicarage 1913.

With this book we are reaching back a hundred years to the antecedents of the present wildlife artists. In one of the first pages there is an announcement about another Gowans and Gray publication:

The Art of Miss Jessie M. King
The work of this talented young artist is now well-known in this country and on the Continent because of its striking originality and the graceful beauty of its design. Her pen-work is shown at its best in a little book of drawings of trees and shrubs called
BUDDING LIFE

which is published at sixpence net (post-free at 7d) and in an edition de luxe at One Shilling net. Her colour work is also shown to great advantage in a charming colour-print called
APPLE BLOSSOM
Which is sold in a pretty paper frame, ready to hang up, at One Shilling net. Its fine taste makes it an ornament to any room, no matter how luxuriously furnished.

I wonder whether Miss Jessie King was happy with the quality of reproduction. Printing methods today do little justice to watercolours. Work in acrylic, a less delicate medium, reproduces better. Peter has never taken to acrylics. He's constantly disappointed by the printed reproductions of his watercolours.

Spurred on by the way he had painted the Hever hens, Ma Barrett hunted down someone to give him private lessons. From the tutor's house in Penmaenmawr, there was a view of Puffin Island, just off the northern shore of Anglesey. It made an ideal subject for painting. Ma's faith in her seven-year-old son's ability was justified when the tutor entered him for a Royal Drawing Society examination and he passed with Honours. On a family holiday in Betwys-y-Coed, they stayed in a hotel which catered for salmon fishermen. Every day the largest catch of the day was displayed on a plate in the hall. It smelt lovely, says Peter. He read up on salmon, intrigued by the way their names and habits and scale patterns alter at different stages of their lives; how the first-year parr have orange-red blotches on their silver scales; how they lose those blotches in the migratory stage when they spend two or three years at sea, before returning at the grilse stage with gunmetal stripes on their silver chainmail. He has an appetite for detail, and still prefers to trust his eyes, what he sees and reads, rather than his ears and the information he's told. In Treardurr Bay, Anglesey, while being urged into the freezing sea by Ma (Come on in, the water's lovely), he asked a man fishing on a promontory the name of the fish he'd just caught. It lay beside him on the rock, its orange and blue striped gill covers attracting Peter's attention. The fisherman said it was a bass. Peter was doubtful and later looked it up in his growing library. He identified it as a cuckoo wrasse.

In our first years in Greece in the 1960s there were all kinds of wrasse in the sea. We preferred to harpoon other fish for supper, bream and mullet for instance. Before they hit the grill pan, Peter would paint an accurate record of them in watercolours. It was these fish paintings which led to his career as a wildlife artist and illustrator.

And it was those early years in Wales that led him to paint fish in Greece.

When the war was over, the family returned to London. They lived for a while in Raynes Park where Peter made friends with local lads who taught him how to kick a football and catch newts and sticklebacks in streams which flowed in those days at the edges of suburbs. Bikes became important. He cycled every day to Sutton to a prep school where he had boarded for the first two terms, an experience he hated. Eventually the family was able to settle in Dulwich. Pa had got his name on the waiting list of a developer who was building new houses in the gaps left by the bombing. When number 114 Burbage Road was ready, the Barrett family moved in. The crater in the garden had been levelled. Now it became a neat lawn, edged with flower beds, with a path that led from the back door to hens, vegetables and the garage. The Herne Hill cycle track lay the other side of the fence, providing open space. Ma was home at last. She never wanted to move from Dulwich again. It was only after her death, forty years later, that Pa was able to leave London. He was 80 when he moved to be near us in Devon. We encouraged him to spread his wings. This was the Bora-Bora incident mentioned earlier. He got as far as picking up brochures. But he had lost his appetite for adventure. An "Edith" who lived in Bath had appeared in his life, or rather, re-appeared. We were startled to learn about this girl-friend from pre-Florrie days with whom he'd exchanged Christmas cards ever since. There were some meetings with Edith and a stay with her in Bath, which startled Jennifer and ourselves until her name faded from conversations.

In Dulwich, in 1945, Peter's interest turned to butterflies. He bred butterflies on the dining-room windowsill, buying the eggs and food plant from a naturalist and broadcaster called L Hugh Newman. (He remembers the names of people influential in his life with ease.) He used to watch Red Admirals and Tortoiseshells emerging from their chrysalises, though never when a meal was in progress. He would not have been allowed to get down from the table to watch. He let these hatchlings go, but at the same time he perfected the technique of catching butterflies with a net. In the same way as he learnt about birds through egg-nesting, he learnt about butterflies through catching them. His boyhood collection, well mothballed in a glass case, hangs on the wall of his studio today, having followed him from place to place over the years. With bones, skulls, feathers, eggs and skins, the collection became a wildlife artist's invaluable resource.

But it was a battle, keenly fought by Ma, to include art in his school life. He went to Dulwich, in the steps of his uncle Charlie. It was not a school that fostered creative talent, save in music. Art lessons ceased when you reached the Lower Fourth. However, the art master Mr Fisher, reportedly stern and humourless, started an afterschool club, which he encouraged Peter to join. He was an associate of the Royal Academy, expert at detailed watercolours of natural history subjects. Later, in Peter's final year at school, Mr Fisher arranged for Peter to go to Chelsea Art School on Monday evenings. It was this out of school teaching that made it possible for Peter to take advanced level Art, as well as Latin, English, History. Out of 1,200 boys only three or four were entered for Art at advanced level.

He avoided the military cadet side of school life by joining the Scouts and working to amass all the badges a Scout could possibly get. He was made a troop leader and at 16 – unusually young, I believe – was made a Queen's Scout. He went on camps in Austria, Belgium, Dorset and Devon. While in Dorset he drew a picture of the Cerne Abbas giant, not understanding why the other scouts were rolling about, snorting and sniggering. He thought the giant was decorated with a crotch to chest pattern of some abstruse Celtic design. His ability to look closely and identify natural detail failed him here. Or was the failure in sex education. Whatever the case, it made a good story when later he was enlightened.

Old Mr. Meacher, then Mr Fisher, followed by R.M. Lockley … these three adults were important influences. R.M. Lockley (nearly always referred to like this, never as Mr. Lockley nor by a Christian name) was a friend of family friends, the Stevensons, who had a son called Bill. Peter joined Bill and his family for a holiday in Wales and they visited the Lockleys who were living at the time in a farmhouse on a cliff in Pembrokeshire. This was in 1948. R.M. Lockley was probably writing at the time "The Seals and the Curragh", his study of seals on the beach below the farmhouse. Peter still has this and a number of Lockley's other books about his life as a naturalist. Reading the Introduction to "Shearwaters" (inscribed *to Peter by Grannie Barrett on his eleventh birthday 1946*), I take a moment to sit back and wonder at this glimpse into life's inner workings. The 12-year-old Peter was inspired by Lockley. When Peter was in his twenties in 1963, he and I searched for an island where he could paint and I could write. We chose an island in Greece; in that choice there was for Peter, I realise now, a faint echo of Lockley and Skokholm. Our Greek island had a population of about 2000. Lockley's Skokholm had a population of one: the writer himself.

"Not everyone," wrote R.M Lockley, *"has the luck to live on, to have an island to himself. It is true that before I could start this ten years' study of the shearwater there were certain formalities to be got through. I wished to settle on this remote Welsh island in order to live simply and undisturbed and alone, but in the company of those things I most cared for: wild birds and animals, wild flowers, the sea and a wide horizon. But Skokholm is no tropic isle where you can walk naked in perpetual sunshine, pluck your food from a bread-fruit tree, and take your drink from a coconut shell. Skokholm's two hundred and forty-two acres lie in the path of a fierce tidal stream and in a latitude subject to heavy westerly and southerly gales. There is little shelter on the island, which is no more than a grassy treeless plateau, rock-bound, and raised about one hundred feet above the sea …*

Elsewhere (The Way to an Island) I have described the work of that first year, and how I found the island, and settled there, was married and became a shepherd, with nothing to think of but my island's precious contents: my wife and home, my sheep and garden, my boat, the sea, the weather, and the wild birds. In this book I tell how, with my wife's help, for we were alone in that second summer, we began to study the birds of Skokholm individually, and in particular the members of the shearwater colony outside our back door." R.M.L.

In 1960, the first year of our marriage, we went for a weekend to Wales. Peter wanted to show me the corner of Pembrokeshire where he had first met R.M. Lockley. We were walking down a lane when we stopped to pass the time of day with a man coming towards us. Extraordinarily, the walker

was Lockley. He asked if we had somewhere to stay. No, we hadn't booked anywhere. Then why not stay at my place, he suggested. He and his wife were living in a large gloomy house called Orielton, in the middle of a wood. They took in paying guests. Lockley was conducting, at the request of Nature Conservancy, a study into wild rabbits, which was published in 1965 as a book: *The Private Life of Rabbits.* Richard Adams found it essential reading when he was starting to write *Watership Down.* In a foreword to a second edition, Adams praised Lockley's book:

"it exemplifies what a work of natural history should be. It is the book of an excellent naturalist, of a keen, shrewd, but feeling mind and above all of a true – that is to say, a sensitive, painstaking and clear-sighted lover of this beautiful earth (well, a lot of it is still beautiful anyway) and of the wondrous works of the Lord." Richard Adams, May 1974.

I wonder what Lockley and Adams would make of the present state of our beautiful earth. To find the wildness he loved, Lockley finally went to live in New Zealand. On one of our trips to see our son in the early 2000s we drove past the turning to the area where he lived. Perhaps we should have taken the time to find him but we didn't want to be pushy, on the basis of such flimsy acquaintance. Now I think he might have welcomed the chance of some nostalgic conversation.

We were by far the youngest in the hushed dining room of Orielton. As I spread butter on my toast, conscious of the loud, rasping sound the knife made, I strained to hear the sotto voce exchanges at other tables, curious as ever to know what's going on around me. Most of the sentences began "Did you see the … ?" or "I saw a …" "We spotted a …" Only then did I realise that I was in the undiluted company of bird-watchers. If Peter wanted to convert me (he says he had no such motive), he failed. I had a lesson in using binoculars in the Orielton woods. But no matter how much I twiddled the knobs, altered the focus, and adjusted the width between the lenses, I never saw a single bird that Peter had patiently pointed out. By the time I was focusing on the right branch in the right tree, the bird had long since flown. That weekend in Wales went down in our memory as the time we met Lockley in a lane, and Peter had a long conversation about shearwaters while staying at Orielton.

Many years later, we went for a weekend to Skokholm. Again, I found myself marooned among bird-watchers. This time, they didn't talk about the birds they'd seen so much as the machinery with which they'd photographed or filmed the creatures. Over the long communal table in the hostel, words and numbers flew back and forth, relating to exposures and film speeds, prices and makes of equipment. I grimly concluded that perhaps this was slightly more entertaining to listen to than the conversation of stamp-collectors.

Peter and I, as I'll describe later, lived and worked on two Greek islands: Sifnos in the 1960s and Amorgos in the late 60s and 70s. In the 80s we returned to Greece to research a book about the landscape, people, flora and fauna of Greece. On the title page of that book there's a pencil sketch captioned: *Manx shearwaters skimming over the waves near an uninhabited island in the Cyclades.* Heading towards that rocky island is Moby Dick, our converted Sicilian fishing boat. Looking at the picture, I can feel once more the buck of the waves as we head across the Aegean. Now I'm travelling again, not towards an uninhabited island, but into a thoroughly inhabited past. The more I travel, the more I see. Time and events overlap, echo, fade – like waves on the sea shore. I'm writing this memoir with Covid 19 hovering invisibly outside my study window and our lockdown door. Meanwhile, in his studio at the far end of the house, Peter is painting a picture that will include all the key people and places in our lives together, managing to do this in oils in scenes the size of postage stamps. How did we come to this point? And who on earth, beside ourselves, will be interested? Perhaps it may survive as a historical document describing a way of life that was possible in the marvellous interval we've been so lucky to inhabit. A childhood, before and during a war in which we didn't have to fight; growing up in a world that was emerging with optimism from dark days of rationing; young adulthood in a decade full of promise; and then a life of freedom to do what we could, when we could.

The present pandemic is likely to have put an end to that period. Whatever comes next will give the lives we've led the gloss of profound nostalgia.

The difficulty with embarking on this memoir comes from the amount of material and the myriad pathways that open up at every turn. This morning

Peter was describing his maternal grandfather. Yesterday it was his naval National Service that he was remembering for me. How can I do justice to these influences and experiences when I didn't live them myself? It's not possible. I can only give a partial view, filtered through my own influences and experiences. Peter's pre-marriage life comes to the page through the style I've developed as a writer. If he were writing this, it would be quite different.

I have the facts, though. Over the years, scraps of information about Peter's life up to 1960 have been scattered through our conversations. I knew its trajectory and content. However, for the purpose of this memoir, I've been eliciting more details from him, almost as though he were a counselling client of mine or someone I might put in a book. Beside me today I have a timeline written down and incidents freshened up. My focus is on finding the origins of his childhood determination to become an artist. There were no artists in his family to encourage this idea.

At breakfast Peter demurred. "My mother, though! She used to paint. She encouraged me."

I never saw anything she painted. Had he? The answer was no. But we remembered her coming to us with a children's story she'd written. She hoped Peter would illustrate it and get it published. But you need luck as well as talent and certainly more of both than just hopes. Peter benefited from her unfulfilled dreams. She helped him become the creative artist she would never be.

As for Peter's father, his overriding hope was that Peter would earn a living in some steady way, preferably an office job with a regular salary and a pension. Perhaps he'd become an estate agent, helped along by Dick Talbot, a good friend of the family. Although he knew perfectly well that Peter would never follow him into accountancy, he arranged for Peter to work as a cashier in the menswear department of the Army and Navy Store during the hiatus between leaving school and starting his National Service.

For six weeks, Peter occupied the payment booth in a corner of the menswear department on the third floor. The suave sales staff would guide customers to Peter in his booth. *"This way, if you please, sir."* Payment would be made, mostly in cash, change given, and a note made of the transaction in a ledger. This hurdle passed, Peter would wrap the invoice around the cash and pop it in a brass cylinder, which he'd send shooting on its mysterious track to wherever it had to go. At the end of the day, all the cashiers assembled in the basement where Peter's father presided. The books had to be balanced. This was a challenge. Peter had failed to get maths at Ordinary Level, although he had first taken and passed the exam at an age deemed too young to count. He says he did get better at addition and subtraction during his time in his booth. But it was *"terribly boring."* In describing his early years as an adult, there is a kind of graph tracking the degrees of boredom, going from a plain boring, through very boring to terribly boring.

At school he'd joined the Boy Scouts to avoid the alternative, which was becoming an army, air force or naval cadet. This choice paid dividends through his life. Many is the time we've thanked his Scout training. But it caused a few difficulties for him as a school leaver. He was outside the mainstream. The majority of those starting their National Service, still mandatory at the time, had been in the cadets at school in one of the armed forces. Now Peter had to choose. He didn't want to have anything to do with explosions and planes, having had enough of these in the war. He chose the navy.

First, he had to join the RNVR by signing on a ship moored in the Thames, *HMS Discovery*. After a short wait, he'd be summoned for a week's training on an aircraft carrier in Portland harbour, *HMS Indefatigable*. He would have to travel in uniform. When the summons came, the family was on holiday in Port Gaverne, Cornwall. Peter struggled into his uniform in the hotel bedroom, with no idea how it should be worn. A school naval cadet would have learnt the intricate ways of putting on the uniform. For a Boy Scout, the bellbottomed trousers presented no trouble. It was the layers from the waist up which posed a problem. First came the white, square-necked, short-sleeved linen top. Over that the tight, navy blue sweater was wriggled into. Somehow connected to these garments was a flap which would hang at the back of the neck. Over that flap another, separate flap had to be added. This one bore three very important stripes, symbolising Nelson's three great sea battles, the Battles of the Nile, Copenhagen and Trafalgar. Once the flaps were in place, a kind of scarf had to be worn around the neck, tucked under the collar and tied in a particular knot in the centre of the chest. Peter felt like a poorly dressed scarecrow who'd be severely reprimanded for bringing the Royal Navy into disrepute.

"That's the hotel," said Peter many years later. We were on our way to Port Isaac where we'd bought a house in the harbour. Back in 1953 and wearing his puzzling uniform in what he suspected was the wrong way, he was driven by Pa from Port Gaverne to Bodmin station to catch the train to Portland After his week's training on *Indefatigable*, he spent the wait for call-up in the Army and Navy payment booth with lunchtimes spent eating his midday sandwich in St James' Park, watching the ducks. After six weeks he began his National Service in the Victoria Barracks in Portsmouth. All naval recruits went through the same process of basic training. There was a cacophony of regional accents. The Glaswegians were a particularly vociferous lot, often drunk. Peter couldn't understand a word they said. There was a great deal of drill and hanging around (terribly boring) but about one weekend a month he could go up to London to listen to jazz in clubs: Chris Barber on trombone, Humphrey Littleton on trumpet and Cy Laurie on clarinet.

"That's where we were," said Peter, when we drove past Portland harbour one day. Like ants scurrying along invisible pathways of their own, we scurry about in our lives, tracing and retracing pathways, meeting and just missing people on their own paths. At one point in Peter's naval life, he came to Plymouth about the time I was being invited to parties on board ships. Our paths didn't cross.

Peter was considered officer material by the War Office selection board. He puts this down to the Boy Scouts where he learnt – in his words – how to get a small troop of boys across a stretch of water with two bits of wood and a feather. Independence and initiative were two key qualities looked for. Earlier, on the family's return after the war to London, there'd been a prep school in Sutton, which taught him how to answer questions in exams.

He'd got into Dulwich College, where his uncle Charlie had been and which pleased his mother no end. The same techniques got him past the War Office selection board to become a naval officer.

He was back in Portland on another immensely large training ship moored in the harbour, *HMS Implacable*. This patch of life in the navy was hard work. They were up at 5.30 to scrub the decks (actually, corridors) before breakfast. Bed at 9 pm in hammocks slung in a very small space. Peter lists the training subjects: drill, gunnery, navigation, signalling, seamanship, anchoring. Oh, anchoring! I exclaim, remembering our adventures with anchors in Greek waters. "Well," replies Peter with his usual pragmatism, "it was a bloody great anchor. We didn't have to do anything. We just watched a section of chain running through a hatch."

I like his descriptions of drill. On a flight deck more than a hundred yards long, Peter would shout orders at a squad of seamen. "Squad! Wheel to the right in fours." This was to tell them in advance what they would have to do when the order was given. Then, barking much louder, out came the order itself, "Squad! Right! Wheel!" The squad obeyed. Amazing! What power!

"I was useless," Peter adds to this description of drill. I can see all kinds of Monty Pythonesque debacles. A squad might march in tight formation on the deck of an aircraft carrier and obediently wheel right to drop one by one into the sea. The image mingles with one summoned up by Peter's friend, John Burge. John did his national service in the army. On a night exercise, he and the squad he was leading were lost on a heath. John saw the gleam of a road ahead. "Come on men! Follow me!" John shouted, waving his arm encouragingly. The men came to an abrupt stop on the edge of a river where Burge floundered, up to his neck in water

However useless Peter was – and probably not useless at all – drill was more entertaining than painting railings.

A side-shoot beckons.

A farmer's son may follow his father into farming. A doctor's son often becomes a doctor. The offspring of several artist friends of ours have gone into finance, keen to make the sort of money it's hard to make as an artist. Were there any artist antecedents in his family? At breakfast this morning I asked about his mother's father. Had Florrie perhaps inherited a liking for art from him? I knew he'd been a director of Waygood Otis, an American lift-manufacturing firm. In fact, he was managing director. They lived in a Victorian house in a good part of Dulwich, with a tennis court at the bottom of the garden. There was a billiard table in a billiard room, under which the family had hidden during air raids. There was an occasional chauffeur called Pocock who taught Peter how to drive. It was entirely possible that Grandfather Day had liked painting watercolours in his spare time, as so many had in those days. But if he had, wouldn't there be a pile of sketch books among the family possessions. No. He was no artist and his son, Uncle Charlie, followed him into the lifts of Waygood Otis.

John Barrett was doubtful about Peter's determination to make a living as an artist. "If you make £1000 per annum by the time you are 25, then good luck to you. I'll have no objection." It was a kind of bet. Pa Barrett liked a bet. He said he'd give me a ring if I gave up smoking. I did. He did. A year later, I

lit up again but I didn't give the ring back. Peter did earn £1000 by the time he was 25, and Pa was pleased.

Back to the navy.

A representative of the outfitters called Gieves came to measure up the new officers for their uniform. Before two weeks' leave, the newly outfitted could choose from a short list of options. "Small ships, Far East," was the most popular choice. Peter got "Small ships, home waters." Peter joined the *Knaresborough Castle*, anchored in Devonport with engine trouble. The slogan *Join the Navy and see the world* rang hollow in the ears of the sailors on board. She set to sea once while Peter on board. They'd barely passed Drake Island when it was realised the engines were not in good enough working order and they returned to harbour. On the graph of Boring the line veered to Terribly. Peter was given the job of chart corrections. I think of the wonderful charts we had on Moby Dick, on which Peter would set our course for the day with set square and ruler. What sort of thing was he correcting? Instructions would come from the Admiralty. A reef marked at 32 degrees latitude by 67 longitude might have appeared after a tsunami. A green light should have been marked red. It strikes me as extraordinary that naval charts should need so much correcting that a midshipman must spend his days altering them. And who checked he'd got them right? Again my cartoon imagination comes into play. "Oops! Sorry! It's marked green on the sodding map!"

His next ship was a minesweeper, the *Cockatrice*. Not so boring, it appears. Peter as a midshipman had to keep a log of important learnings and events. His log was filled with more drawings than words They swept

for mines off Harwich, a necessary occupation as the sea was still thick with them, a decade after the end of the war. The first lieutenant was a jolly chap which made a difference. But then Peter was moved to another minesweeper where the people, rather than the tasks, were *boring*. They sailed north to Invergordon. "That's where I was," said Peter last May, pointing from the car when we explored Scotland for my first time. Peter's memories were

evening classes after school, and now he was offered a place there. He also had the possibility of sitting the Cambridge entrance exam, having been granted a State scholarship on the strength of his advanced level results. But he wanted to get on with life itself, to learn through experience. This was the moment Pa Barrett challenged Peter to earn a thousand a year by the age of 25. Five years was a generous amount of time. He was willing to help Peter on his way, too. He talked to the boss of Fleet Illustrating in Argyll Street, the commercial art studio which produced the Army and Navy Stores' catalogue. I can hear the conversation. "Oh, by the way, Melcher." (Name unknown but I want to indicate Pa Barrett's throwaway style. He would get to the point fast.) "My son's good at drawing. He wants to be an artist. Can he make a living at it?" "Yes, of course, he can. I'll give him a chance."

constantly jogged. He remembered exercises in Loch Ewe, and being sick as they sailed around the northern coast. He was on night watch and had to be brought a bucket. The ship was pretending to be escorting a North Atlantic convoy. I thought of my friend who'd recently had her novel published, a wartime love story set in Loch Ewe, with convoys and the Merchant Navy the background to the plot: *The Restless Sea* by Zoe Kenyon.

After this, Peter's naval life perked up. His ship sailed up the Bristol Channel and into the Avon to anchor right in the middle of Bristol, expressly – or so it sounded – for cocktail parties where there were – wait for it – *girls*. There were trips to Ostend and Amsterdam. Drink was duty-free. In the Officers' Mess, it was tuppence for a gin, thruppence ha'penny for a brandy, only thruppence for whisky. We were drunk all the time, says Peter.

Finally came the course which, in the recounting, has always entertained me. He was sent on a Signals course in a country house in Hampshire, *HMS Mercury*. Peter liked signals. He learnt Morse code, how to use code machines and how to type. How different my life would have been, had he taken to computers, which – technically – he could so easily have done. But he could see no point in computers in his life as an artist. Whereas I latched on to wordprocessing with enthusiasm, buying something called a Screentyper in 1985. On that I wrote our first book on Greece, revelling in the technology. Result: I am often being Mr Peter Barrett on digital forms. Hello Peter! says the Tesco website, when I make an extra online order.

Peter was among the top three in the Signals class. A good friend he'd made during training was also on the course. Peter Daniel would later be chosen as Peter's best man. When I first heard about this patch of life, I was staggered to learn of the morning ritual. The trainee officers were brought cups of tea in bed by Wrens. Do you imagine that the custom continues today? Or maybe the situation is reversed? Cups of tea brought to female trainees by sailors in bell-bottomed trousers! Mmmm …

When I first heard about the Wrens' visits with cups of tea, I laughed with amazement – but not any unease. It fitted the context of the era. Only later did I feel outraged at the way the Wrens were expected to be servants and the young officers were expected to be served. Hierarchy had to be emphasised to promote obedience and the smooth running of ships. Enough now, though. Peter, in this story, has come to the end of his national service.

In October 1955, he was out of the navy and making his way as best he could towards a career as an artist. He'd been to Camberwell Art School for

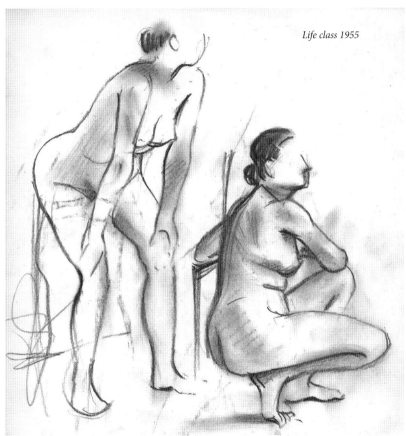

Life class 1955

So there was Peter, out of the navy and into the offices of Fleet illustrators. They were highly skilled with air brushes, showing the shining toe caps of shoes and the fashion details of men's and women's clothing. This was more interesting than his weeks as a cashier in the Army and Navy Stores. But there was no way that he could be given anything to do, except run errands. He emptied and filled water pots, picked up proofs from block-makers, watched typographers, and learnt a bit about the production process. It involved a great deal of hanging around. The line on the boring graph hovered around the *very* and *terribly* mark. Even if he would eventually be let loose on a catalogue page, this was not the career he had in mind.

We sometimes have discussions about the paths we could have taken but didn't. Had Peter gone to Cambridge or art school (both possible choices) how different would his career have been? He'd probably have ended up teaching art as so many artists have to, in order to make a living. We both, in our individual ways, dived off into the undergrowth to see what we could do on our own. We'd both had enough of institutions when we reached the age of choice.

Mr Melcher, perhaps seeing that neither Fleet Illustrating nor Peter was benefiting from the arrangement, suggested he should become an advertising account executive. There was an advertising agency on the floor below and the boss took Peter on. This was a step totally off track. Think of the graph – see the line stagger to *terribly*. There was one bright spot: the chap who showed him how to schedule advertising campaigns was a jolly guitar-player called Brian Concannon. Peter's social life developed promisingly. He'd been a member of a Dulwich tennis club since school days, as a way to meet girls – a preoccupying theme for most young men, as it was for the girls to meet young men. There'd been various exciting meetings while he was in the navy, particularly a Liz in Bristol. Now, into the story comes Valerie who was learning fashion design at St Martin's school of art. She was the girl friend who would last for nearly four years. Peter is such a steady man that I think he must have been longing to find someone like Valerie. But once found, inertia set in. I guess she was so steady that she brought Peter to a standstill. They became engaged and stayed engaged for years. When I look at the diamond wedding picture Peter is painting for us, I can see that the two of us have never stood still – except in staying married to each other.

I'm glad to say that the friends Peter made at this time were relieved when he eventually slid out of his engagement to Valerie, two weeks before their marriage in 1959. At last, they said, he'd got rid of "that terrible girl". Poor Peter – he'd suffered from being too nice. He couldn't bring himself, earlier on, to hurt her. As a result, he hurt her even more. This happens. I hope she found a man that suited her down to the ground and is a contented great grandparent somewhere in south London, not far from the Crystal Palace flat that Peter and she considered as a possible home.

When and where did Peter meet these friends, John Burge and Pete Rose, who found Valerie a little – a lot? – on the dull side. He says these two really educated him. We left him at G.S. Gerrard where he'd lost his direction. After a very short time there, he cast about for a job which would suit him better. (In his career, he's been swift to make changes. In relationships, otherwise). He got an interview in the design department of Thomas Cook. He was asked to design a brochure for Paris. He managed to do it well enough to be taken on.

He says that this is where he really began learning – about life as much as work. His tutors were Reg Hayes who was a good artist and designer, and Pete Rose, a nuts and bolts man full of advice and guidance. A tall, laconic chap a few years older than Peter, a jazz enthusiast and simply a very nice man, Pete took young Peter in hand. Beer drinking and jazz clubs were one of the ways this education happened, alongside the business involved in

producing brochures. Peter was soon able to design and illustrate brochures on his own. He also started doing book jackets for publishers on a free-lance basis. In 1957 he took another step out and up. He wanted to learn about typography so he got a job in the public relations department of the Monotype Corporation, designing brochures and advertisements to promote new typefaces.

This was the most interesting job he'd had so far. Work and social life had looked up. He was learning useful new skills; he had a steady girlfriend. Valerie, though, abided by very strict rules. There were boundary lines all around her, pretty well from her neck down. It seems that Peter's line on the boring graph was hovering between *very* and *terribly* for this was the point when he booked an assisted passage on an emigrant ship to Canada. He'd have told Valerie that emigration wasn't his aim. It was the means of getting across the Atlantic to see something of North America. Would that

Peter's early sketch books record visits to jazz clubs, classical music concerts, life drawing classes, West Country harbours and six months in America

19

have reassured her? On an assisted passage, the £10 fare wouldn't have to be repaid if he stayed there for three months. The Canadian economy needed workers. The government hoped that the ship's passengers would stay for ever. Many did. Peter stayed for six months.

His time in Canada and America is recorded in several sketch books. It looks and sounds like fun from the start. On the ship to Montreal, he made friends with a lively Cambridge graduate called Mallory Wober. In Montreal, Mallory, Peter and Colin Lewis, a friend from G.S. Gerrard days who he'd crossed with, found a flat to share. Peter landed a job with a printing firm with the Dickensian name of Rapid, Grip and Batten. The name was memorable; the job, too, in a different way. He had to paste blocks of type together with a make of glue he'd never come across before. He found it impossible to handle. He was sacked after two weeks. After this he found a nice job in a design group of amenable people. Not that long ago, at a party in Devon, Peter looked across the crowded room and recognised one of the group, Jed Falby, sprawled in an armchair. "Didn't you work in Montreal at one point?" Peter asked. Jed was standing for the council of Budleigh Salterton. Circuitous pathways.

After the two months learning more about advertising design, Peter answered an advertisement. A co-driver was wanted to drive to and from San Francisco. They would spend a week there and share the cost of the fuel. On the way back, the car broke down 50 miles before they reached Albuquerque. The other driver disappears from the story, probably with more cash to get back to Montreal. Peter got himself to Santa Fe. He had very little money but he did have, briefly at that time, a beard which was more ginger than blond. The older locals exclaimed. He was a reincarnation of D.H. Lawrence who'd stayed at a ranch in Taos County in the mid-1920s, thirty or so years previously. Whether it was due to the beard or not, it led to a most disconcerting experience. He was chatting with the assistant in a tourist shop selling Native American artefacts when another customer joined

in. He had lots of similarly interesting things at home; perhaps Peter would like to see them? Yes, said Peter, he would. "Good. My car's outside." Off they went. But once he was in the man's home, he realised the real purpose of the invitation. "I've got to get back," he said hastily and left. He had to walk a long way back to the town. The experience was a lesson markedly different from, but as useful as, typography. From there he got a Greyhound bus back to Montreal with the pressing need to find a job.

Mallory and Peter decided to try Toronto. Peter managed to pick up some freelance. His portfolio of sketches and printed work was growing. His confidence increased, too, after he won a prize organised by an art shop – a set of artist's materials but he asked for the cash instead. He and Mallory both wanted to head west. They went to meet someone advertising for co-drivers. An old man greeted them. His plan was to drive across the States to rescue the Doukhobors. What on earth did he mean? Mallory and Peter learnt that the Doukhobors were a Russian religious sect that had come to America in the late 19th century. They were being persecuted and, according to the advertiser, needed rescuing. "The man's raving mad," said Mallory when they got away. Instead, they bought an old car, which broke down irrevocably, 10 miles out of Toronto.

Having written that paragraph, I decided it would be fun to track down Mallory Wober. I googled him and was led to LinkedIn. He answered my message within an hour or two. We went on to exchange a flurry of emails. Here's an excerpt from the one he sent yesterday evening, May 27th.

Strangely, I recently had a fleeting thought about the Doukhobors – not having had them anywhere near in mind, for decades.

Vanity decrees – I decide to send you a picture which I am nearly sure that Peter will have taken – we drove from Detroit, crossed the Mackinac bridge, and along the shore of Lake Superior stopped somewhere quiet to look at the water …

(I don't have many pictures of those days and would be interested if Peter does have any …)

Cheers

Mallory

Peter, looking over my shoulder, reports that he didn't take the photo of Mallory contemplating the shoreline of Lake Superior. But pictures, yes; he filled his sketch books during his six-month stay. It was going to come to an end soon, but first he and Mallory got onto the new car delivery system, the most popular way of getting from east to west. They went to Detroit. the centre of car manufacture, and from there they drove a new car (what make? This is not the sort of thing Peter remembers) to Seattle. Mallory remained there while Peter went on to Vancouver where he stayed with an old Dulwich College acquaintance, now manager of a logging business. Winter was coming on, cash was running out again, the prospect of scrabbling for more work was not appealing. He sold his guitar so that he could get the bus back to Montreal. Once there, he phoned his parents.

"You can pay me back later when you find work here," said Pa Barrett, and sent him the passage home.

Peter was home in time for Christmas.

Soon after this he and Valerie became engaged.

From Peter's American sketch books

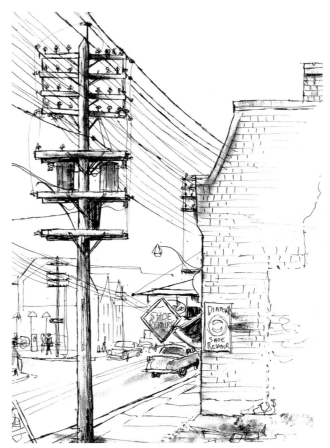

Peter shaved off his beard and started hunting for work in January. After a few weeks of disconcerting joblessness, he was taken on by a small advertising agency. It had been set up by two friends who'd fled from Nazi persecution in Germany before the war and joined the RAF to fight for the British. Peter Laufer changed his name to Langford and the agency was called Hausman Langford. Tragically, in the 1960s, Wally Hausman and his wife were killed in a plane crash.

The job suited Peter. He worked under the single graphic designer, Peter Hounsell, who was talented and a good influence. Peter was building up his portfolio with respectable specimens. He was also getting a few freelance commissions from publishers for book jackets. His circle of friends and contacts was widening, mainly through drinking beer in pubs after work. John Burge, who became a good friend, was the agency's copywriter and entertaining company. Pete Rose had been a friend since Thomas Cook days. Despite his six months' absence, Valerie was still part of Peter's life but she was not part of the pub scene. By now she was visiting schools as a representative of Simplicity, selling dress patterns to the girls. On one or two occasions, she was lent her father's Rover to drive to a school far out of London and Peter went with her to keep her company. Then he took the train home, while she stayed the night after the sales session in a hotel. She was the only child of elderly parents: the model daughter of an Aquascutum salesman, a nice, sweet girl. They became engaged in the autumn, having known each other for three years.

By this point, Peter had moved on in his career. This was the way to proceed; you took zigzag steps from agency to agency, moving ever upwards, to more interesting jobs, to greater responsibility, to better pay. Peter was given a job by Ken Dickinson, who ran an independent design department within McCann-Erickson, one of the best known and biggest American advertising agencies. The Monotype Corporation where he'd worked before going to America was on the ground floor of McCanns' offices in Fetter Lane and his knowledge and skills in typography helped get him the job in Ken Dickenson's department. Pete Rose, Peter, John Burge and Mike Cole, who John had met during National Service in the army, were a regular foursome in the Printer's Devil, the pub across the road where Susan Withington would soon be drinking beer, too.

I'm glad to say I was not the cause of Peter's break-up with Valerie. They were due to marry in the spring of 1959. Two weeks before the occasion – the invitations had been sent out long before – Peter's cold feet became so cold that he simply had to act. He told Valerie he couldn't go through with it. I can imagine the combination of feelings: shame, guilt and intense relief. During the two weeks he'd booked off work for the honeymoon, he went to Paris with John Burge.

FREEDOM!

*Peter tracked his travels in
America in sketch books*

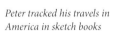

IN THE MAKING
SUSAN

It's May 8th 2020, the 75th anniversary of VE day. As a French friend remarked in an email, VE should stand for Victory against the Epidemic. In France they're coming out of lockdown ahead of us. Gatherings of 10 – family and friends – will be allowed from Monday onwards. On Sunday Boris will announce his roadmap for lockdown release in England. It's predicted that groups of up to four family and friends will be allowed in the open air. May this be so.

We're longing to hold in our arms the latest addition to our family: our great-granddaughter Davinia, born prematurely on April 2nd. She was actually due yesterday, May 7th, which was her father's, our grandson Mark's,

birthday. Today Rio, her mum, put a photo on Facebook: Brinley, aged two and four months, holding Davinia, now five weeks old. It's a wonderful photo, and makes the Covid pandemic seem horribly cruel, preventing us from seeing them. I suppose we should think of a virus as a life form with as much right to exist as we have. Rather a stretch, that, for the imagination.

As I wrote that last paragraph, our son-in-law Nick arrived on the terrace and made all the difference to the day. He fixed the base of the parasol with the tool that was missing from the socket set given to Ben and left behind by him in a typically haphazard state many years ago when he started travelling. Nick reports that Sophie is making scones and will be bringing

Seen from the slopes of Cox Tor,
the town of Tavistock is all but hidden
in its valley beyond the western edge of Dartmoor,
Susie's much-loved childhood home

them up with cream and jam to join us under the parasol at the new garden table. I felt my spirits rise, as clearly as the level of mercury in a thermometer. Social distancing, now in its seventh week for us, is beginning to drag me down. Social contact is more important to me than I'd realised. "I don't think it affects you quite so much?" I suggested to Peter. He agreed, with an expression of slight mystification.

That thought leads me back to where we were in the last section. I was looking at what made Peter. Now I'll turn the mirror on myself.

I was born by Caesarian section in Plymouth on June 24th 1938. In my imagination and in psychotherapy training I have re-enacted that experience. Whether I'm guided in this by my adult knowledge or by physically and emotionally held memories in the deep unconscious, I cannot say. To me it is intensely real. I feel myself thwarted in a natural movement forward. Again and again this happens – going forward, being stopped, going forward, being stopped. Eventually I come to a halt. There is a fading into non-activity, nothingness. There's nothing wrong with this state of affairs. I can give up, be quiet, do nothing. It doesn't matter. But then I am roused and suddenly, I reach air. I'm exhausted, stunned but peaceful. It's wonderful out here.

My first conscious memory is of daffodils. I'd woken up from delicious sleep to find myself gazing up at the trumpet heads of yellow daffodils. The air was fresh and gentle around me. I could hear birds singing. I had no knowledge of any of these things. I knew nothing by name. But I knew from my senses that I was there. And it was glorious. Later, I could point

to the exact spot in Markham's garden where this occurred. Memory or imagination – who knows.

Jane, my elder sister, was probably not thrilled by my arrival. She was two years older than me, having been born on May 11th 1936 in Hong Kong. She turned blue on birth, so the succinct story goes. This was the cause of great anxiety, of course, but especially as our parents had lost three previous babies. I learnt this from a cousin of my mother's when I was an adult. Jane and I survived. Our parents were not young; my father was born in 1893, my mother in 1900. They'd been married at the end of the first world war and became parents just before the outbreak of the second. They'd had nearly twenty years of childless life, spent in various outposts of the Empire while my father served as an army officer. There'd been golf, tennis, bridge, lots of servants and parties. In 1937 they returned to England with Jane. The following summer I was born in a Plymouth nursing home. My father was commander of the Royal Engineers in Devonport at the time and they were renting a house in Tavistock. This must have been a good year for my mother. She had her husband with her, and her two little daughters. She had domestic help; a nurse, a cook and a maid who wore a little headdress, white detachable cuffs, and a pinny. Later, I was to find her uniform in a strange piece of furniture in the box room, a treasure house of mysterious suitcases and trunks covered in exotic labels. The brief interval of easy living came to an end when war was declared in September 1939. Father was sent to France for the second time in his army career. He'd fought in the First World War, and now he was to go through the Second.

I can imagine my mother's anxiety but I have no need to imagine what her wartime life was like. I have a wonderful record, distilled from family letters exchanged between cousins throughout the war. This was the brain child of my father's Cousin Alice. A member of each family of cousins dispersed by the war would send monthly news to her in Rye, Sussex. She would bind these together to circulate around the contributors. She called it the Cousins Family Chronicle and by January 1940 it was well under way. By 1945 there were enough newsletters to fill a suitcase which Alice bequeathed to a cousin in a younger generation. When I was lent the suitcase in the early years of the 21st century, I was inspired to make readable sense of the collection. The result was a book I brought out in 2016: *Alive in World War Two, The Cousins' Chronicle, commentary and memoir.*

My mother, Molly Withington, was a keen contributor. She loved writing and receiving letters, so she was in her element. In January 1940 she wrote from her parents' Godalming home. It's clear that the year of ease I'd imagined after my birth hadn't really existed. The Devonport position had come to an end, and they'd moved to York before war was declared.

"From Molly Withington, Downderry, Godalming
This month we had once more to migrate. Dick left York on the 1st to report at Aldershot. I came down with him in the car, leaving my sister-in-law who was staying with us in charge of the house and family. We stayed a week at Downderry while Dick was busy collecting his staff and kit. I returned to York on the 8th and Dick went across to France on the 10th, he is Chief Engineer (Works) on South L of C (Lines of Communication) I had a busy week myself settling up all our affairs & packing up – we have left the things we had collected up there in store. The furniture was hired so no trouble about that. One wonders when we shall have a home all together again! I came down here on Jan.18th with the children, nurse and the large black dog! Though rather an invasion we are preferable to the 4 noisy schoolboys that were billeted here till Christmas time! Jane and Susan are well and jolly, & have quite settled down here. Jane goes to a dancing class once a week at a school on this hill. Dick writes cheerful letters from the B.E.F. (British Expeditionary Force).

We don't know where he is, he seems to have a very extensive area. His H.Q. is in a chateau & the Comte and his family occupy one wing. There is central heating but no bathroom!

It has been immensely cold in France as reported in the papers. Dick has met a lot of old friends & acquaintances during his tour of the area."

Something I find fascinating and strange is that, when I ring Jane, she is receiving the call in the house she and her Peter built in the early 1960s in a quarter of the garden of Downderry, a Victorian house a short step off Holloway Hill, the "hill" of Jane's wartime dancing class. On this hill our great grandfather built a house in 1850 and called it Holloway Hill House. Our mother stayed for long periods here while her parents, my grandparents, were abroad in the army – in Bermuda and India. When they settled in England on retirement, they lived in Downderry. We used to drive from Devon to Godalming for Christmases with our grandparents who we called Mop and Pop. Mop lived until she was rising 103; Pop, until he was 98, My mother ended her days in Downderry's converted stables. She, like my father, died from a stroke in her 70s. She'd been photographed as an 18-year old

bride on Downderry's lawn. The roof of the stables where she was to die on her wedding anniversary 58 years later can be seen in the background. While I've lived in any number of houses since marriage to Peter, Jane is still with her Peter on this family ground. Continuity in families and houses has often haunted the background of my fiction.

For the next month's newsletter, Molly Withington wrote:

"Dick writes frequently and cheerfully from his H.Q. and sent some snapshots of himself with the grandchildren of the Comte who owns the chateau. They are about the same age as Jane and Susan. Dick is hoping to get 5 days leave in April. The Comte gave an afternoon Bridge party one Sunday in Dick's honour – tea and very rich cakes were followed by glasses of port and then they sat down to Bridge.

Holloway Hill House, Godalming, and Susie's mother's family

I have been working at the Red Cross Supply Depot. As I am such a poor hand with a needle, it is rather a penance but I've made a beautiful pink dressing jacket for a Finn! Featherstitching and all!"

I'm enthralled by the image of the Finn sitting up in bed in a pink jacket. Peter, who has brought me a coffee, likes this line, too. Needs a cartoon, he says.

'Poor hand with a needle' writes my mother, yet she managed featherstitching. Well done, Mum! I'm about to follow a video on how to make a mask. The friend who sent the link has made one and says it's simple. Wait and see what a merry dance I make of it.

Masks today, bed jackets then. The wartime spirit is being evoked by our present prime minister who appears to think of himself as a reincarnation of Churchill. The bluff and dramatic approach seems gauged to whip up more popular support than one grounded in solid good sense.

I learn from my mother's March 1940 newsletter that she and her two daughters were still staying with her parents in Downderry. Markham had been sublet when my father was moved to York. He was now in France but had joined her in Godalming for a four day-leave. There's a photograph in the original collection of newsletters that must have been taken at this time. Cousin Alice gave my father the title of Brigadier, but I think he was still a colonel at the start of the war.

"Dick looked well and was cheerful though not particularly optimistic about a short war. He is impressed with the spirit of the French and says the Entente is much more pronounced than in the last war in every way. He is very comfortably housed in this 15th century chateau and the H.Q. has now got a hut in the grounds as the Mess, with an anteroom and kitchen and shower bath as well – the latter necessary as the chateau has no bathroom. Dick was delighted with his daughters and they with him. Susie has produced 2 eye teeth lately and has just learnt to walk up and down stairs unaided. This accomplishment she finds so entrancing that she seems to spend a good deal of time indoors on the stairs! Jane is growing so fast that she had been promoted to a skirt and jumper on Sundays which gives her intense pleasure."

I have no recollection of my two-year old self, although I can recognise the person who was entranced by learning something new and doing it over and over again until the shine wore off. My memories of Downderry date from after the war when we used to drive from Devon to Godalming for Christmas. The staircase was exceptionally steep in relation to the size of the house; a design fault, we reckoned, as we were used to Markham's two flight, gently graded staircase. Downderry's telephone was fixed to the wall at the bottom of the flight before a few more stairs turned the sharp corner into the hall. The phone had a wonderful, brass-rimmed receiver hooked up at the end of a long flex. I don't remember anyone ever speaking into it. In my memory the stairs are connected not with this antique phone, nor with my first unaided climbs but with the ritual of Mop's descent for the day after breakfast in bed. Lily, the live-in – I can't possibly call her maid; it would be like calling Everest a hillock – Lily, who reminded me of a red-cheeked Toby Jug, and who had brought us early morning tea with thinly sliced and buttered brown bread, stumping up the steep stairs with the trays, one each, three journeys, and had drawn our curtains, and had long since seen to other tasks including getting Mop up and dressed – now at 9 o'clock would call out loudly "Madam's coming down!" Everyone removed themselves from sight. Mop had one leg shorter than the other, after being knocked down during the blackout on her way home from the Bridge Club. She wore a shoe with a substantially built-up heel and moved very slowly with the aid of two sticks. She hated to be watched but we could hear her go clump, ker-clump, clump, ker-clump as she moved along the landing to the stairs. Only when she was safely down and sitting in her chair opposite Pop, either side of the glowing coal fire in the dining room, only then did we emerge from wherever we'd been hiding and join our mother for breakfast. "Porridge! Aren't you having porridge?" barked Pop without fail. Later, it would be the time for the Times crossword. I learnt how to do cryptic crosswords from Pop, my mother and her brother, my uncle Dicky.

Downderry and our mother's family were important elements in our childhood. There was Aunt Mary, our uncle Dicky's wife who was an invalid and died young. Before that happened, she sat beside us at Downderry's dining-room table. She gave us coloured pencils and exercise books. She drew squares and made a pattern of dots within them; some had more dots, some had fewer. The dotted squares had a sign between them, followed by another sign. We counted up the dots and wrote down the answer with a number. Four and three makes seven! Entranced again.

Mary was fragile and died very young. Uncle Dicky eventually married again. Before Mary died, Dicky had joined up, following Pop, a career soldier, into the Royal Artillery.

From Molly Withington,

The Withington contribution is late this month, I am so sorry. We moved back to Devonshire on the 20th. I motored down in the Standard with the dog as company and spent the weekend with a friend and near neighbour so that I could get everything unpacked and ready before Nannie brought Jane and Susan down by train. We found everything in good order and Tavistock seems comparatively peaceful, though we have many troops back from Flanders resting here at present and there are quite a lot of R.E in the town, too, now. Jane and Susan are very well and seem delighted to be back with their sandpit and their swing and to see their old toys again. My family has increased during the last few days! After some hurried telephone messages my cousin George Mellersh sent his two children and their Nurse down here on Friday last from Sussex. Antonia is 3 and a half and gets on very well with Jane, and Nicolas is a lovely baby of 8 months, and they are really very good indeed.

I have been getting letters rather irregularly from Dick since the invasion of Belgium, naturally, but he is perfectly well and I hope safe and sound. My brother is in good form, his R.A. Base depot was moved back and as far as we know he is still at the Base.

I have been putting in some hours' clerical work on several days lately at the local Food Offices, issuing the New Ration Books. This is such a very large Rural Area. I am also pretty busy in the house as I have only one daily maid from 9 – 6 so I cook the breakfast."

Shortly after this, the cook who I remember well – Bessie – must have appeared. I always had the idea that my mother didn't learn to cook until Bessie left at the end of the war. I remember her ringing up a neighbour, saucepan and wooden spoon in one hand, saying "I've added the flour, what do I do now?"

Thinking of the Covid epidemic as a kind of re-run of the 1940s I feel I should be taking part in the "war effort" as my mother did. But I'm not. I am just abiding by the rules. My biggest effort is ordering food online. I have never liked making shopping lists. I prefer to browse the shelves. But we have not set foot in a shop since before March 16th when we were told to stay at home, being over 80. My mother was 40 and had a daily maid and Nannie.

"Dick got back from France on the 18th (June). He crossed in one of the last ships to leave St Malo. It was of course crammed full of troops, but as a senior officer, he got a berth. I had a phone call from London the day before from one of his staff to say Dick would soon be arriving which saved me some anxiety. We were also very anxious about my brother as no news was received from him for many days. However, he turned up at Southampton safe and sound and was sent to Cheshire, then Ascot, from there he got 48 hours leave and he is now under orders for 'abroad', destination unknown.

Dick arrived here by the same train as my cousin's wife, Rachel Mellersh, with her cook and her cat, and masses of luggage! So we **are** *a houseful! Dick looked very much better for the leave as he was very tired and strained. He has gone to the 11th Corps as Chief Engineer. The Headquarters are near Bishops Stortford. I have only had a hurried note from him. It is a very large area and he will have a lot of travelling to do.*

Tavistock has been in the midst of alarm, if not excursions, lately, as we have had 8 air raid warnings in six days last week. The raids were over Plymouth, nothing very drastic up to date, we understand, but I definitely do not like to go far from home, because of the children. All four have slept through the night alarms, and we haven't disturbed them, as there seemed nothing anywhere in the vicinity, and it's so bad for their nervous system to be disturbed. I find it rather difficult not to be irritable! Though this has proved to be anything but a 'peaceful spot', we have an excellent hidey hole under the stairs about four steps down, and I really don't think the Germans will come here in malice, but merely offshoots from a raiding party on Plymouth. There are a lot of troops in the town, though the R.E. have left. We had a small sherry party for some of the R.E. Officers while Dick was here.

Susie was 1 on the 24th and we have a nice little party for about 24 people for tea. It was so lucky that Dick should be home for it; he found Susan very much advanced in the months since he had seen her as she is now very talkative. Of course, she wants to do everything Jane does."

Parties! I've inherited the party gene, if there is such a thing. Our diamond wedding anniversary party for friends and family, originally planned for June 20th is postponed. Until when? Who knows. In this Covid lockdown it's become clear how important social life is to me. I like being on my own very much but now I realise how much I enjoy planning things with other people – meals here, meals out, parties.

Where did all the cousins, cooks and nannies sleep? Markham had six upstairs rooms: moving from the right of the stairs, first there was our parents' double room with father's dressing room next door; then down the landing we come to the boxroom; turn the corner to find the single room that later I painted a horrific salmon pink when it became mine; then back

past the bathroom (a lovely, west-facing, warm room) to the nursery in the corner, a big and important room in early childhood with a gas fire and towels drying on a folding, wooden clothes airer which I still possess; back towards the stairs past a single bedroom, another room that became mine in the end. Its window opened onto the roof of the verandah. I could climb out and down the roof into the garden.

The bathroom was a favourite room. On summer evenings I liked to gaze out of the open window feeling the rays of the setting sun on my face. The garden lay below, sloping away over the vegetables, past the hens, to the garage where there were two cars – the Standard and a little Austin 7 put up on bricks for the war. Trees hid the hill down to the town and the roofs of the town itself but I could see the hazy line of trees along the top of the hill hemming in the town's valley. It was a blurred and bumpy place that I thought was India, where elephants and Uncle Dicky lived.

The bathroom contained a vast airing cupboard with lots of racks. I liked to climb up onto one of the racks and go to sleep. Underneath the sheets stacked on that shelf were the swimming costumes (that's what we called them) of the previous summer, smelling of seaweed. I had a voluminous, red, rubbery garment with a bodice and straps, but also a pretty, yellow and white check costume, an elasticated and frilly affair. Possibly these were of different eras, and never thrown out even when replaced.

Another place into which I climbed for a sleep was the old pram standing in the verandah. I remember a particularly delicious sleep from which I slowly awoke to the sounds of a man's steady voice coming from the dining-room's open window. I knew this meant it was one o'clock and this was The News on the wireless. Where else did I sleep? Not on a branch of the conifer at the corner of the house where, if I'd fallen asleep, I'd have fallen off and tumbled down the steps leading to the back door. That was just a favourite hiding place. I could hear the voices calling out. *Where's Susie?* I remember the wonderful feeling of being safely lost, an observer of a scene rather than part of it. The hallmark of all writers?

*An Austin 7 laid up on bricks in the garage
was a get-away vehicle in wartime spy games*

These wonderfully sunny days of April and May this year, I've kept my reclining deck chair permanently ready on the porch.

"What did you do in the Great Covid, great grandmamma?"

"When I wasn't asleep, I wrote a memoir."

On the phone with Jane the other day, we were comparing memories of VE Day. On May 8th 1945 we walked down the hill with our mother to join the crowds outside Tavistock Town Hall. I remember waving a small Union Jack. I was nearly seven, Jane would be nine on May 11th. We both remembered the red, white and blue crepe banner was laid over the damask cloth on the dining room table for her birthday tea. We talked of our mother's war work. From the time I spent collating the Chronicle's newsletters, I remembered a mention of digging potatoes. "But I don't think she did that for very long," I told Jane. I've always remembered my mother as a party-loving, game-playing absentee. Now, with my more focused attention on her contributions to the Chronicle, I learn that my mother didn't just dig potatoes, she did all kinds of jobs. She was a serial volunteer. After her efforts with a needle for the Red Cross supply depot when she feather-stitched a bed jacket for a Finn, she began putting in a few hours' clerical work at the local Food Offices, issuing the new Ration Books. (Pa Barrett in North Wales was busy at the source of these, the Food Ministry in North Wales). Then, in October 1940, she reports:

"The local WVA is really beginning to function at long last and I'm on the Committee of the Tavistock Branch.

I have also taken on a small canteen job in Whitchurch where a company of the Regiment has its H.Q. I only go once a fortnight on Sunday evening from 4 – 7 as my nannie is out every other Saturday. Anyway, canteen work is always so popular, they have no difficulty in getting helpers."

Then came the potatoes.

"Another wartime activity I have been drawn into is Land Army work and I have been out 'potato dropping' rather a nice outdoor occupation but quite tiring. I found one has to accept payment for this and I was quite proud of my wages.'

This is a rabbit warren of a chapter about myself. So many new paths open up at every turn. I always had the idea that I didn't know my father until his retirement after his last position as commander of the Royal Engineers in Kenya. Yet from the Chronicle I see that, after he got back from France and was stationed near London, he was often on leave, coming down to Tavistock to play golf and see his family. Here's an excerpt from a newsletter written in the autumn of 1940. I was two and a quarter.

"Dick got back for a week's leave in early October, which was a great excitement for us all. He looked very well and was very cheery and thoroughly enjoyed his little holiday and the society of his family. He played golf every day except one when it was too wet. Our dear old friend General Curtoys (who has since died after some months of illness) lent Dick his beautiful sports Bentley and we had a lovely drive one day through Dartmeet and Ashburton, Bovey Tracey to Moretonhampstead and back across the moor to Postbridge where we had tea in an "'otel' much to Susan's joy. "Tea party in 'otel with Daddy" was her theme song for the afternoon. The week went all too quickly, of course. The country was looking beautiful with autumn colours which is the loveliest time on Dartmoor, I always think."

My mother's mother, Mop, used to talk of otels, not because she dropped her aitches – she didn't – but because she was a Victorian at heart. I believe it was thought correct to pronounce hotels in a French way. Or was I perhaps imitating Nannie or Bessie?

The hotel was the Lydgate House Hotel which we continued to visit occasionally throughout my childhood. As an adult with Peter, it once again became a place for treats. It was the site of my 80th birthday party, two years ago. We filled five of the six hotel bedrooms with the family: Sophie and Nick, Mark and Rio, Olivia and Bertie (and their dachshund Rufus) as well as our good friend Christine Walker who'll often be mentioned in future pages. William and Jill Fell joined us for the Saturday evening meal; they, too, may feature later. They have both responded well on reading the novel I gave them for their golden wedding: *Greek Gold*. It was an appropriate present, not just by virtue of gold but also because the novel is set in the Pindos mountains. We first met the Fells in the Vikos gorge. Surely more of that later on.

Home!

An emotive word. On the surface, and immediately, it brings to my mind everything most desirable. It also contains for me the slightest tinge of desperate, unfixable sorrow. This is a remnant, a scrap of emotion, left over from childhood. I have tracked two sources of the tears that can mist my eyes at any evocative moment.

The first is from 1944. During my recent page-turning of the Cousins' Family Chronicle, I came across a few lines in a newsletter of my mother's dated March. I was five, My father had nine days' leave. We'd gone into Plymouth, *"now outside the banned area,"* writes my mother, *"to see a film about a lovely collie, Lassie Come Home. It was very good indeed but very affecting – Susie and I wept nearly all the time!! However, after many adventures, Lassie did eventually arrive home, I'm glad to say!"*

She doesn't mention any display of sadness by Jane or my father. I remember the weeping well. I was uncontrollably awash in tears. I could not stop. It makes me realise now that I "take after" my mother more than Jane does. Yet I used to think it was the other way around; that I was more like my father, and Jane, my mother. It's not a matter of feeling things more deeply – how can one compare depth of emotion – it's the exhibition of feelings that can be compared. Little Molly Phillips was farmed out to live with her maternal grandparents in Holloway Hill House for long periods of her childhood while her parents were abroad. She also went to a boarding school in Kent. She probably wept buckets on her first nights away from her family and home.

I soaked my koala bear in tears every night of my first three weeks at The Royal School. It was January 1949. I was ten and a half. The long title of the school (for Daughters of Officers of the Army) conveys its style at once. Founded in 1865, it was modelled on Rugby, the famous boys' school. It was a massive grey stone building with a distinctive tower. Conditions were spartan. Jane was already there and it was thought that she would look out for me. But she was in the senior school in the main building; I was in Laggan (the very name gives me unease), one of the two junior houses on the other side of Lansdown Hill. I managed during the daytime, being intent on working out the system. But at night homesickness struck: an unshiftable ache filled my rib cage, taking up too much space between my stomach and heart. Tears didn't relieve the pain. I was barely conscious of them. Koala and my pillow absorbed them.

Jane could do nothing to help, nor did the school expect new girls to need special attention. They just had to get on with it. So I did. I was the only new girl in Laggan, as far as I remember. Another girl was appointed to 'mother' me. Bad choice of word, there. I didn't take to her and looked out for someone who might become a friend. Diane Brittorous seemed

Picnics on the moor were an essential part of Susie's childhood and are still part of our life. Here's our present picnic basket on the grassy bank of the river Dart near Huccaby Bridge

likely. She was a no-nonsense, athletic sort of person. We were proud to be tomboys. We started a couple of idiosyncratic games. One was swimming along the top of a laurel hedge – horribly uncomfortable but we thought it very clever. Another was a daringly high jump off the top of the wall at the back of the vegetable garden. Soon we had five or six girls shrieking and jumping. A clean landing was laudable: a neat bend of the knees and then straight up and away. We had no thought at all for the ground on which we landed. However, the house mistress had a visit from the gardener, incensed by the destruction of his carefully tended rows of lettuces. Diane and I owned up and I was told to write a letter of apology to the gardener. I was thrilled to be asked to do something I really enjoyed. The start of my career.

As I went up through the school, there were other occasions when I was asked to write whatever letter had to be sent from the girls at the school. I was in the Upper Sixth when I was selected to write the official letter of thanks to a benefactor. I have no memory of the content but I do know I aimed to bring a smile to the benefactor's creased and care-worn face, as I imagined it to be. Miss Goss, the headmistress, called me to her study in the tower. She was extremely disappointed, she said. I was flippant and superficial. I must re-write the letter in a suitably serious way.

I worried about being superficial for many years after that. Is it pay-back time? Yes!

Here is another legacy from Miss Goss. Well into the last term in the upper Sixth while or after taking our advanced level exams, we were called in to see her. We were to tell her what we aimed to do when we left. I looked at her as I weighed up the pros and cons of confiding in her my only aim in life. She had a tight roll of grey hair that went from one ear to the other around the back of her head. It looked like a barricade against any sensation from her body to her brain. Her back was straight, her form well-padded, her eyes hidden by spectacles. She was not thought by any of the girls to be a warm and likeable character. Yet I bared my soul to her.

"I want to be a writer." I said.

I remember the toothy smile which accompanied her shocking bark of laughter.

This needed time for thought. She hadn't laughed when I had been amusing. Now I was being serious and she'd laughed. All I could think at the time was that I'd made a stupid mistake. Best to keep my own counsel, I decided, and this I've largely done all my life.

The expectation for girls in those days was to study something useful for later life as the wife of an empire builder: a secretarial, cookery or fashion course was recommended. Alternatively, for the more determined, academic and public-spirited, social work was a popular choice. Jane went on to the London School of Economics to study social science. Miss Goss approved of Jane. She talked generally to me of possible careers, after we'd got over the writing debacle. I said I wouldn't mind being a Wren. There were a number of charming retired naval men in Tavistock, friends of my parents – Admiral Sir William this and Captain Ogilvie that. There were one or two sons who were doing their national service in the navy. I might marry into the navy. Miss Goss didn't approve of this either. I should use my brain.

I shall slot in here another bone of contention to chew and discard. In the January before we took advanced level exams, it was arranged for two girls to sit for the scholarship to Bristol university. I was selected with Sara Thackwell, the head of school. She'd take the maths papers while I was entered for History. It meant a day spent in Bristol, *out of school*. Wonderful! It turned out to be the worst occasion I'd yet experienced, the very stuff of nightmares. Imagine an enormous cathedral-like hall filled with carefully separated desks and chairs, a scribbling student at each. Now into this scene place me, a born scribbler, sitting transfixed at my desk, immobile for two hours. I'd learnt about King Arthur, Norman castles, the Magna Carta, nineteenth century European revolutions, the Reform Bill, the Boer War … I was up to my neck in the Tudors for advanced level … I could write reams about Henry the Seventh, the Eighth and Elizabeth the First. But that was not what I was asked to do. The questions set before me were designed for students of a period of history that I knew absolutely nothing about. As far as I remember I did write something, if only to be seen to be doing it. I used my imagination to describe how and why Pitt the Elder advanced the cause of something or other in the latter years of the 18th century. The examiners must have read my brief contribution with extreme puzzlement. I daresay I put in something amusing to bring a smile to their faces, as I had done in my letter to the school benefactor. Superficial again! But Miss Goss, why didn't you check what period of history the examinees would be expected to know? You only entered us to demonstrate the RS's academic credentials. A tall order in the first place and an abysmal failure as far as I was concerned. I think Sara managed better. She could at least understand the questions in her maths paper.

At the time, I felt no resentment towards Miss Goss, simply because I couldn't work out what had happened to me. It was like receiving a cricket ball on the back of my neck. I didn't know where it had come from, or who had thrown it. Only years later, probably when I was seeing a therapist as part of my counselling training, did I say to myself *Hey, that was not fair*. I was used and humiliated simply for the sake of the school's reputation – which I let down in any case.

Now, in the summer term, Miss Goss thought I should stay on at school for the autumn term and take the Oxford and Cambridge entrance exam; then read English or History. This could be seen as a reasonable suggestion, even if hindsight tells me that the school's reputation was again the motivating factor rather than my personal needs. I was taking English, History and Art at advanced and scholarship level. But I was not going to remain a schoolgirl a moment longer than I had to. The thought of being the only girl to stay on, no matter what privileges I was given, was too chilling. I left.

On the strength of my exam results I was awarded a county major scholarship. Had my father not been above the means-test level, I might have gone to Exeter or Bristol. But as I wrote in a previous chapter, my father was above the level of state help, yet not rich enough to support me without continuing to work. If I spent three years at university, he could not retire from his job as bursar of Kelly College. In 1956 he was 63. It now sounds ridiculously young. I can still not blame him. He'd been through two world wars – 1914–18 and 1939–45. That would be like Covid 19 lasting for ten years.

Giving up the thought of university was not too disappointing. It meant I wouldn't have to exert myself unduly. I could spend time living at home. *Home*!

This doesn't mean to say I was unhappy at school. On the contrary. If ever I'm asked, I reply that I enjoyed my schooldays. I had no trouble fitting in. I made good friends, two of whom I'm still in touch with. I was good enough at rounders, netball, hockey, lacrosse, cricket and tennis, without shining at any of those games. I was picked for "Star Gym" – which meant we had extra time vaulting; and I was awarded a posture stripe which had to be sewn onto my school games sweater. But at some point during the next term I decided I didn't want to be small, keen and bouncy any longer. I wanted to be tall, languid and lazy. I began to slouch. My posture stripe was taken away. So that's the price? I realised I didn't have to gauge my worth with a bit of ribbon. My best friend in my form was Diana Davis and she seemed to get by very well without fitting herself into the expected Royal School shape.

Diana (known in adulthood as Diny) and I were both bright and we liked to take a slanted view of the world. We are still friends. In an email she sent the other day from her home in America, she described how she thought I was 'normal' while she was not. But it's hard enough to remember what we were like as individuals in those years when we were putting ourselves together, let alone remember what other people were like. I would never become tall and languid. Lazy was another matter.

I didn't understand, nor like, the way the English mistress singled me out, making me her star pupil. But there was nothing I could do about that. I loved reading aloud and writing essays. I wasn't going to slouch in English, History or Art. Besides idly thinking of becoming a Wren, I much more seriously considered becoming an actress (Shakespearean) or an artist. Drama school or art school beckoned. But becoming a Writer was my single ambition. I knew from reading the biographic details of authors given on book jackets that I should put together an interesting list of occupations: coal miner, bus conductor, ship's cook, sausage factory worker … there were endless possibilities. The summer when I sat at my father's knee and told him that he could retire, I had simply no idea how to proceed. The easy answer, the family decided, was that I should follow in my sister's footsteps. Jane had left school in the perfect RS mould. She wanted to become a social worker. She needed more advanced levels to get into the London School of Economics so she went to Plymouth Technical College to gain them while also doing a secretarial course.

It still astonishes me that I followed suit. I didn't need more advanced levels but I took the same courses as Jane had taken: British Constitution, Economics and Economic History. I escaped sitting the exams because the dates coincided with Jane's wedding in Godalming, Surrey, and I was her bridesmaid. A wonderful and welcome excuse! There was one major benefit from my year at Plymouth Tech. I learnt how to type and take shorthand. The shorthand I should have kept up, it would have been useful. The typing is more than useful; it's invaluable. I touch type fast. Only now have the well-worn synapses involved in touch-typing started to play tricks: my

fingers sometimes transpose letters, so I might see *lettres* appear on the *paeg*. Checking slows things down. Fear of dementia haunts our age group. One of our good lifetime friends, a brilliant journalist called Katharine Whitehorn, is sitting in an armchair in some North London care home, with no idea what's going on. I don't want to tempt fate, but I hope to finish this memoir before I can't finish it.

A significant lesson learnt at Plymouth Tech came from the man who lectured in Economics and Economic History. I will make up a name that would fit: Ken Weill. That's suitably spikey. The surname I've chosen for its pronunciation, not its national origin. Ken Vile was an ardent socialist.

"Will Miss Withington of Markham Lodge – or is it Court? – like to honour us with her views on …"

I could only shrink onto the bench I was sharing with another student, while forcing a little laugh to show what a good sport I was. Why was Ken Vile getting at me? Was it for the way I talked? My social background?

My life to date had been among people who talked in the same way. Our RS ears were critically attuned. We knew that the Matron of our house came from a different background to us. I judged her not by her accent but her character and whether I found her likeable or not. (Middling). At home, I took in the way my mother sorted people into those she'd cultivate as friends and those who would never be included. Her great friend, who was my godmother, was a more socially rigorous discriminator. "So and so is NQWWW," she'd say. This stood for Not Quite Want We Want. My mother would chime in. I felt acutely uneasy, trying to make out how to react to this. The army, of course, is a classic hierarchical system. The school Jane and I went to was for *officers*' daughters. There was a girl whose father had come up through the ranks. She was thought rather non-U, in Nancy Mitford's vocabulary. "His men loved him," mother said of the soldiers under my father's command. There were social strata with definite edges. This was my background, but I hoped it would not be my own approach. I picked out the more left-wing papers in the school library.

Ken Weill, from his socialist convictions, made a point of emphasising the divisions. You'd think someone who wanted a more equal society would try to do the opposite. I was surely not a suitable target for his resentment. Markham was not grand in any way and it did not belong to us. We rented it from our nextdoor neighbour! As for myself, I think I was more of a mouse than a monster to be cut down to size.

The result of my experience with Ken Vile: I have never wanted to differentiate people by the way they talk. Yet I know I harbour a fussy, little, elitist selector inside me. When in 1998 the Royal School amalgamated with Bath High School, I was extremely upset. Bath High brought in much needed funds, higher academic standards and bright girls from a broader spectrum of society, but … BUT! The RS was adulterated, as though water had been added to wine. NQWWW. I squirm at my residual snobbery but this doesn't make it go away.

I tell myself, and I have written about it as far as I can recall, that it's a human need to sort people into them and us, and everyone does it in different ways all the time. As I write, there are violent demonstrations in America, sparked by the death under arrest of an unarmed black man by white police. One of the four policemen keeping him down on the ground put his knee on the man's neck and held it there. He suffocated.

Perhaps today, now that I'm all but 82, I could stand up to Ken Vile and have a good discussion. I doubt it, though. I've always found it easier to write than talk.

Across the road from the portcullis archway of the RS was Kingsdown, a boys' school. It existed on the edge of our consciousness, strictly out of bounds but ever present in our minds; much in the same way that Moby Dick swam in the same seas as Captain Ahab. One of the most astounding things I learnt after leaving school was that a girl in our year had *married a Kingsdown boy*. They'd got together while at school. How can I convey the extreme unlikeliness of this piece of news? How had they met? When and where? It was baffling. I still don't know the answer. We were kept within the boundaries of the school as tightly as East Germans behind the Berlin Wall. At a certain level – the fifth form? – we were allowed to walk down to Bath on Wednesday afternoons. Diny and I had a weakness for Welsh Rarebit and Rum Babas at a swanky café in Milsom Street. Cream teas on Dartmoor in the summer holidays came a close second to the extreme pleasure of these Wednesday escapes. Perhaps the girl who married a Kingsdown boy had met him over a cake in Milsom Street. I've only just thought of this solution, so embedded were the rules of purdah in my mind.

But there was a single occasion each year when the oldest Kingsdown boys mingled with the oldest RS girls. It was agony. Weeks of anticipation were followed by a day of intense excitement and uncontrollable nerves. At the appointed hour, twenty or so Kingsdown boys stumbled into the School Hall for the Summer Dance. There was much shuffling and staring at the ceiling and the floor, with quick sidelong glances that took in essential details. Spots? Short? Tall? Dandruff? Gawky? Good-looking? Somehow or other the opposing groups shifted and broke up. Pairs took to the floor. One of our mistresses was on the platform in charge of the gramophone, an awkward version of a later DJ except that she was there, not just to ease things along, but to put a stop to any inappropriate behaviour. One foot on the accelerator, one on the brake. As though there'd be any need for the brake! We were all rigid with fright, or so it seemed to me. We girls had had lessons in ballroom dancing. We could waltz and fox trot and do all kinds of intricate, little, feathery steps. Even the girls who were not so nifty could get around the polished parquet in time to the music. I loved dancing. As a nine-year-old I'd danced in a performance in Plymouth – with a stage-full of others, admittedly. I was a natural ballet dancer, said the lovely person who gave the lessons in Tavistock, who thought I should be sent to ballet school. Many are the girls who have the same fantasised, what-if history. I was probably only just a bit above average. I had my own line in dancing, a mixture of ballet and whatever came into my head in the moment. I used to do dances for my mother. "Now I'm Helen," I'd say, emerging from Helen's home beneath the nest of tables that I still own. I must have been very small. I'm not sure why I danced best when I was Helen. It wasn't because I was shy. My mother wrote in 1940: "*Susan has just started dancing lessons. She is the youngest in the class but follows reasonably well and is not in the least shy.*" That was me, eighty years ago. In our early days of marriage I used to do dances for Peter,

sometimes sensuous, romantic glissades, sometimes comic turns to make him laugh. Whenever the right sort of music started, up I got – particularly in Greece. Now I can only stagger to the nearest chair.

In the School Hall, the music started and off we went.
"Sorry!"
"Sorry."
"No, it was my fault."
"Sorry!" echoed a hundred times around the hall. As I said, agony. There was one boy I liked and he wasn't a bad dancer. But the whole event left me feeling that it was a mistake to hope for the best; the best may not exist. In any case, we rather suspected that the Kingsdown boys were NQWWW. Our fathers and brothers would have gone to the well-known public schools; if not Eton or Harrow, then Winchester, Rugby, Sherborne, Uppingham, and Marlborough among them, besides the equivalent army officers' school for boys, Wellington in Shropshire. *Not*, we hurry to add, the one in Somerset.

While Peter was in America hoping to meet girls and meeting them, I was in this last year of school, not meeting boys except for the Kingsdown ones on that single occasion. I did meet, though, a young Russian naval officer called Boris. Through my mother's cousin Beryl, a member of our family was invited to stay for a week in Malta as the guest of friends, a naval officer and his wife, Benedicta and Ronnie Burville. Jane had now left home – she was in London – so I was chosen. This was heady stuff. The flight, for a start, was thrilling. Then to be greeted on landing by the warm glow of a yellow sun in a clear blue sky; being driven to the city of Valetta: becoming aware of the background bustle of streets, with voices talking in another language; arriving at the Burvilles' flat in a street of honey-coloured stone houses with terracotta tiled roofs and French windows with shutters opening onto wrought iron balconies; all this was a revelation. I'd come from a grey land.

Benedicta arranged a small cocktail party for me and the Russian navy – well, a few of its young officers, at present in a ship anchored in Valetta harbour. I sat on a firmly upholstered, wood-framed sofa in between two of them. I fell in love at once with Boris on my left. He spoke a little English. I had a fit of trembling. I couldn't stop. "You cold?" The temperature inside the flat was well into the 80s. This shivering happened once or twice in the next year until I grew used to being in close proximity to anyone of the opposite sex.

This is a strange phenomenon. I'd been friends from the age of four with a boy called John. John wanted to marry me. I was doubtful. He was a year younger than me, and I had the idea that, on these grounds, our marriage would never be allowed. Not wanting to disappoint him, I prevaricated. "Let's see when we grow up," I told him. (A precursor of "I think so" to Peter in 1960.) There were other boys. Kit Brown and Robert Wills were bruisers of about six. They put me on a bike and pushed. This happened on the moor outside our back gate where a cropped grass drive alongside our garden hedge led down to the gate that gave onto a footpath to Down Road. It was the very edge of the moor, the small apron called Whitchurch Common which held, too, the golf course and a cricket ground. The gate was set in the moor's boundary, a Devon bank with thorn trees huddled among granite boulders at its foot. I careered down the hill, clinging to the handlebars and wondering how one stops a bike. I didn't learn in time. When I got to my feet and dusted myself down, I saw Kit and Robert, rolling around, slapping each other, unable to stop laughing. Kit was the first to recover. "Look," he said, demonstrating the brakes. He was the nicer of the two but he didn't hang around later on when I lived at home, as Robert did. By then Robert had a motor bike and used to take me at stupendous speed over the moor, mostly by road.

My father had an olive-green BSA Bantam motor bike which he let me ride. Wonderful independence! Wind in my hair! I can go anywhere! He taught me how to drive the family car, too, a Ford V8 with the number plate KTA. Then Nasser the Egyptian president took control of the Suez Canal; petrol was in short supply and driving tests were cancelled. Kindly, the government decreed that learners could drive on their own, without a qualified driver beside them. I was up and away. Nowadays, whenever we visit Tavistock and approach by the road from Two Bridges, I relive the moments when Katy the Ford and I began gathering speed just the Tavistock side of Cox Tor. How does one slow down a car? My lesson in braking had obviously been forgotten. We hurtled down the familiar road, taking corners at amazing speed, past this, past that, past the road coming in from Mary Tavy, the road to Kelly College, the bridge, the river, the shops but how to slow down, how to slow down, how to slow down? We swept into the square and somehow or other my foot was on the brake and we stopped. It took me longer to stop shaking.

Braking is not my forte.

Is it time now to list boyfriends in my pre-Peter life? There were boys I liked who never became boyfriends, simply because we were itinerant between home and school. We met in the holidays at parties and dances. Our mother was indefatigable at arranging entertainment for Jane and me when I was old enough and Jane hadn't yet left home. There was one Christmas holiday when we totted up at the end there had only been two empty days in four weeks. That may have been the year when I couldn't decide if I preferred Winslow or Paul Foot. Winslow was the better looking but Paul was better company; sharp-witted, clever, sardonic. One of those what-ifs, but our paths only crossed briefly in Yelverton, halfway point between Plymouth, his home and Tavistock, mine. I'd been at prep school in Yelverton where I'd made friends with a wider circle, and spent later holidays stripping the willow and hopping about in eightsome reels in the Village Hall. A lot of anxious time was spent clinging onto the iron railing that enclosed the cast-iron stove which roared away in an attempt to dispel the moorland chill that seeped into the long room. I liked the Scottish Reels for the dancing and for the chance to wear the new dress I had those holidays. It was made of taffeta, in bottle-green and black stripes, with a tight-fitting bodice, cap sleeves and full skirt; it went swish when I spun around. I began to get the idea that I looked alright.

Let's go on to the time when I'd left school and went to Plymouth Technical College. The general thought was that I'd make lots of friends at college. Not a bit of it. I had a single compatriot, a fellow RS girl called Sarah who was living with her grandmother near the Hoe in order to do a course at the tech. She was good-natured and she and her granny had me to lunch occasionally which was kind. Most of the time, I was utterly miserable. I had

no idea how to interact with the other students. There were no openings. They seemed to know each other and regarded me as a visitor from outer space. I used to sit on a bench in Royal Parade and smoke cigarettes. I was as hopeless at smoking as I was at braking. I never got the hang of inhaling, which was probably a very good thing. The department store Dingles, rebuilt with the whole of Royal Parade after the blitz, was a slight attraction. It smelled delicious on entry. John's father, Stanley, was one of the directors, or he might have been the managing director. But that was of no account or advantage to me. I was not a shopper. If I had pocket money, I have no recollection of the amount. My father must have given me an allowance for travel, lunches and oddments. I'm still not at ease with a purse. I find it difficult to spend money on clothes and I'm not certain what will or won't suit me. This is not a surprising characteristic in those of our generation. In the war years, we had cast-offs. Everything was made to last; seams were let in and-out, hems taken up and down. Clothes rationing went on until 1949. I was still inheriting Jane's clothes in my teenage years. When my mother began to buy me new things, she chose garments that were versions of her own. I have a photograph of Jane and myself wearing hats and coats which make us look like women on a Mothers' Union outing. We were, at a guess, 18 and 16. But she did go wild one day in the branch of Dingles in Exeter. We were on a major trip over the moor. She fell for a long-sleeved, wine-red dress, with diagonal raised seams across the bodice and a pleated skirt. I thought it was far too expensive and I said I didn't want it. She insisted. The diagonal raised seams were a challenge to my emerging bosom.

What seems to me the ideal for people of any age is the availability of lots of cheap clothes and the freedom to make our own mistakes. It wasn't until I was at Plymouth Tech that I started choosing my own clothes. I remember a kind of enlarged baby's matinee jacket in bubbly cream wool. It swung out and around from the armpit area. It was probably a bad mistake but I was thrilled with it. Sometimes I held my red umbrella over my head. It had to be raining, of course, but I might have done it anyway as I loved the warm red light it shone on me. Like footlights? I wanted to be an actress at that point. I felt like Marilyn Monroe as I trotted in my Cuban heels down to the station to catch the train to Plymouth. Dr Beeching did away with the line that took me to and from Plymouth. It was the line we used for blackberrying, too. Clearbrook Junction was where we got off for the best blackberries.

This is where James comes in. We must have met at a party, as he wasn't the son of any of my parents' friends. He took a shine to me and he had a car. I was willing to go out with James for the sake of sitting in his Austin 7. What a cachet to have a boyfriend with a car! This, sadly, was a lesson in priorities. Personality, I discovered, was more important than car ownership. *Poor James* is how my parents began to refer to him. I was trying to put him off, but very cackhandedly. He persisted, regularly turning up at the station to meet me on the train from Plymouth. In desperation, I got off at the previous stop, Whitchurch, and walked home across the moor to avoid James and the Austin 7. Two or three miles of foot slog to save me from, as I saw it, hurting his feelings but it was more a case of not daring to be honest.

A parallel with Peter's long engagement to Valerie comes to mind.

In my year at Plymouth Tech I was sinking into a dismal frame of mind.

Instead of having a whale of a time, I was bored and lonely. I began to worry that I wasn't normal. From my bench on Royal Parade, I'd watch lunchtime couples meander up and down, holding hands, faces close. On the evening of the Bristol scholarship exam fiasco, Sara and I had walked down to the Quay with a posse of boys in our wake. "Pay no attention to them!" I hissed at Sara. To my consternation, she did the opposite. She slowed down and began responding to their questions and remarks. "*Sara!*" It was no good. We ended up in a line at the counter of a café. I retreated into myself. Sara, I realised, was in her element, flirting. And I'd thought her a very strait-laced character. As for me, easy-going and popular, I was being an icy island. It was all very puzzling. Would I ever fit in?

Apart from trembling at the side of Boris, my feelings had not been stirred by anyone, male or female. I knew I wasn't lesbian, a word and phenomenon I'd heard of. At school there'd been whispers about the history mistress and the mathematics mistress, found wrestling on the floor in fits of giggles. Perhaps they were only playing but it was interpreted as a demonstration of intense, same-sex love. Weird, I thought. Was that like being an amoeba? In the fourth form, we'd done the life cycle of frogs, having previously learnt of single-celled life forms and had progressed onto reproduction. It wasn't news to me. When I was at the Yelverton prep school, Deidre Tuckett, dressed as a demure squaw while I bagged the Brave's gear, told me how babies are born. She'd learnt from her mother who had produced a little brother for Deidre, which was why she'd come to Markham for the day. Apparently, a little while ago her parents had loved each other so much and kissed so hard and for so long that they'd made this baby which had popped out of her mummy's tummy button. But Miss Maths and Miss History! How incredible. Might they have a child? Was that possible?

In my early days at the RS, I'd been asked who I was "cracked on". It struck me as a totally pointless exercise to get all silly about one of the senior girls. However, pressure was exerted. I had to be cracked on somebody. In the end, I chose one of the prefects: a blonde, blue-eyed, pony-tailed girl, good at sports. I didn't want to emulate her. I didn't want to giggle and blush when she appeared in the corridor I was walking down, which was the accepted mode of action. On the other hand, when I became a prefect – though never blonde nor blue-eyed – several little girls were cracked on me, and I was definitely flattered. I acted towards them as graciously as a queen.

This was my preparation for life after school.

I expect my mother thought I would have learnt The Facts of Life at school, so there was no need for her to give the lesson. She must have filled in my sister when – and this had been a mystery at the time – she refused to let me into the bathroom when Jane was having a bath. Why not? We're having a little talk, she said through the locked door. Very much later I realised that this must have been when Jane had her first period, a passage of female development I have never been through. This is another story, and where does it belong? When I, aged 76 or so, was one hundred per cent reassured that I am entirely female with two x chromosomes? Or at this point, the start of my exploration into my sexual nature? Let's go, for the sake of clarity, chronologically.

The year at Plymouth tech had a lasting benefit at the cost of the boredom. I got a job as a secretary to the manager of Lloyds Bank, Tavistock. This must have been on the strength of my parents' standing in the town, and not down to the standard of my shorthand and typing. I would sit in his office with my shorthand pad on my lap and make squiggles which I then tried to turn into words back at the enormous typewriter on the desk I shared with Mr Trevelyan and his account ledgers. He did income tax and – poor man – had a dreadful scalp disease. I cowered from the showers of skin flakes that fell from his bald head. He was very patient and kind but he had bad breath, too. Oh dear. My shorthand squiggles were indecipherable, so I perfected the art of careful listening and accurate recall, if not word for word, then according to the sense of it. "Did I say that?" asked the bank manager, looking vaguely puzzled. He'd sign the letter with a flourish, pleased with his ability to express himself. Or at least he let me get away with it. The same ability to hear, remember and summarise what people tell me served me well as a counsellor. "Exactly!" they would say, relieved to be understood.

Mr Manager wanted me to become a Lloyds Bank trainee. He must have mis-read my character. I go all over cold and prickly when I see figures in columns. My brain is not geared to cope with sums. Both Peter and I had trouble with maths at school, and still have trouble. Is this going to cost us £1000 or £10,000? If we need to work out how many cubic metres of cement is needed to make a foundation, we draw pictures of the space.

A career in a bank was never going to be for me. The purpose of the job at Lloyds, Tavistock, was to make it viable to spend another year at home. (*Home!*) To stave off boredom, a friend of my mother's suggested I join the local amateur dramatic society. They concentrated on plays by Shakespeare, which suited me. I was in love with William. If he hadn't died in 1616, I'd have gone up to London and hung around the stage door of the Globe. Instead, I fell in love with the Duke Orsino. I was Viola.

"What would thou?"

"Make me a willow cabin at thy gate …"

Oh, so lovely, to be in love, such a dream of a state to be in. Robert taught English at Kelly College. I told him I wanted to be a writer. He didn't laugh. Rather, he encouraged me. He told me to write something and show it to him. I did. Or was it he who wrote the story about a merman and a mermaid, and he showed it to me? I can't remember. It was a love story, obviously. It became a matter of meeting to discuss the plot, and we had to plot to meet. I knew we shouldn't meet but I was not going to refuse such excitement. So it went on. Soon Robert said he would teach me something about my reactions. He did this in the top floor bedroom of his house when everyone was out. I was invited to join his family on holiday in Cornwall, ostensibly to help with the children. That's the first time I had a close look at an erect penis, shown to me when he entered the bathroom he'd told me to leave unlocked. I remember climbing out of a bedroom window in my pyjamas, to avoid being seen to leave a room in which he was alone. I went for a week's art course in St.Ives. He came down to see me and we spent a day, lying on a rock in Prussia Cove. We lay in woods, too. He never went further than foreplay, though if it had been solely up to me, we would have. This was an area where I did not want to brake. I had not a shred of moral feelings – or, if the smallest shred of awareness did exist, I was not going to pay it any attention. Curiosity ruled, and perhaps the need to prove my femininity.

At school, I noticed the girls who lined up in the corridor outside the Nurse's room, next door to the dining room. It was ages before I learnt that they were queuing for sanitary towels. I hoped no-one would notice that I never joined. You'd think I might have had heart to heart talks with my two good friends: Diana, my best friend in lessons, and Sheena, my best friend in our House. But no, the subject never came up. I didn't want to think or worry about my failure to menstruate. My mother, who did broach the subject when I was about 18, was reassured by our doctor that some girls are very late. I was dangerously innocent about everything to do with my body when I played Viola and fell in love with Orsino.

After some months, there came a time when he said, "*The writing is on the wall.*" I found this enigmatic. Was it perhaps a literary allusion I should know about? Was it the title of a novel I should have read, like *The Grapes of Wrath*? I was invited to have coffee in the local café with his wife and two of her friends, all in their early 30s. They talked together in a conversation which seemed aimed at me, but which I could not enter. Of course, they knew exactly what they were doing, as Robert knew exactly what he was saying. In their heads they gave me a clear message. We had to stop seeing each other. We did. My feeling of anguish was painful and I held on to it for a long time. Even after I left for London, I would write to Robert. I had asked at our last meeting if I might write occasionally. I used to call them Blue Moon Letters. They petered out eventually as London life became absorbing.

On our separation, Robert told me to meet boys nearer my own age. There were not many around and those in Tavistock held little appeal. (Remember James with the Austin, and Robert with the motor bike). However, there were parties in Plymouth and I passed long evenings in non-stop kissing sessions in various armchairs. Joey, who briefly came back into my life by chance forty or fifty years later, was a very good kisser. So was Patrick, a dashing second lieutenant in a cavalry regiment. He had to return to Germany and we took to passionate letter-writing. It was obvious we would get engaged when he had his next leave. A couple of days before I was to meet him at Waterloo, he let me know that his mother would meet him and I was not to be there.

Another bitter disappointment and blow to my self-esteem.

What I was not acquiring in these years was any kind of determination to act on my own behalf. I was imbued with the necessity of looking after other people. At a very basic level, this was indoctrinated by the *mores* of RS meal times. We could not ask for anything. We had to sit with untouched, saltless food until a neighbour noticed and asked if we wanted anything. This meant we always looked after our neighbours on either side, which I still think is the right thing to do, and I'm ashamed when I forget to do it. I couldn't believe it when I later met people who simply helped themselves to everything. How sensible! "How did you sleep?" I'd ask Peter after I'd had a bad night. He'd tell me in detail about his night and his dream, but never showed any curiosity to learn about mine. I let this go by for many years, until eventually I began to change my own behaviour. Simply *ask for what you want!*

I've come back to my study an hour after writing the last few pages. Of course! I have only now realised, 64 years later, a possible explanation for the strange, indeterminate, extremely awkward meeting over coffee with Robert's wife and her two friends. At the time, I simply felt horribly guilty and ashamed, knowing what I'd been doing with Betty's husband. Yet what did Betty actually say to me? There were no outright accusations in the conversation, just weird allusions to people having 'crushes' on older men and generalisations about marriage. Today the novelist is at last at work on a possible explanation for the lack of clarity. Here's how it might have been.

Betty to Robert: Is something going on between you and Susie?

Robert (alarmed); Why?

Betty: Mrs Pinkerton saw her coming out of the house on your afternoon off.

Robert: Oh? That must have been the day she wanted my advice about her children's story.

Betty: Mrs Pinkerton thought you and Susie had been in the attic bedroom.

Robert: Good lord, why on earth?

Betty: You weren't? You haven't done anything you might regret?

Robert: Of course not! Susie does have a bit of a schoolgirl crush on me, that's obvious. I've tried to put her off, but she's persistent.

Betty: Don't worry. I'll handle it. I'll have a word with her.

Robert: Oh, don't do that! What will she think?

Betty: Really, you're not to worry. I'll do it gently. I'll invite her to coffee at The Crib with Angie and Hazel.

Something along those lines would make sense of that ghastly hour over coffee. In fact, I did base my first novel on this happening. I gave it the clunky title "The Attendant Vultures." I don't remember what I wrote and I burnt it years ago. However, it got enough encouragement from a couple of publishers for me to continue writing fiction. So I did get something out of the experience, besides the experience itself. Better than going down a coal mine although impossible to put in a biographical nutshell for a book jacket.

Time to pick up my path from Tavistock to London. I'd had enough of home by the summer of 1958. There'd been another Robert after the Merman. This second Robert was in the Horse Guards. I remember we went together to find my father in his dressing room which was also his study. We told him excitedly that we wanted to get engaged. I think I really meant it, though I didn't really like this second Robert. He seemed to me to need an inordinate amount of attention, on top of his pleasure in himself. Luckily, my father said we were too young. Besides that, his parents disapproved of me. I think they'd heard floorboards creaking during the night I stayed with them in their lovely house in East Anglia. They said I should go home straight after breakfast. I'd led their son astray. Another life lesson.

In September I packed my ex-school trunk with the things I thought I might need for the rest of my life. London was the place where I'd become a writer. First, I would need to find a job and somewhere to live. Until I found these things Irene, the wife of my father's cousin, Trevor Becker, would have me to stay on arrival. They lived at number 70 Eccleston Square, Victoria. Ah, more and more side tracks beckon, which I will not succumb to now. Within a week I'd found a bedsitting room and a job. The job was as a secretary to one of the editors of Thames & Hudson. The room was in Edge

Street, off Kensington Church Street and near Notting Hill Gate. Barbara Twigg, a fellow old RS girl, invited me to take on the vacant bedsit on the top floor. It was a thrill to have my own place and it was easy to get to Thames and Hudson in Bloomsbury Square by tube. Bloomsbury! A publishing house! A start?

I got the job simply because I learnt that the editor interviewing me had been to Charterhouse. I can't think what made him divulge this information. Oh, *Charterhouse*, I said. My great-uncle taught music there, and my grandfather umpired their cricket matches until quite recently. We went on to chat idly about Godalming. I became his secretary the following Monday at, I think, £7 a week which seemed a fortune. I left my handbag containing my first pay packet on the tube. I got it back from the Lost and Found Property office, complete with seven pound notes in their small brown envelope. How lucky can you be.

I'm afraid I was no better at taking dictation from the Old Carthusian than I was from Mr Lloyds Bank Manager. I made up all kinds of things in the letters I typed from my indecipherable, shorthand squiggles "Did I really say that?" asked the editor, echoing Mr Manager. I got away with it once again. This time, I had a fellow conspirator. Rosie was another Guardian reader and crossword completer. We were both useless at our jobs and never mastered the arcane filing system. Flimsy pink, blue, green and mauve copies belonged in different filing cabinets in different rooms in the two adjacent three storey houses of Thames and Hudson Publishing. Rosie and I ran hither and thither, up and down the staircases, desperately stowing copies right and left, messing up the system. I left after a month because Diny's husband offered me a job as a trainee copywriter at McCann Erickson, in Fetter Lane.

Here's the back story.

Diana Davis had left school at the end of Ordinary Levels, as had my other good friend, Sheena. I went on to stay for another two years, feeling left behind. They were out in the world, the lucky creatures, finding out the answers to all the unanswered questions we'd stored up. Diana sent me parcels full of chocolate and delicious sweets. One day in my last year at school I received a card signed *With love from Diana, Francis and Vicky*. Who on earth were these people? Flatmates, I guessed. They weren't. Francis Wilkinson was the head of McCanns creative department. Diny had been his secretary. Vicky was their first baby. This was staggering and exciting in equal measure. My goodness me, how far her star had taken her! A married woman! A mother!

During my first month in London, I must have met Francis and he told me that, if I liked, he'd give me a job as a trainee copywriter. He talked about the accounts they handled and what I would learn to do as a copywriter. I didn't dare let on that I had no clue what he was talking about. I silently hoped that the accounts wouldn't entail any adding up. I'd only passed ordinary level maths at my second attempt. However, I was confident I could manage the writing part of the job. If it meant imitating a literary style, I'd enjoy that. Diny and I had done a spoof Shakespearean play together, which we'd been very tickled with. Maybe she'd told Francis about that. If it meant actual handwriting, I'd manage that, too. I'd recently learnt how to write with an italic pen which gave a stylish twist to my rounded, clear RS hand.

Am I making my ignorance up, I wonder? Whatever the case, I took up the offer gladly. This was the start of the long history of Francis and Diny being our benefactors.

I was put in an office at the end of a long corridor, to be trained by Marie Stroud, a dynamic, blonde, older woman who had a husband and children on the Tulse Hill, Dulwich border. I was in awe of her, although she wasn't the sort of person to invite veneration. She was fun and very good at the job. Her office attracted a continuous stream of droppers-in and passers-by, exchanging fast chat and swift repartees. I found it hard to follow so I mostly smiled, laughed and otherwise stayed awkwardly silent. There were a couple of copywriters who gave me much the same treatment as Ken Vile had done at Plymouth Tech. They teased me for being what they saw as posh. They were not vile like Vile. They were amusing. But I felt uncomfortable; I didn't know how to respond.

Gradually, I got the hang of things and developed an ability to come out with quick, flip remarks. I also learnt how to write copy. Mazola Corn Oil, Findus peas and Westclox clocks were among the accounts I cut my teeth on. Marie helped me to come up with "the peas with the picked today taste" which was the answer to Birds' Eye "sweet as the moment the pod went pop." I was well paid, and the creative department was a buzzy place to be.

By now I'd moved out of the bedsit and joined an RS school friend in her flat in Primrose Hill. Rosie Hutchinson had been given a nickname early on at the RS because there was at the time an elderly mistress with the same name. It took me ages to think of her as anything other than Baby Hutch. She had been a confederate in the last two years of school and we're still in touch.

Like my sister Jane, Rosie was studying social science at the London School of Economics in order to become a social worker. She and a fellow student called Pam had taken on a flat for four. I and another old RS girl, Moira Groves, made up the numbers. The flat was a hub of attraction for a number of young men living in Hampstead. One of them was called Barry, a social anthropologist from California, studying at the School of Oriental Studies. I know he'd got his eye on me before I left Edge Street because I remember he visited the bedsit and then walked all the way back to Hampstead having missed the last bus. Joey, my lovely kisser, had driven in his van from Plymouth to London to see me and had parked in Edge Street. I don't remember if Barry and Joe had coincided on the doorstep, but they coincided in my mind. I thought how difficult life could be. Would I ever learn how to manage things gracefully?

My mother's second cousin Beryl had wanted to bring Jane and myself "out", in other words, to present us at court. She'd fund us as debutantes and we would, two years apart, do the London season. Fortunately, this was only talked about and never happened. I was saved from that horror.

There were several other potential boyfriends. The best man at my sister's wedding hovered for a while. I went on a Yugoslavian camp holiday with Lucy Harington-Hawes, another ex-RS, who had taken Moira's place in the flat. On a day trip to Venice from the camp on the Istrian peninsula, a massive Slav with straw-coloured hair *en brosse* arranged for a friend of his to take a photo of us on the Bridge of Sighs. The Slav had an arm around my waist and the other clamped on my left breast. I looked to later

– taken on my camera – I remembered the moment. Discomfort, unease, embarrassment, confusion and thrill made a typical cocktail of feelings during these two years before I reached the safe haven of Peter.

It was Barry who became the serious boyfriend and it was during a night with him in my Primrose Hill almost-double bed that I learnt what the phrase 'making love' actually entailed. What a painful let down. Barry told me I'd enjoy it more next time. I thought sadly of my first Robert and wished he'd been less restrained. Barry was still around for my 21st birthday in June 1959. On the day itself he took me to Harrods and asked me to choose what I wanted. I homed in on a very good powder compact with a mirror – *very good* in that it was well made, it opened and shut with a satisfying click, the case looked like gold, and the powder inside smelt delicious in a restrained, expensive way. It was a happy 21st birthday and I was generally happy with Barry. He was not like anyone I'd ever met before. The same must have been true in his response to me. I, and the other girls in the flat, represented for him a certain slice of England as seen in some Hollywood films. For a Californian, we were – at a guess – like the cast of an Agatha Christie film come to life on Primrose Hill. He called us puppy-dawgs and chanted a version of a Disney sound track as we went back and forth from the kitchen to the living room of the flat, bearing mugs of coffee or wine. *Dee-dumpty-dumpty-dumpty-dum*, wagging his shoulders in time.

A lot of drink must have got spilt on the carpet. There was a week of evenings when Rosie conducted a carpet-dyeing task force. The result was hideous. The dye chosen turned the beige carpet a fluorescent emerald, interspersed with splotches in bilious, olive green. We lived with it.

I hadn't learnt a lot about housework. After a really long time, months and months, I fished for something under the bed. My arm came out covered in some strange, clinging stuff the colour of a donkey. What on earth was this? Should I leave it there, or get it out somehow? I fairly quickly identified it as dust, London-type dust. I had a go with the flat's duster before I decided the broom might do a better job. At school we never had to clean things. At home we had Mabel, who lived with her devoted sister by the river in the town, followed later by Mrs. Reddicliffe, a vigorous and thorough cleaner who didn't want to be known as Gladys. She called me Soos, having understood this was my name as she heard my mother talk of Sue's room. She often came out with remarkable verbal transfigurations. I should have kept a notebook when I was still at home. Rodeedanglums for rhododendrons was one I remember. Mrs R would have dealt with the fluff under my London bed, with no trouble at all.

During the autumn of 1959, I was growing a little bored with Barry and beginning to keep my eye open for someone new. By now I could pretty well hold my own with the boisterously joking copywriters and designers who gathered in Marie's office. I was able to deal with the double-entendres which were the speciality of a particular duo, who I later fed into a novel (*Moses,* Michael Joseph, 1970). Across the corridor was Derek Robinson whose company I liked. A visitor to Derek's room was one of the account executives, Mike Cole. They were at university together and were on the same graduate training scheme at McCanns. Mike, as mentioned earlier, had been in the army with John Burge, so he was part of the crowd gathering

after work in the Printer's Devil. They made me laugh besides talking about interesting things. Next door to Marie and me was a bigger office in which sat about four designers. They were a lively bunch and there was a spilling over of jokes, stories, and hilarity between the offices. I sometimes escaped for a quiet time to the library, halfway down the corridor, where one could go and read the day's newspapers. At the end of the corridor was a small room with a sink where the designers went to change the water in their water jars. I liked the look of one of the designers who worked in the big studio near Francis's office. He had fair hair that flopped over one eye and he always wore a tremendously baggy, blue sweater over his jeans. I learnt his name was Peter Barrett, and when I joined Mike, Marie and one or two others in the Printers Devil, Peter Barrett was there, too.

It's something of a surprise to me now to work out that Peter and I were on the same floor of McCanns for so long before we took any notice of each other. In my memory we'd homed in on each other very soon after he, or I, joined the agency. But no. It took months before we each realised that here was someone we'd get on with on a deeper level. I have to examine the dates and our separate histories. He joined McCanns in the autumn of 1958. He was engaged to Valerie at the time. I started as a trainee copywriter in the same autumn of 1958 and was soon involved with Barry. In the spring of 1959 Peter broke off his engagement with Valerie, and was suddenly free. John Burge took him in hand and they went to Paris to do whatever unattached young men might do in Paris. Peter also took on the rent of a flat in Tite Street, so that he could stay longer and later in pubs and jazz clubs, instead of getting back to Dulwich. He was not on the lookout for another girl friend who might cramp his style. Meanwhile, I was still seeing Barry although not exclusively. My sister had written to my mother saying he was a boor and should be discouraged. I was upset by this, but I saw what she meant. That autumn I was being taken out by several hopefuls, more fodder for a future novel (*Jam Today*, Michael Joseph 1969) I was beginning to worry about my morals. I vowed I would not become involved with anyone else unless he and I were absolutely serious.

These first sections of our memoir describe our separate lives up to the time in late 1959 when we were both in the library with the aim of catching up on Flook, the Mail's strip cartoon. Physical proximity, shared interests, a sotto-voce conversation (it was a library, for heaven's sake); then, later that day, meeting in the Printers' Devil after work. I've described the precarious start to our friendship: the missed first date, the impounding of the mis-parked car, my mother's stroke, and my return home to nurse her. But I left out the crucial, make or break minute. For me, the key, decision-making time was on New Year's Eve at a party given by Marie Stroud. The usual McCanns crowd was there, including Peter although by now he'd left McCanns and joined Young & Rubicam. During the evening, I was acutely aware of two men, Peter being one of them. I knew – as one sometimes does know these things – that when the time came to leave the party, both would want to leave with me, and we'd go on to spend the night together. I would have to choose between them, and I knew my decision would be a life-changing one. I chose Peter. We were engaged in April, and married in June. Sixty years ago this month.

THE 1960s

A parcel arrived in the porch yesterday. Inside was a bottle of champagne sent by my sister's eldest son, Michael, a present for our diamond wedding anniversary. He's just celebrated, in lockdown fashion, his 60th birthday. He was born on May 11th 1960 not quite six weeks before our wedding. In one of the wedding photographs, he's held on Jane's lap, between our grandparents, Mop and Pop Phillips, in the grounds of the Lake Hotel, Godalming. The 18th was a bakingly hot, June day. The photographer, Miss Muddle, spent hours hidden under a black cloth behind the camera she'd fixed to a tripod. The ushers were John Burge and Derek Robinson. Peter's bestman was Peter Daniel, Peter's friend from naval days. We'd been married, like Jane and her Peter, and like my mother and my father, in Busbridge Lane Church, with Downderry as our base. My mother and father had stood on Downderry's tennis court for their wedding photograph in 1918. In the background is the roof of the stables where my mother ended her days after its conversion to a house on my father's death. The sight of that roof is a reminder of the transience of moments set in amber by the camera.

I stayed the night before our wedding with Cousin Beryl in Bear's Barn, her beamed and ancient Surrey cottage where she'd hosted my 21st birthday party the year before. To my relief, the Vidal Sassoon cut and set, which had made me cry with despair in Peter's arms when I emerged from the salon in Berkeley Square, had become flattened during the night. I changed into

The bay of Kamares on the island of Sifnos
provided our first Greek home for painting and writing

41

my wedding dress in a Downderry bedroom, helped by someone I barely knew. Mrs Talbot was a friend of the Barrett family and the mother of my bridesmaid, Julie Ann, a girl of 10 or so who I'd certainly never met before. Mrs Talbot zipped me into the dress that Peter's sister Jennifer had made for me. "Are you sure you want to marry him?" she asked.

This wasn't a question I was expecting. It shook me. Of course, I wasn't sure! Who is, with half an hour to go before wedlock? "Oh yes, absolutely sure," I replied.

There was the slightest hint of Withington family disapproval that I should have wanted to get married so soon after my mother's stroke and Jane's production of a baby. In retrospect, I think my mother managed well and without complaint, remote controlling the run-up to the wedding from Devon. I may have done quite a bit of organising from London but I don't recall any hassle. Godalming was the obvious choice for our friends and Peter's family. I don't think I had any firm ideas about what I myself might want. In typical RS style, I accepted the things over which I thought I had no control. Here's an example of where this thorough training led me. In April, when Peter and I announced our engagement, there was a discussion at Burbage Road about rings. After a while, I realised Florrie was offering me her mother's engagement ring. I didn't *have* to have it, she said. It was just that Peter had given Valerie a very expensive engagement ring and it hadn't been returned, Florrie fetched her mother's ring from her jewellery box. It was a Victorian five-stone diamond cluster. "Oh, how lovely," I cried, sick at heart. "Are you sure you want to let me have it? Thank you, thank you!"

A slow burn. Much later, I worked out what I'd, politely and feebly, let happen. Peter has given me endless rings to make up for being a silent

co-conspirator with his economical mother. A single, inexpensive ring chosen especially for the occasion would have done the job in the first instance.

When I inherited my grandmother's similar ring, but a bigger, brighter version, I sold Florrie's mother's ring with great satisfaction.

How small are the things that can feature so large in a lifetime!

We spent our honeymoon, first in Paris, then in Antibes where the Wilkinsons had taken a villa and invited us to stay. They had two children by now. Sara had joined Vicky eleven months after Vicky was born. Now Vicky was a lively toddler, while Sara sat happily on the sand, a chubby triangle as immobile as a road cone. This was the first of many times we were on holiday with the Wilkinsons. We made an easy foursome, somehow fitting each other's varying requirements. We laughed at the same things and found the same books and films interesting. We were young company for Diny; Francis was twenty years older. He appreciated our difference from the people he mostly dealt with. We liked the Wilkinsons' humour and intelligence and the way they could show us a world we'd never be part of.

In Juan les Pins we went to a night club and watched someone glamorous called Kiki La Moustique sing and prance around rather badly. The other tables roared and clapped. Were we Londoners too sophisticated to find her as talented as they did? It wasn't until a few days later we learnt she was a man. Ha! That was one of the many episodes in our mutual lives we liked remembering.

Back in London, we used to play golf with Francis occasionally, with Mike Cole making the fourth. He had married his long-term girlfriend Annie in a secret registry office ceremony in the summer of 1960. They'd also been honeymoon guests of the Wilkinsons in Antibes, before or after us, I'm not sure. None of the golfing four took the game too seriously although seriously enough to like winning. As teenagers both Peter and I had spent hours on golf courses with parents. Peter's father was a good golfer with a low handicap, down to scratch at one time. Both my parents played constantly, and my mother often won competitions. Peter and I, with these golf-playing parents, might have played more and better, but our hearts weren't in it although Peter was a natural games-player. He'd played tennis, squash and hockey for Dulwich College. He was a member of a rugger club when we first got together. I stood on the sidelines one Saturday and peered through the freezing fog, trying to identify my new boyfriend. *Sod this for a game of soldiers*, I said to myself, an expression picked up from John Burge. I never went again and Peter gave up rugger. In any case, he'd fallen out with the captain for turning up late. Other games we played during our early London years were shove ha'penny and bar billiards in pubs with Pete Rose and John Burge.

Our life was carefree and fun. Peter had left McCanns and joined an agency called Young and Rubicam. He had been bumping up his freelance work in advertising design and illustration and there came a point when he was able to set up on his own, backed for a certain amount of work by Francis, who was now in partnership with a colleague called Jack Clark. Clark Wilkinson became a small advertising agency, with Mike Cole hired as their account executive. In our spare room today is the two-drawer table that Peter used as his desk in the offices of Clark Wilkinson.

I'd moved out of the Primrose Hill flat in the month we got engaged and we took on a semi-basement flat just off the Westbourne Grove. We invested in a double bed and, although Peter still lived at home in Dulwich, our love-making took place in comfort. Early on, in fact I think it was after the New Year's Eve party, we'd checked that we would get on. I remember thinking that you don't really know a person until you have made love with them. Apart from the matter of whether a window should be open or shut at night (I won, and since then we've always kept the window open, even if only a crack), we discovered we certainly got on. Between the time I returned to London when my mother had recovered well enough from her stroke and our engagement in April, we had two what were known as "dirty weekends", one in Rye, one in Cambridge. I bought a plain, gold ring for the purpose in a Chancery Lane jewellers. We were old hands by the time we were on honeymoon, so it was of no concern when Peter spent our first night, sleeping on the floor. Driving down through France, we had to stop every so often to fill the car, a convertible Morris Minor, with water. After our stay with the Wilkinsons, we went on to a hotel in Menton run by friends of the Barretts where Peter sickened further from the sunstroke he'd suffered in Antibes. He had a high temperature and very sore throat. A doctor was called. After his inspection of Peter, the doctor in his natty suit and co-respondent shoes (black and white with airholes) paused in the doorway and turned back to us. He thrust his arm towards the ceiling. "His bowels must move by morning!" he cried out, as though inciting us and a crowd of followers to storm the Bastille. Poor Peter was not at all well and stayed in bed for several days. I drove the Morris into Menton and ate bouillabaisse in the harbour. A mixed pleasure. A thrill to drive on my own – I hadn't passed my test. The bouillabaisse was superb. Yet I was mournfully alone and missing Peter. I rang London to explain. His boss at Y&R did not believe the extra honeymoon week was due to illness. There was a lot of teasing on his return.

The two-roomed flat in Monmouth Street had a door out onto the tiny garden where the pink of hollyhocks matched the bikini I sunbathed in that summer. Just outside the door was a wedding present, a beautiful, stoneware pot with a lid in which I'd casseroled and burnt to smithereens a rabbit. The pot with its blackened contents stayed there as long as we did – and longer. It

could still be there. Like the dust under the bed in the flat, I didn't know how to deal with it. There were other things occupying my attention. A surprise visitor knocked on the front door. I thought he'd come to read the meter and showed him where it was. He was as disconcerted as I was when we both realised our misapprehension. We were number 4A. The house across the road was number 4, an active brothel.

Ronald Searle lived around the corner and we were invited there for a party by his wife Kaye Webb. Peter was doing work for her at Puffin

HOW A PUFFIN IS MADE

1. The author writes the book and sends it to a publisher.

2. The editor reads the book and says his firm will publish it.

3. The sub-editor prepares the manuscript for the printer, and the designer decides what sort of type it should be printed in.

4. The editor (and sometimes the author) chooses an artist to illustrate it.

5. The printer "puts it into galley". These are long sheets of paper which look like this.

6. The artist delivers his drawings and they are photographed into metal copies, called blocks.

7. The author and the sub-editor correct the galleys and the typographer fits the illustrations and type into pages.

8. The printer prints the type and drawings 16 pages at a time. The edges of the pages are cut by a "guillotine", and they are bound in the right order.

9. The finished books go back to the publisher, who sends copies to the author, to critics and to the bookshops.

10. Publication day comes, and you go into the bookshop and buy the book. Hooray!

Books. I did a tiny booklet for her, too. It was titled "How A Book is Made", and I illustrated it with cartoons. Was this during our Monmouth Road time, or later? Never mind. All memories crowd together. At the Searles' front door, James Mason handed me his grey Homburg. "Thank you SO much," he drawled in his honeyed voice as he continued towards the staircase and the party upstairs.

It was a good place to live. We painted one wall Thames Green, a ghastly colour that we thought marvellous, and hung a striped, Indian cotton curtain from the ceiling to divide the cooker and sink from the sitting area. We bought a rocking chair from Portobello Road and, from a shop in Paddington, a jay in a glass case and a French skeleton clock on a marble stand. Peter will correct me if these acquisitions belong to later days when we lived in Putney.

From Monmouth Road, (we had to re-paint the Thames Green wall white before leaving; quite right, too, I say now as a landlord), we moved to a small, modern, terraced house in Westleigh Avenue, off Putney Hill. My father had arranged for us to receive some money from my grandmother, as Jane and her Peter had been given a quarter of Downderry garden on which they could build something called a Croft home, made out of wooden panels.

It still stands; it'swhere Jane and Peter live to this day. With Mop's three thousand pounds, we could put down the deposit on number 9 Westrow, and get a mortgage for the rest. The total asking price was £4,900 and we were the second owners. We inherited a front garden deep in discarded wine bottles. In fact, when taking on each of our many houses, we've always done month and months of clearing to start with. Had we but foreseen our future piles of other people's rubbish, we'd have thought the wine bottles child's play.

How many houses have we owned? Peter has painted miniatures of each of them for the diamond wedding anniversary picture. The gift of the deposit started us off on the property ladder which has benefited us, in our generation, so well. It gave us backing for the haphazard life we've led.

Westrow was a group of 10 houses around a central lawn, with numbers 8, 9 and 10 in an extended row, making the tail of a Q. The architect Eric Lyons won a prize for the design of his Span houses; there was another group of them in Blackheath. The lines were clean; the material, glass and wood; the ground floor was open plan but with folding doors which could shut off the section that made an L of the living room. Floor-to-ceiling windows let in the light and parquet flooring reflected it – when and if polished. (I was getting more practised at housework).

We Span owners felt smug. We were at the cutting edge of modern architecture and had chosen to live in this select group. In number 10 there was a Dane, Kaj Bec Anderson, his wife and children. Kaj worked for Shell as the editor of their Danish magazine and, later, he commissioned Peter to illustrate a brochure which entailed a trip to Denmark. Our neighbours in number 8 were the Hobbs family. Bruce, known officially as Eric, was a graphic designer famous for his work on the Guinness account, producing witty and memorable advertisements. Eugene his wife was known as Jean. They had two teenagers, Sally and Adrian. Some years in the future Adrian became a photographer and visited us in Greece. So did Bruce and Jean.

Peter and Susie at Westrow, photographed by Adrian Hobbs

Paul and Gloria Ferris lived in number 7. Paul was well-known for his writing, mainly as the Observer's radio critic. He also wrote novels. Another novelist who came to live in Westrow briefly, was Freddie Raphael, his wife Bea and family. Freddie came back into our lives more recently, through a good friend we met and made during our second patch of Greek life. With this friend, Christine Walker, the travel editor of the Sunday Times, we visited the Raphaels in France. Just the other day, Freddie wrote some kind words about the novel I brought out in 2019, *Greek Gold*.

The couple who lived in number 11 were called Jones and they held a party on a particular night in November 1963, remembered vividly by everyone who attended as the occasion President Kennedy was shot and killed in Dallas. The news shocked us, and millions like us, to stunned silence. Another famous Westrow party was the one we gave as a farewell before leaving for Greece in 1962. The Temperance Seven, having been at the top of the hit parade with "*You're driving me crazy*", brought their instruments into number 9 and blasted the surrounding neighbourhood into submission. I don't know if we'd actually invited them. I rather think that Colin Bowles, drinking in a Putney pub with us earlier that week, had taken it into his head to bring the Seven to the party. Colin was at the Royal College (as were all the Seven) when Peter was attending evening classes at Camberwell after work at G.S. Gerrard. Colin couldn't bring his piano to the party, but Cephas Howard made up for this on the trumpet. We heard, many years later, that this party had gone down in Westrow folklore. "The time when …"

We owned number 9 for almost ten years but from 1962 we only lived there when we were not in Greece. It was in the summer of the party that we'd realised that, if we were going to fulfil our separate ambitions, we would need to leave London for somewhere where we could live cheaply, save money, and give ourselves the time to see if we could paint and write for a living. The year after our French honeymoon we had driven to Spain in the Morris Minor (its water tank mended, presumably) and landed up staying in a fishing village called Cambrils, not far south of Barcelona. There was a small hotel at the back of the beach with a balconied room overlooking the bay with its dark blue and green fishing boats and skeins of drying nets. We had the most delicious paella every day, its standard never reached by any cook since. We dallied with the idea of finding a place to rent where we would paint and write for a good length of time. Instead, we went back to London, as we had to. I'd changed agencies, in my individual zigzag of progression, and I was enjoying working at Pritchard Wood & Partners in Knightsbridge. I was in a room with someone who was new to copywriting, she was also new to marriage. I was, to her, a kind of young Marie Stroud, though I wasn't going to be the fount of all wisdom for Joan, who had quite enough of her own ideas about the way to go about things. We had a lot in common, besides having husbands in the same line of work. Terry, her husband, was a graphic designer and illustrator, ex Royal College and recently back from studying in Germany. The four of us became good friends. The Dalleys later moved to Putney and stayed there. They were one of our many overnight resting places when in London. And like many other London friends, they are no more. R.I.P. Joan and Terry. Each death makes us hold each other's hands for a reassuring moment or two.

"Do what you can, when you can." I first used this motto in a novel called *Making A Difference*. I heard it attributed to a South African boy, but I think that derivation was concocted to make it sound authentic. Whatever its origin – it probably dates from the first few homo sapiens – I cling onto it. It has been our motto. We often remark how glad we are that we started all our travelling and living abroad when we were young.

That first time, we decided to try Greece. We needed a Mediterranean country for the sun, the food, the way of life and the lower cost of living. I'd been to Italy and together we'd been to Spain. So Athens was our destination. I was given leaving presents by the creative department of PWP: a tartan travelling rug and a copy of a fat book of maps called Europa Touring. With these, Peter's portfolio of specimens, an umbrella (insurance) and a suitcase, we took the train for Dusseldorf. Our idea was to buy a Volkswagen in which to drive to Greece. When we arrived, we discovered that anyone connected with cars, making them, mending them, selling them, was away on annual holiday. Through an advertisement we came across a private seller. His VW dated from the time when the models had no petrol gauge. When you heard the engine begin to struggle, you had to switch a lever with your foot to go onto the reserve tank. Peter put on his canny mechanic's face and looked at the engine. Thankfully, he knew enough about VWs to look for it in the boot rather than under the bonnet.

The car got us through Germany, Austria, Yugoslavia, and northern Greece. It wasn't until the last ridge of mountains before the descent into Athens that the engine faltered badly. We managed to limp into the city where we parked outside John Burge's flat in Kolonaki's empty streets a stone's throw from the centre. These days, it's hard to imagine Athens as a small, contained city with clear skies and little traffic.

John had spent his year in Greece, teaching English and writing the novel he'd come here to write. Did he finish it? I'm not sure now, at this distance. I read a bit of it, full of expectation that it would be amusing and interesting.

John as a person had these qualities. This was when I learnt that good talkers may not make good writers.

Today it's June 18th 2020, our 60th wedding anniversary. We've exchanged our 'cards': the Diamond Wedding Anniversary picture and the sixty-line poem I wrote in response. Peter has decided to do daily sketches of the view from his studio window. He started today and it took him no time at all because the view is blanked out in white mist and steady rain. We can only just see the front line of the garden: tall yellow evening primrose, mauve hebe, purple elderberry bush, green choisia with a few white flowers remaining. The tall Leylandii hedge to the side of the lawn is like a liner being launched down a slipway into endless, grey sea.

We are still in lockdown, although shops have started to open. This afternoon I will take my printer back to Curry's, Taunton, as its colour cartridge holder snapped weeks ago. It should be covered by guarantee. We'll have a tin of sardines for lunch. All is Covid-normal and we're perfectly happy, particularly as Sophie and Nick will look in after their work this evening. I say "look in" but that is impossible in lockdown conditions. We can only see other people in the open air. Since March 16th when we went into isolation, the weather has been mostly beautiful; strangely so, for England. Our terrace has become a living room, in the way Greek terraces and balconies are. The party for 40 or so we had arranged to happen this Saturday, June 20th, was cancelled some time ago, when we realised that Covid 19 was with us for months. Instead, we're inviting friends, in twos and threes, to join us around the terrace table to sit two metres apart. How quickly unusual behaviour can become normal. As our anniversary featured in our local parish magazine, we've had cards and messages from more people than usual. One of the cards was from Mary Tancock, who with Stan was our neighbouring farmer at Goodiford Mill, Kentisbeare. Another was from her friend, Ruth Tartaglia, who remembers helping with our 25th wedding anniversary, held on the lawn between Luggs cottage and the Barn. So much life and living – I'm wondering how on earth I can do it justice in

Cambrils, Spain

45

this memoir. I've reached a period which I've already written about. Two years ago we published our second book with Greece as subject matter which covers the years we spent in Athens, Sifnos and Amorgos before we decided we should bring Sophie and Ben up in the English school system. I would like to give the flavour of that ten-year period, without repeating myself. Then again, the same dilemma will arise when I reach the period when we produced our first book on Greece, *Travels with a Wildlife Artist*. We were travelling around Greece from 1982 for another few years, sketching and writing, gathering material. How will I deal with that patch of life? As always, the best course is to bash on and discover how to do something while doing it.

We imagined our time in Greece would be a year-long experiment. We'd have six months in Athens in the winter, earning our keep and saving enough to give ourselves six months on an island. We'd taken the Greek Linguaphone course out of Putney Library on a weekly basis and had managed half of the six-month course by the time we left England. We stunned the occupants of the taverna, the scene of our first meal in Greece, by trotting out a few phrases of Linguaphone Greek. Of course, we couldn't understand a single word in the excited torrent that came back at us, but it was a start and we worked hard at learning.

John wanted to show us Hydra and Crete before he returned to England, so off we went with him. It became clear that he, as a single man, was attracted to the very places we wanted to avoid. However, we did make one life-long friend on Hydra. She, like us, was beating a retreat from the harbour cafes where loud-voiced foreigners were talking about the novels they were about to write and the paintings they were about to paint. We each stopped for breath near the top of a steep and otherwise deserted hillside. Red-haired Elizabeth Dun was an artist, the sort that paints rather than talks about it. We became friends at once.

After time on Crete, we were anxious to get back to Athens and start looking for work. We'd brought enough money to last about three weeks. If we didn't find work in Athens, we would return to London and advertising. We didn't really think that would happen. Peter's experience gave him the confidence and the portfolio of specimens to chance his arm. For my part, I had confidence in him. Also, as an eternal optimist, I reckoned I'd be able to teach conversational English to willing Athenians, as John had done for a full year.

All happened according to hopeful plan. We found a flat, Peter found work in a design group, I gathered pupils of various ages to teach, and at weekends we took new Greek friends out in the VW to explore the countryside and coastline of the mainland. We had the car, they talked only Greek; it was a good bargain. The friendship has stayed the course. Yannis and Vaso were with us in 2017 on Cefallonia when inspiration struck for our second book on Greece, covering this first period of Greek life.

We saved drachma notes under the thin, striped mattress on the iron frame of our bed and they mounted up satisfyingly. We lived very economically, spending little. In the spring we calculated we had enough to start the hunt for an island on which to paint and write. Rent from the Putney house was paying our mortgage, the initial non-payer having been ousted by Peter's parents and our solicitor. That had been a bad start to the year's letting. The estate agent drew up the agreement with someone who simply didn't use money, a way of life that was discovered at once but not fully understood and acted upon for several months. I was fascinated to learn of the various ways this was possible. When we returned to Westrow, we were regaled with stories of the tenant's charm and tricks. He had 'borrowed' the cash from a series of different neighbours to pay the waiting taxi. He even managed to 'borrow" his taxi fare from the shop assistant from whom he had just 'bought' a pram for his pregnant 'wife'. "Poor woman!" said Florrie, who had camped out in the garden to make sure he finally left number 9. "He must have conned her, too."

Only in later years did I realise how good both sets of parents were to us. Mine had moved from Markham, Tavistock, Devon (my mother's favourite home) in 1960 in order to be near their two daughters who lived in London. They bought a bungalow a couple of miles from Liphook. My mother's parents were still both alive, living in Downderry, Godalming, so that was a convenient location for the three generations. But soon after they settled in Liphook, Peter and I left England. We were to be mostly absent for the next ten years, raising grandchildren on a Greek island for great chunks of time. As for Ma and Pa Barrett, they willingly provided the home base support, while our sisters took over our share of family duties, interest and companionship.

Did our parents receive anything in return? That's the question to ask. Perhaps they gained vicarious pleasure in our life and work. I wrote long letters home, and both sets of parents came out during our first Spring to visit us. In March, my father drove my mother and two women friends across Europe. In those days the roads were winding and narrow. It would have been a strain – leaving aside the chatter of three female passengers – for a man of 73. He was a very patient man, and now I come to think of it, he was fascinated by Norah, the younger of the two female friends.

Norah was the unmarried sister of our family doctor. She'd served in the navy in the war. Today people would describe her as 'bubbly', not a description I like to use but it fits in this case. Her head was covered in glossy chestnut-brown curls; her dark brown eyes and white teeth glistened, her lips gleamed luscious red. She smiled and laughed a lot, and she was also kind and sympathetic, murmuring her genuine sorrow over any reported mishap. "Oh, poor Susie!" "Oh, poor Dick!" I can't imagine her saying Oh poor Molly. Of course, I realise now: she was an intoxicating recipe for any man, as tempting as the shortbread and chocolate buns she used to make for her café in Tavistock. I once saw my father's hand creep around her waist in the kitchen of The Crib, the scene of my confused comeuppance at the hands of Robert's wife and her two friends. Was Norah in on that story? She gave no hint. In retrospect, she might have regarded my involvement with Robert as the merest, passing flirtation, to be enjoyed and forgotten. That's what it would have been for him. For me, it had a lasting effect. No-one would ever make real the love that he had sketched out but never made reality himself. This may be overdramatic. From the vantage point of 64 years my view is surely distorted, either belittling or enlarging events. Possibly the best outcome was in the way the experience provided the material for my

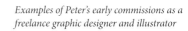

Examples of Peter's early commissions as a freelance graphic designer and illustrator

first novel, which I was about to write when we'd found the island for our summer of work. I don't remember much about the plot, beyond the fact that it dealt with gossip and affairs in a small town. Its title was "*The Attendant Vultures*", which summed up my feelings of being a picked-over carcass laid out on the floor of The Crib.

Betty Whateley was the fourth member of my parents' group. She was some kind of family connection and lived on Dartmoor with her sister, also unmarried. She was an intelligent woman whose company I liked, as did my mother. They enjoyed reading the same historical biographies, besides doing the Times crossword and playing Scrabble. Peter and I still use the Scrabble dictionary Betty gave my mother.

With our parents, one set after the other, we covered a lot of ground. SPRINGTIME TRAVELS 1963 is the title of the section in *The Garden of The Grandfather* in which I describe the times we spent exploring, and showing off our favourite places. Seven pages of text, black and white photographs and sketches in ink, cover this period. Delphi, Monemvasia, Mycenae, Nafplion, Aegina, Paros, Mykonos, Delos, Serifos – and, finally on our own, we came to Sifnos. As soon as we arrived in the bay of Kamares, we resolved to stay. Only a couple of places were available to rent in the port but, on the far side of the beach, a potter called Costas said we could have the two-roomed cottage where his sister Smaragtha sometimes slept to save her returning to their mother's house in the main village on the top of the island. We could have it for as long as wanted it.

That was the start of our first summer on Sifnos, not knowing at the time that we were forming a template for the future. The pattern of our days was governed by the arc the sun drew across the sky from the valley's olive-treed head to the bay's seawater rim. Rough bread, sweet jam and black coffee on the terrace while the sun dispelled the shadows and the goats came past, a cascade of tinkling bells and tumbling stones. A morning spent in separate rooms, Peter at his easel, I at my Olympia portable typewriter. Afternoons lying on a rock and slipping into the sea, fishing for our supper with harpoon guns. Back for another few hours of painting and writing; before supper grilled on charcoal on the terrace, and bed. Was this the very best summer, because it was the first? Or were there many others as good in their different ways?

Two of the paintings Peter did that summer hang in his studio here in Devon. Built up with sand from the beach, they show the gaunt hillside behind the sprinkling of white houses that made up the port of Kamares, one in the yellow light of midday, the other in the violet light of evening. They were part of the first exhibition he was given by Halima Nalecz of the Drian Galleries. My first novel was read by a couple of publishers and gained me encouragement for the next I would write. It went up in a bonfire's smoke after my second became my published "first". That's often the way. You'll have read in a review: "this second novel does not fulfil the promise of the first." In fact, it's the other way around. The publisher will bring out the more ham-fisted first novel *after* a successful second, saving the writer a novel's length of time and effort. But all this lay in the future. When we left Sifnos at the end of our first summer there, we had no idea how our painting and writing would be received.

Peter constructed a huge cardboard sandwich of his canvases, made more weighty by the sand he'd incorporated, and the bulky package was taken across the beach strapped to a mule to await the arrival of the twice weekly steamer on its round trip from Piraeus. A low hoot announced its arrival at the mouth of the bay. All was hurry and excitement on the quay. The small boats. loaded to the brim with packages and passengers, chugged out into the middle of the bay. With a great clatter and rattle, the anchor chain spilled out into the blue water and the small boats clustered around, like chicks around their mother hen. Peter's awkward cardboard sandwich was manhandled up the swaying companionway onto deck. I could imagine the rope which bound the parcel slipping out of position; whereupon the summer's worth of oil paintings and black ink sketches would slither into the sea.

That was just the start of the paintings' long journey back to England on the roof of the Volkswagen. After much queuing in hot offices and dealing with Byzantine bureaucracy to release it from the place where it had been impounded by Customs, the Volkswagen accepted the ungainly parcel on its sloping, rackless roof, as meekly as the mule had done. Then, with our suitcase, an icon, Europa Touring, Peter's bulkier portfolio and my Olympia typewriter, we said goodbye to the friends we had made – among them, Yiannis and Vasso, Nikos and Oliga – and drove back to London.

Having written the last two paragraphs I said over lunch to Peter, "How brave you were!"

"Why?"

"Painting so many huge and heavy paintings which would need to be got home to have any chance of being seen and sold."

"I didn't see there'd be a problem," he said.

And there wasn't.

The Volkswagen got us back to England without breaking down, against all expectation and despite the battering it took on unmetalled roads during our Greek winter explorations and its six months' baking in the customs pound. The journey was arduous but entertaining, with a new place to stay every night of the five days it took. In that era before easy air travel, crossing Europe by road was a useful time for re-orientation. Slowly your eyes got used to softer, greener landscapes. By the time you reached Dover, you were familiar again with rain, tidiness, and clearly defined boundaries – but not to driving on the left. That caused a jolt of confusion at the first roundabout. A worse shock, though, had been our arrival in the bedlam of Piraeus, after months spent on the island where there had been only a short stretch of unmade road between harbour and main village on which travelled the island's three vehicles: the bus, the lorry and the taxi.

Back at Westrow, we were regaled with tales of our conman tenant's exploits. He'd provided gossip material, even if no income for us. After he left, we'd had good tenants who paid the rent regularly which fed our mortgage. Now that we were home, it was imperative to start earning again. Peter, his portfolio under his arm, called on his various contacts and some new ones. I got in touch with friends in advertising. The grapevine came up with a vacancy in the copywriting department of an agency called Greenlys and I was taken on. I can clearly recall my time at McCanns and later at Pritchard Wood but I am greeted with a blank when I cast my mind back to

Greenlys. I have no idea of the accounts I was given to write copy for. Only John Pitt, the head copywriter, comes to mind. He was a mild man, not tall, and easily overlooked in all manner of ways, but when he sat down at the piano he came into his own. He could play anything. Where was the piano, I wonder, on which he demonstrated his talent? I think it must have been in his home. He and his wife Jo moved to Putney, and in due course their children were to become friends with ours. Our son Ben called a favourite soft toy Matthew Pitt. It was a kind of Noddy with a bell on the tip of its pointed blue cap, made by Granny Barrett. Ben and (the real) Matthew Pitt, Sophie and Katy Pitt, were all at Whitegates Nursery School on a future return of our family to London.

Advertising was the safe harbour for all kinds of creative people – poets, novelists, musicians, artists, film-makers. Peter and I, as hopeful artist and novelist, were by no means unique but we were luckier than many. Peter very soon had been booked by Halima Nalecz of the Drian Galleries, Porchester Place, for a one-man show the following March. He was also commissioned by various publishers. On the strength of these introductions, I sent my novel to the editors of four of these publishers. Over the following winter, it came back regularly, unaccepted but with remarks that were encouraging enough. One editor suggested I re-work it as a serial for a woman's magazine. This, though it sounded dismissive, was a route I might have followed. On the other hand, to write stories that appeal to a massively large audience, you have to enjoy reading such stories. I don't and never could. I was not down-hearted; just determined to have another go at my sort of novel one day in the future.

Peter had a successful show at the Drian Galleries in March. We'd developed our friendship with Elizabeth Dun, the artist/social worker who we'd met legging it away from Hydra harbour's café tables. Through her, we met Oliver Campion, another very good artist who became a lifelong friend. As did the Lyalls, Gavin and Katharine Whitehorn, first met on Sifnos when they asked us to help as translators. Elizabeth, Oliver and Gavin – all good friends – are no more. Katharine has lost her (exceptionally keen) mind and so is lost to the world as well. This memoir, I can tell, is fast becoming an *In Memoriam.*

 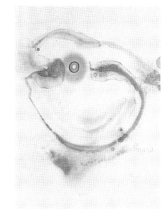 

Let's go back to Peter's show and recall its warm reception. Rosie Hutchinson, my one-time school friend and flat-mate, wrote her response to the paintings on the back of the catalogue. Her words were welcome, but carrying more kudos were those of the critic in The Arts Review.

Peter Barrett's "*first and very impressive show … records the development of his intuitive appreciation of the unique character of the country. The early deeply coloured paintings become more bleached and abstracted, growing in strength as the bones of the landscape appear through the richly textured and eroded surfaces.*"

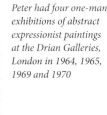

Peter had four one-man exhibitions of abstract expressionist paintings at the Drian Galleries, London in 1964, 1965, 1969 and 1970

Our London life was proceeding at a fast and lucrative pace when we decided we could afford a holiday in Greece. We went by train to Venice, where we left our underwater fishing gear in the left luggage office so that we could spend the day at the Biennale. In the evening we returned to pick it up before the ferry left at 10 pm. The assistant behind the desk disappeared for ages, eventually returning to throw his hands in the air and wave

*Inspired by the landscape
of the Cyclades Peter sketched
continually, often with
later paintings in mind*

50

them about. It was easy to understand that the two guns and the hold-all containing the flippers, masks and snorkels could not be found. There was nothing for it but to leave our English address and hurry to catch the ferry.

It was sad to be in Greece without the ability to re-introduce ourselves to its underwater world. But we met up with our original underwater friends, Yannis and Vaso, and borrowed some gear for a trip to an island we'd had in mind for some time – Folegandros. If it had been the first Cycladian island we'd explored, we would have loved it. But our first had been Sifnos and we were embedded there. If we'd had longer – the journey to and from England took most of one week out of our three-week holiday – we might have gone back to Sifnos, but we couldn't bear the thought of being there, just on holiday. It would be torture not to have "our" house, and stay there, painting and writing for months.

On our way home we had a day in Athens and Peter went to say hello to the design group where he'd worked eighteen months previously. We were to meet after this in a central square. I sat on the marble edge of a flowerbed to wait, recalling the derivation of its name, Klavthmonos. It was named Weeping Square after the civil servants who in the 19th century worked in the nearby government offices. They were political appointees. If their party lost an election, they would gather in the Square and – naturally enough – lament loudly at the loss of their jobs.

Unlike Peter, who at that moment was being offered one.

"Guess what?" he said, finding me in the Square. "I've got an interview this afternoon."

A new magazine was being launched and the design group owners had been asked for recommendations for the job of Art Director. They considered Peter the perfect candidate.

This threw us into turmoil. If he was offered the job, would he want it? Would we want to come back to Greece to repeat our first year, and more?

Acceptance would mean some quick re-arrangements back in London: I would need to give notice to Greenlys and we would have to find tenants for 9 Westrow before travelling back to Greece. It would have to be by road. Would the Volkswagen manage it? If he accepted, Peter would need to start work in Athens in six weeks' time.

We paced up and down. In retrospect, the choice seems glaringly obvious. It didn't at the time. Had we stayed in London, in what direction would our careers have developed? I was already a fairly well-paid copywriter. I would have climbed the advertising career structure. I was writing commercials for television. Might that have developed? What about fiction writing? Would I have had the time? Peter, similarly, might have made more of a name for himself in graphic design; he'd have had no time for painting. But that's a fruitless exercise for the imagination. We opted for Greece and we repeated the pattern of the first year – working in Athens and exploring at weekends in the winter; spending the summer back on Sifnos, painting and writing.

With that repeat year in Greece, we drew nearer to achieving our ambitions. The second novel I wrote in the summer of 1965 on Sifnos made the rounds of publishers in London and was accepted by Michael Joseph, thanks to the agent I found through doing cartoons which Katharine Whitehorn showed to the art editor of The Observer. The art editor called me into his office. I told him I wasn't really a cartoonist; I wrote fiction. He introduced me to his brother-in-law, a literary agent called Jonathan Clowes. Toby Eady was his latest recruit. Toby somehow or other got in a taxi with Mia Farrow and told her about my novel. He persuaded her she would love to play the main character, and on the strength of this taxi ride, film rights were sold to Anglo-Amalgamated film studios. Lucky breaks can take circuitous paths.

Over the next seven years we spent more time in Greece than in England,

putting into practice our aim of painting and writing for a living and at the same time bringing up a family. That last ambition was the one which was the most problematic to achieve. It had suited me not to worry about my strange lack of menstruation. No birth control of any kind was necessary, and I was healthy and normally female in every other way. But as time went by and friends had children, we began to think we should look into the situation. In the autumn of 1965, we were back in London. There was a story in the press about a breakthrough in fertility treatment being conducted by the Queen Elizabeth hospital in Birmingham. We decided I should get an appointment. Had I really imagined I'd be a suitable subject for treatment? Perhaps I did have an ounce of such a hope but I was not surprised when the consultant, after his examination, told me his opinion. He'd love to open me up, he said, and see what was going on inside me but in his opinion there was little chance of eventual success. I was lucky to have a beautiful body (I was slim and tanned from Greece in those days). It would be a shame to mess it around. How much better, he thought, if we accepted the situation and adopted children. I thought at the time, and I still do, that he was a wise and kind man. In a way, I always knew this would be the answer so my breakdown in tears in the hospital Ladies was brief. Boarding school upbringing no doubt helped. There are still unshed tears over the non-existence of our genetic offspring. I cannot read aloud the poem I wrote for our diamond wedding anniversary without releasing a few of them. Yesterday I read it aloud for Mark, our grandson, and his partner Rio, and just made it to the end. They got to their feet, moved around the table, and took turns to hug and kiss me.

We have a family, thanks to Sophie, and thanks to the decision we made in the autumn of 1965. As I couldn't produce our own children, we would adopt. Peter's mother provided support and encouragement and immense practical help. My mother – I'm sad to say – was always, at times of emotional need, geographically distant. I can't say she was emotionally distant, too. She wasn't. She was very loving. But she wasn't a hands-on mother. I guess she hadn't learnt the way. Like many children of

army officers stationed abroad, she spent more time in England with her grandparents than with her parents and, as a teenager, at a boarding school in Kent. In contrast, Florrie Barrett was not such an expressive personality but she attended with single-minded purpose to the details of motherhood – overmuch, her son and daughter might say. What I was like as a mother is not for me to say. The early years when I was learning had its strains and stresses as they coincided with my first acceptance as a novelist. By the time Sophie was two and Ben was a five-month old baby, and his adoption had gone through, we were back in Greece and needing help. Over the next few years in Greece, we had a series of au pairs who looked after Sophie and Ben on weekday mornings while I wrote. We found them through advertisements in the Times personal column: HELP WANTED ON GREEK ISLAND. You can imagine the mass of applicants we received. Our Westrow neighbour, Jean Hobbs, helped us by interviewing and choosing from our top three choices. Maureen was the one who shared the most gorgeous sea journey of our lives; from Amorgos to Sifnos in our small caique on a flat, calm, June day, the blue of the silent, spacious sea melting into the blue of the sky, with visitations from dolphins and, for a brief half hour, a turtle. Ben took his first unaided steps on Kamares quay. Jennie, the last of our helpers, is still a good friend. She and I spent our evenings in meandering and fascinating conversations while we embroidered, crocheted and sewed in the flickering light of oil lamps. Did we damage our eyesight? I have macular degeneration, first diagnosed ten years ago. Jennie seems to be able to see well. She has just helped me by spotting all the typos in the first printing of my latest novel, *Elfrida Next Door*. I shall ask her to do the same with this.

The early years of combining work and a family were mainly spent on the island of Amorgos, years which are well enough recorded in photographs and text in *The Garden of the Grandfather*. But in this memoir I want to tell the more complex and longer story of our sixty years together.

Whatever I experience nearly always makes its way in some form or another into my writing. This does not mean it appears in true-to-life form. Rather, it's like a lump of clay to be shaped according to my aims. I like to produce realistic, credible fiction. Readers think I am describing a real person, a real place. I protest that I'm not. Yet everyone and everything I encounter may contribute to the raw material for my imagination to work with. The shock of London life after long periods on a Greek island fed the ideas for my fourth novel *Rubbish* (1974). Visiting my uncle Dicky in his care home inspired the novel *A Home from Home* (2014). The experience of adoption was the background for *White Lies* (2016). There can be a lengthy time lag between real life and the page.

My first falling in love formed the material for my first attempt at writing a novel. My second novel, *Jam Today,* the first published by Michael Joseph in 1969, was inspired by the period between 1956 and 1960 when, between leaving school and marriage, I was learning about human courtship rituals. During this time I came to the sour conclusion that men were attracted by my body not my brains. It seemed their interest in me was driven by the sole aim of getting me into bed. At the back of my mind I was saying: *You're a nice, intelligent man. Couldn't we just kiss and talk?* The novel that grew out of this was a fantasy about a lively Londoner who tricked men into

paying her for the bed-time she avoided in a variety of imaginative ways. "*A jolly romp. I found this hilarious,*" said the Daily Telegraph. Making people laugh was the way I'd found to express the disappointment that had accrued during my single years and any anger at some of the men I'd met on the way. The publisher came up with the flagline *Tales of a Virgin Prostitute,* or words to that effect. I was left smiling at its success but fundamentally uneasy. There was a shakiness in the novel's logic which needed more than laughter to sort out. Perhaps the faultline came from the fact that I had not based the content on real experience.

Jam Today was published by Michael Joseph in 1969 and opened the path for my agent to place my next three novels with them. "*Susan Barrett is that rare bird – a good, modern, English comic novelist,*" wrote the Liverpool Daily Post. I was mentioned in an article in the Times as one of the few female writers who can make people laugh. That pleased me but I was keen that each novel, besides inducing bursts of surprised laughter, made a pertinent point about human nature and social customs. "*Taking a few swipes at materialistic society on her way, Susan Barrett contrives some marvellous muddles,*" said a review of *Noah's Ark* in 1971. The photo on the back cover shows me feeding deer in Richmond Park. It must have been around the time when Ben, racing downhill in the park, fell over a log, cut open his cheek and needed stitches in hospital. I fainted while holding his hand. He was stoical.

Raleigh Trevelyan, a charming and civilised man, was my editor at Michael Joseph. He invited Peter and me to a meal in his Mayfair flat on a couple of occasions. We met there someone whose novel Raleigh was bringing out and who also had connections with Greece. This was Polly Hope. She and her husband John had a house on Rhodes. Over the course of the next forty years we kept in intermittent touch. This was typical of our times back in London. Circles of friendships often overlapped. Polly gave wonderful parties in London. She was a networker and through her we met old friends and made new ones. Martin Young, a friend of ours from our first Athens winter, invited us to his London wedding and Polly was there. Later, Elizabeth Dun, met first on our brief visit to Hydra, came across Polly through paintings and tapestries. Through Elizabeth we met Oliver Campion, whose paintings we admired. In memoriam: Raleigh, Julia, Polly, John, Theo, Oliver, Elizabeth.

While spending most of our time in Greece, various reasons took us back to London. There was the excitement over the film rights of *Jam Today* in autumn 1969, and the shock of my father's sudden death in January 1969. There were Peter's four exhibitions at the Drian Galleries, in 1964, 1965, 1969 and 1971. Peter had to keep in touch with the publishers who were commissioning him for illustrations and book jackets: Puffin children's books, Penguin Modern Poets, and a series of educational books for Anthony Blond. For one particular book jacket, Peter arranged for our Westrow neighbour's son, Adrian Hobbs, to take a photograph. When we were about to christen our newly adopted Ben, we asked Adrian to be his godfather, as well as Oliver Campion. Adrian visited us first on Sifnos and later on Amorgos. He and I shared the flight back from London after I'd been on my own to meet the Hollywood film producer. A thunderstorm as we were coming in to land meant we had to circle over the runway for some time

while lightning ricocheted off the mountains that encircle Athens. In those days the airport with its single runway lay tucked between the sea and the foot of Mount Hymettos. The ferry from Piraeus that week went only to Aiyiali at the other end of Amorgos. On arrival on the island we had one more leg of our journey by caique. By the late 1960s plane travel was cheaper and there were more frequent flights, but the ferries between Piraeus and the islands were still infrequent and slow in comparison with today's superfast and enclosed carriers. The enchantment of island travel has been lost for us who remember earlier days.

Among the many book jackets that Peter designed were – naturally enough – those he did for my novels, with dispensation from the art director of Michael Joseph. My second novel with them was *Moses*, published in 1970, the story of a single, female copywriter who wanted keep her baby as well as her job. But of course, a parent cannot look after a young child at the same time as working full time.

I knew this in theory before taking 11-day old Sophie home from the hospital in March 1966. I was happy to give up the daily tube journey from Putney to the agency. Five months later after she'd become legally ours, we returned to Sifnos and were dismayed to find a German couple in "our" house. Costas and Smaragtha gave us a room in the potteries to live in with the use of another room for Peter who was working to a deadline. I began to learn the reality of being a fulltime mother. I rinsed the terry towelling nappies in the sea before washing them in the stone sink set in the sea wall, in water drawn up from the well. Sophie sat in her Moses basket on the beaten-earth terrace and learnt to say "bilow" to the cats that roamed the potteries. I made a sling out of canvas to carry Sophie so that I could, in principle, take her along the rocks or across the beach to Kamares. Without the back-up of Peter, I was a wimp. Was I shy? Nervous of the attention? Uncertain of speaking good enough Greek? Anxious for Sophie's safety? I believe an adoptive mother is hypernervous, still riddled, however faintly, with her pre-adoption concern that she's looking after someone else's baby. Whatever it was that kept me bound to the single room and the terrace behind the sea wall, I waited until Peter emerged from his room, the day's work done, before venturing away from the potteries. Eva and her half German, half Greek Costas, who were in "our" house, became good friends. At Christmas they turned a corner of the main room into a magical candlelit

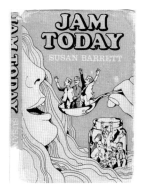 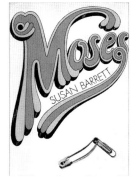 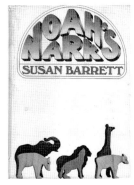

grotto of decorated fir branches and a hand-carved nativity scene. "Blow me, fuck it!" is the rough translation of Nikos the fisherman's response to the sight.

We moved in January 1967 to the newly-built house at Ta Nera on Amorgos. Peter continued to illustrate books for publishers. Sophie was my entire life. A typical moment I remember was when we sat on the hillside above our house surrounded by wild flowers, Sophie wearing the strange woollen dungarees I'd knitted for her from island wool. I counted 23 different flowers within an arm's reach – although to be certain of the number I would need to look at the book Peter and I did in the 1980s about Greek nature, or at the book we did in 2018 describing this period of our lives in the 1960s. Another example of how our life feeds our work, and our work is our life.

Today I received an email from France on our website.

Dear Mrs Barrett

After 24 hours of disinfection period in our entrance hall, your exquisite book has reached our sitting room. It is just charming and wonderful.

Stray comments that come in like this make the hard grind and hazards worthwhile. Even more meaningful than the compliments was the description of the writer's personal knowledge of a boat we'd photographed in 1964 in Piraeus harbour. The photograph is reproduced on page 43 of *The Garden*. As a 12-year old Alexis Payne had been on board the *Saita*. For him it was "the most beautiful yacht in the world." It belonged, he writes, "to Alain and Mary de Rothschild before it was sold to Hubert de Givenchy." His father knew Patrick Leigh Fermor and Lawrence Durrell.

Such reminders of the myriad overlappings and interminglings of time, people and lives are precious, especially when the reminders come out of the blue.

We always intended to have two children, so we returned to London at the end of the summer 1967. Again Peter's mother provided crucial help. We were led, via her doctor, to expect the imminent delivery of a baby in a Southampton nursing home. On December 5th, the baby was born. A boy. We went to see him as soon as we could. My father came with us and pushed Sophie around in the pram (a pram! Possible on pavements!) while we went in to see the baby. A nun brought him downstairs. "Would you like to hold him?" she asked. We took turns. I looked down at the baby's solemn face. His eyes were bright blue and wide open and he regarded me with what I fearfully imagined was distress. "Please don't cry," I said. His mouth didn't crumple. His gaze remained steady. The name his mother gave him at birth was Jonathan which we retained as his second. Five months later, Benjamin Jonathan became a Barrett. "Now we can go back to Greece!" Sophie told the judge in her bright, two and half year old way. We'd been keeping our life on a Greek island as dark as possible during the trial period, not wanting to appear a feckless couple. The judge didn't comment. The court order had been signed.

It was during the months in London, waiting for the adoption to be finalised, that I began to fret at my mother's role. I longed to get back to writing. I was not one of those wonder women who scribble away at the kitchen table with a baby slung over each shoulder. I grew severely depressed and consulted the doctor who prescribed Valium. The Rolling Stones' "Mother's little helper" was the hit of the time. The little yellow pills they sang about slowed me down so effectively that nothing got done. I was at a standstill which worried and depressed me even more.

A critical moment was reached when my agent arranged to bring someone in public relations to meet me. I invited them to supper. (Giving people delicious food is still my preferred way of deflecting attention from me as Writer. The thought is "At least I cook well.") This is one of my most vivid and embarrassing memories. I'd got Sophie and Ben bathed and in bed. Peter was probably reading them stories. Supper was in the oven. I'd cleared away the carpet of toys on the parquet floor and was getting out plates and cutlery. The pointlessness of presenting myself as a writer with a novel to publicise struck me with sudden force. *But look at me, I'm a harassed mother, not a novelist*! I downed tools and went to the cinema in Wimbledon, leaving Peter to greet Toby and the PR man at the door and somehow explain my disappearance. I still feel bad about this.

Parenting is the most valuable contribution anyone can make to society and parents need all the help that society should and could provide. It's very simple but I am not sure any society in any time or place has yet achieved a fair solution to the conundrum of how to manage this fairly for parents. In the present Covid pandemic, it's the women who have taken on the brunt of the home teaching as well as the housework. The job and preoccupations of the man in the household still take precedence over childcare. In the 17th and 18th century women were starting to cry out in frustration. An idea I have for my next novel circles around an 18th century female poet, smarting under the restrictions imposed by her gender. By the 1970s I'd read *The Female Eunuch* and was inspired by Germaine Greer's clarion call to do whatever we can to hasten equality. I resolved to use my novels for the purpose. Thanks to my helpers, by 1972 when we returned to make our base in England for the children's education, I had written and had published: *Jam Today*, (1969) *Moses* (1970), *Noah's Ark* (1971), and *Private View* (1972).

My writing desk on Amorgos was a pine shelf built under the bedroom window. A door led out onto the blue-painted wooden balcony. I'd look up from my Olympia portable typewriter and see the children wending their way up from the sea with the helper of the time, who would concoct lunch from whatever could be magicked up: nasturtium leaf salad and a tin of mackerel comes to mind. It was a wonderful period of our lives, with time for everything – childcare, work, days out, boat trips. We progressed from the small boat with inboard motor to a 20-foot caique with a hold big enough to line with rolls of sorbo-rubber so that we could spend nights away. It had a mast and sail but mainly we chugged along to the steady thrum of the ancient engine. On a long trip to Astypalia, we called in for the night at Levitha, a very small island inhabited by a single family. The single child, a daughter, had never seen another child before and prodded Sophie in the chest, testing to see if she was real or a doll.

Today in August 2020 Peter has just come into my study with a photograph that we'd mislaid. It's precious to me. On the back I'd written the date, October 1968, and a note that this was the last time I saw my father. I'd returned to England on my own to meet the Hollywood producer who had bought the film rights to Jam Today. I stayed with the Wilkinsons in Albion Street and took the opportunity to visit Jane and family in Godalming, My parents came over from Liphook to see me, and my father drove me to the station for the train back to London. The four Owtram boys, Michael, Robert, Francis and Jocelyn, came too. Chris, Jane's youngest son, was not yet born. Jane took the photo. I'm wearing the coat Diny lent me. My father is holding his diary, wanting to know when I'd be back in London for Peter's third exhibition at the Drian Galleries. The answer was February. In January, he died from a massive stroke while playing golf. His two dogs were with him. I learnt of this a few days later when someone came to the house at Ta Nera with a telegram.

We flew back to England with the children for the funeral and stayed on for Peter's exhibition. The Wilkinsons' basement was our home for two months. How on earth did Peter's paintings get back for the exhibition? Fortunately, Peter is here to ask.

He's sitting on the sofa in his studio sorting through piles of contact strips, thumbnails of black and white photographs, with inclusion in this memoir in mind. I have brought back to my room a strip which shows Nanny Guerini (from my early childhood in Tavistock) holding a quite substantial baby Ben on her lap. The photo is black and white but her fluffy fur hat was pale blue, as far as I remember, matching her speedwell-blue eyes. I think she must have been happy to visit us in Westrow, to meet Peter and our two children, and to remember her wartime years at Markham with the Withingtons. For me, she was hugely important. For her, I was just one of the many children she looked after over the years. Seeing her in Putney reminded me of the dreadful hollowness I felt when she left us. At the age of 4, I could not fathom how someone so central to my life could give me up.

She must have long since hardened her heart in some way to have been able to love a child for a while and then move on. But the visit to Putney brought back the tears that flooded our eyes, hers and mine, in 1942.

Now the answer to the question about the paintings. Peter tells me that he took them off their stretchers for the journey. With the stretchers in a parcel and the paintings in a big roll, he got his work onto the plane. In a room in the Wilkinsons' Albion Street house, he fixed the canvases back onto their stretchers ready to be hung at the Drian. In this room he also managed to do some work for Pete Rose who was the advertising account executive in an agency called Fordham Sadler. The job was to design ads or maybe brochures for a business called Vinyl Products. Money coming in! Very important. The exhibition was a success, too; his best work yet, in his opinion. We went back to Greece before it was over, leaving Halima and Diny to deal with the unsold paintings. Halima entered two for the Royal Academy summer show and they were accepted. The Wilkinsons housed the remainder, and continued to do so over many years, in France and America, offloading the ones that they could not accommodate in the process. We hope that whoever has a Barrett abstract expressionist oil painting hanging in their home now is as pleased with them as Nanny Guerini was when she held her Baby Sue's baby.

Susie on Godalming station saying goodbye to her father and four nephews

Peter's sketches were often the source of his abstract paintings

THE 1970s

During our time in Greece, Peter had always drawn or painted the fish he caught before we ate them. He also recorded plants and birds; in fact, he drew and painted anything in nature that caught his eye. My agent, Toby Eady, saw his work and introduced Peter to a fellow Etonian called Virgil Pomfret, who was with Artist Partners, one of the top London agencies for illustration and design. "If you can do this, and you obviously can," said Virgil, "I can get you lots of work." This was the start of the wildlife bonanza in publishing. Peter became known for his ability to paint panoramas. This was the word for large double page spreads showing a number of animals in particular habitats. He could make unreal scenes look real in every detail. Each leaf, each feather, each hair was painted accurately in delicate watercolours. Peter began to get commissions which he carried out over the following years wherever we were based at the time.

Our smallholding life began on two and a half acres at Goodiford Mill, a Devonshire watermill which pre-dated the Domesday Book

Our house on Amorgos now had a second storey and he worked in an upstairs room with big windows. One window looked over the 'garden'; in other words, over the stone-walled triangle of dry, red earth, struggling vines and flourishing almond trees. He could see down to the thyme-covered, rocky headland and the little whitewashed church of Agios Pandeleimon on its promontory jutting into the bay. Peter could keep an eye on the caique, which we'd named after the church and kept moored offshore. In wild, winter weather it was sometimes necessary to race down and fend the caique off the rocks. Even the most solid mooring – an anchor pinned down by a pile of rocks assembled by Peter over a number of dives – was not heavy enough in a howling storm. I could imagine it breaking into smithereens.

The other window in his work room looked towards the gate onto the path that led up the hill to the spring. On the other side of the path lay the house of Father Lorenz, the Austrian priest who lived in Athens. He had bought a ruin and created a one-roomed holiday home. He was a welcome neighbour. Whenever we had an English helper he very kindly let us have the house. Good to keep it aired, he said.

The children knew they were welcome in the studio only at special times

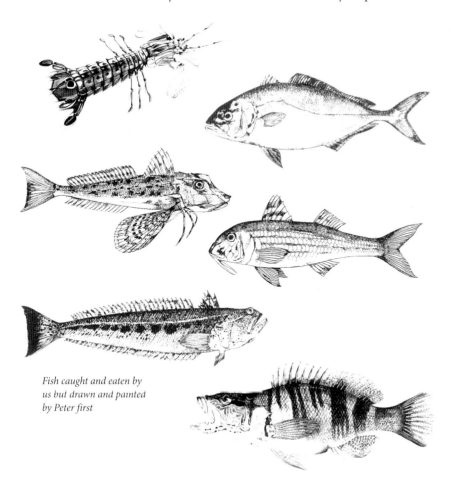

Fish caught and eaten by us but drawn and painted by Peter first

and by invitation. On one such occasion Sophie was sitting on Peter's lap and he gave her a pencil and a big sheet of paper. She drew a jagged line. That gave me the idea for a children's book, an idea which Peter elaborated with brightly coloured illustrations in oil paints. Eventually the idea evolved into three books which were published by Ward Lock; *The Line Sophie Drew, The Square Ben Drew*, and a third for Peter's niece, *The Circle Sarah Drew*. His nephew Graham missed out when the publisher drew his own line under the series. All the same, the books were read on television's PlaySchool, which of course, thrilled the family.

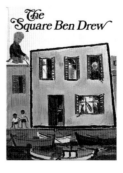

Sophie started school on Amorgos when she was five and completed the first year, as described in *The Garden*. She was bright, flaxen-haired, and fluent in children's Greek. This made her something of a pet mascot in the harbour community. Ben, on the other hand, was having difficulties. Most of the time he was a happy, normal little boy but he was prone to the tantrums of a two-year old long after he was two. We had to tread delicately. Only recently have I discovered that there is a name for the syndrome which we think he has suffered from all his life. In recent years, there has been research into a behavioural pattern which sounds like his. Half way between psychosis and neurosis, it's given the label Borderline Personality Disorder. At the time, we just responded to each child in the way that seemed best: an example of the subtle and continuous interaction between nature and nurture. Adoption colours this interaction in a particular way. One of its benefits is that we had no idea what to expect, so the children were raised without the pressure of parental expectation.

Our life on Amorgos was just what we wanted, even though it was no longer the idyll that it had been when we chose our spot, which I've described as the centre of the front row of the dress circle. At first we'd lorded it in an empty valley overlooking the outer reaches of the bay, the only other building in view being the church on its promontory. But of course one house attracts more. Dionysia, who'd left the island and lived in Athens with her husband, looked at the land she owned on the hillside above the newly-built Englishman's house and thought '*that's a good idea.*' They had two children much the same ages as Sophie and Ben, and the children played together in the summer weeks when the family were there. A German architect threatened to build a holiday village on the nearby hillside. Fortunately, he and his wife succumbed to the charms of Ta Nera and just built one house for themselves. Jutta became a good friend. Kris and

Alan Bushley, an American couple who'd spent time working in Athens, built a one-roomed house on a rocky knoll in the bay beyond the church on its promontory. A summer cabin, they called it. Their children came to play. In later years, they would lend us the cabin for our own summer holidays. Father Lorenz invited friends of his to build onto his little house. Erica and Etele had two boys. The family came for the summer holidays, bringing Erica's mother to help. But she wanted a holiday, too, so it was often convenient to park the boys on our terrace. We became a kind of PlaySchool of our own.

It is still hard for some people to understand that our home is our place of work. We are not on a never-ending holiday, nor are we retired with a comfortable pension as many of our age group are. Matters are worse for me, because writing is generally an invisible occupation. However, with the Covid epidemic, there's been a huge increase in the number of people working from home. We even have our own initials now. WFH is understood and approved of.

In the small community of Katapola on Amorgos we were known for our way of life and Peter was admired for his work. They'd bring him dead birds to stuff and draw. He was asked to paint signs which he would always do, fitting these in between working on the commissions for wildlife illustration that were coming in from 1970 onwards. One of his first commissions came from a publishing firm called Mitchell Beazley. Peter did a number of illustrations for their Atlas of the Earth. As a result of this work, they wanted Peter on their next project, another big work with a similar title: Atlas of World Wildlife. Virgil phoned from London. The Katapola telephone lady sent someone around the bay to alert Peter. The walk, without stopping for chats, took half-an-hour. Peter went over to Katapola and phoned Virgil back. It had taken over an hour for Virgil to speak with Peter, a call that today would be instantaneous. Still, in 1971 or so, it worked well enough in Katapola's telephone exchange where the phone's battery had to be fed with water. Peter said yes, he was interested.

First of all, he had to get to London for discussions and to do a trial rough of an African panorama. An airplane ticket would be waiting for him at the Olympic offices at Athens airport. It was summer and there were several boats a week. Within two weeks Peter had got to London, roughed out a trial panorama of an African savannah and its wildlife, and returned to Amorgos. Some months later, he received the next request. He was to go to London to rough out and collect the reference material for the next six panoramas. It was now winter, snow was lying on the hills, the seas were rough and there were many days without ferries. He was given a lift to Syros by Mitsos, the captain of the small steamer which took goods between the Cycladian islands. From Syros he could take the daily ferry to Piraeus. But it wasn't until two days later that he reached Syros. The engine broke down off the coast of Sifnos. Hours were spent wallowing in the heaving seas, breathing in diesel fumes. Peter was sick, re-enacting his hours at the helm of the minesweeper in his national service days, off the north coast of Scotland. He finally reached Piraeus 20 hours after leaving Amorgos. In London he stayed with Ma and Pa in Dulwich, commuting daily to the Mitchell Beazley offices. He was away for a long two months.

I had Jennie for company. After I'd put the children to bed, we'd light the lamps and stuff a few twigs and spindly logs into the antique stove which never drew properly. Jennie and I would resume the conversation that absorbed us for the entire year she spent with us. While we talked, we sewed. It can't have been very good for our eyes, peering at tiny stitches of embroidery or crocheted lace in the flickering lamplight. We might listen to our few tapes on the battery-fed cassette player which made Mozart sound as though he was being played by a skiffle group in an echoing barn. We were happy.

By the time Peter returned, Sophie had learnt to whistle. We went over to Katapola to meet the boat we hoped he'd be on, Sophie whistling all the way in preparation for showing Daddy her new skill. Back in his studio, Peter set to work on the panoramas which he gave to the ταχυδρομος, the 'postman' who dealt not with letters but with goods, to and from the island and Athens. He delivered the artwork, parcel by parcel as it was produced, to the Olympic Airways office for its flight back to London and the Mitchell Beazley offices. Amazingly, none went astray.

You can see from this that it was not easy to earn money as a freelance illustrator while living on a Greek island.

From the early 1970s Peter received an increasing number of commissions for wildlife from well-known publishers, including Reader's Digest and Mitchell Beazley

Today, August 26th 2020, Peter is suffering from kidney stones. He had a scan two days ago in the ESAC unit of our local hospital. That stands for Emergency Surgical Ambulatory Care; in other words, care of the walking wounded. He's in pain but he says it's not the agony he felt when he had kidney infection. This was in 1973. We were at the time in London, and about to return to Amorgos. Peter went into Putney hospital and then to Dulwich to finish the artwork for a book on insects, one of a series under the umbrella title *Fantastic*. He had to meet the publisher's deadline, which had been delayed by his infection, while I and the children flew back to Athens. On the journey, the children developed – was it chickenpox or measles? Naturally enough, they were miserable. With two feverish and fractious children, I humped the luggage by taxi to an Athens hotel; from there to Piraeus and onto the ferry to Amorgos; then from Katapola and the long walk back to Ta Nera and the house. Although Peter could hardly be blamed for his infection, I slipped easily into the role of martyr but mollified by the thought of Peter's earning capabilities. Those continue today. Peter's American agent has a suitcase-full of his early wildlife paintings which is slowly gaining present-day attention in auction houses in the US.

Even before the increased demand for Peter's wildlife illustration, we were beginning to look ahead with the children's education in mind. At some point during this period, we'd managed to buy a much bigger house in Putney which we let out for long periods as we had done with Westrow. Now with the junta in power and Sophie believing miraculous tales of saints and martyrs, we decided it was time to make our base in England, not Greece. The house in Montolieu Gardens was a generous, Edwardian, semi-detached house with a small garden made into a dog run by the previous owners. We had fun creating a new layout with a corner patio that caught any sun that dared peer through clouds. Inside, we redecorated every room and converted the attic into a studio. We bought a colour television. There was the miracle of electricity and running water in the house and a launderette in the Upper Richmond Road, a short drive down an asphalt road. The ease of daily life compensated for our removal from Ta Nera. "Skinny Lizzy!" a lad called out to me, as I shopped in the grocer's while our laundry tumble-dried. I was wearing Peter's tight naval top. Our Greek island years had been good for the figure.

Being country-born and bred, I was still at the stage of loving London. I had no help but, beyond the occasional evening sitter-in, I didn't need it. Sophie started at the local primary school and Ben went to Whitegates Nursery School, where he fell foul of the kindly but firm head. I was working away at my novels which were being regularly published by Michael Joseph. All was well, as far as I was concerned. I liked being a mother among other mothers. There was Annie Cole down the road, wife of Mike, with their

Animal paintings for the Closer Look series, Archon Press

"Butterflies" for the Sunday Times colour magazine

children, Alexander and Olivia, my god daughter. Joan Dalley, friend from Pritchard Wood days, had also moved to Putney with her artist husband Terry. Ben made friends with Matthew Pitt, the son of John Pitt who I'd worked for at Greenlys. We weren't far from the Barrett parents in Dulwich, nor from Peter's sister, Jennifer, with Sarah and Graham in Sydenham. There were films and exhibitions to see, and an increasing circle of interesting people to meet.

However, Peter, having spent his teens in Dulwich, loathed suburbia. He railed against the uniformity of the cherry-tree lined, residential streets, and the tedious journey into central London to see clients. He hated the overhead roar of aircraft coming into land at Heathrow, one every two minutes. To lift his mood, we arranged a week's spring holiday in the west country.

We stayed on a farm not far outside the town of Wiveliscombe in Somerset. The lanes were studded with primroses, speedwell, campion and umbellifers. In the steep, green fields, lambs practised skipping. Ben rode a trike helter-skelter down the bumpy track outside the cottage, a foretaste of his teenage years spent as a reckless, black leather-clad biker. We had the children's secondary education in mind. A London friend had remarked that there was a very good comprehensive in a big town called Tiverton. One day we visited this town and parked outside an estate agent. Don't go in, I pleaded. Don't leave our name. If Peter did, I was certain they'd send us details of something irresistible and we'd have to move.

This is exactly what happened. As soon as we were back in London, we were sent details of an ancient mill with two acres of land near Cullompton in Devon, not that far from Tiverton and its excellent comprehensive. (We learnt later that the town with the excellent comprehensive mentioned by the friend was *Totnes*, not Tiverton.) The mill was coming up for auction in a week's time. I went down with flu and in my fevered state I could not get the agents' description of Goodiford Mill out of my head. I phoned my sister Jane. "Would you like a swift trip to Devon?" I asked, knowing she would. Down to Devon we went, planning to stay the night on the way back with friends of the Owtrams in Dorset. We both fell for the Mill. I then had the task of persuading Peter, who hadn't seen the place, that we should take part in the auction.

Hardly a difficult task. Peter picked up the idea and ran with it. He phoned a fellow Artist Partners artist who had moved to Devon. Through him, he was introduced to a local estate agent who would bid on our behalf. On the day of the auction Peter rose at five in the morning and headed west. He visited the agent in his Wiveliscombe office before continuing to Cullompton, passing the Mill in Kentisbeare on the way. If he'd thought the place looked frightful, he wouldn't have continued to the auction. He could appreciate its romantic promise at once. His heart sank when, at the auction, bids passed our limit. The auction closed. Peter had only a few minutes to register the loss of the brief dream we'd shared of a mill and two and half acres of orchard, stream and field in Devon. The agent explained that the higher bids were "off the wall". The Mill was ours.

We moved from London to Devon three months later, having sold Montolieu Gardens just in time. Finding the buyer was a stroke of luck. On my return from viewing the Mill with Jane, I'd spotted someone walking slowly past the house, looking up at our roof. I leapt out of the house to intercept. "Can I help you?" I asked. She said she was interested in the house next door

Illustrating the World Guide to Mammals for an American publisher took a good two years. At the same time Peter was illustrating books for Flammarion, a French publisher

65

and had heard we'd converted our attic. They would do the same, if it was viable. "Come in," I said and showed her not just the attic but the whole house. The next day they made an offer and the solicitors got to work. With a completion date fixed for early September, we flew back to Athens for the summer holidays on Amorgos.

It's startling to remember how confident and relaxed we were. On booking our return flight we'd allowed ourselves just one day to get the house ready for the removal men. Arriving at the airport in Athens with a day in hand, we learnt the flight was cancelled. It would be 24 hours before the next. We phoned Ma and Pa Barrett who had the key of the house in Putney. They went into action, dismantling light fittings and taking down curtains. We arrived home at five a.m. beating the removal men by four hours. Then off we went to Devon, Sophie and Ben excited by this latest development in their lives. If they were at all apprehensive, they didn't show it. They were used to changes in their environment. We were the constants in their lives.

There'd been a mill at Goodiford for many centuries. It was entered in the Domesday Book. By our day the wheel had gone but the water that had turned it remained, a frothing, white curtain of tumbling water right outside the living room's double-glazed French window. You could sit on one of our low 'scoop' chairs (covered in beige corduroy, cutting edge fashion in the early seventies) and let yourself be mesmerised by the constantly falling sheets of water. Sometimes, after heavy rain, we had to hurry to raise the sluice gate higher up the land, so that the stream took an alternative course across the fields. Almost at once, the waterfall dribbled to a silent, sad standstill.

The next owners of the Mill diverted the mill leat and stopped the waterfall permanently. They were worried that their two small boys would fall into the pool. Surely it would have been better not to buy the Mill in the first place? In our opinion, the Mill was nothing without its water. But it's no good being sad over possessions you no longer possess.

It was a romantic property. The mill stream divided the land into two fields. In one field, once a cider apple orchard, there was a large wooden henhouse on wheels parked under one of the few remaining trees. We promptly bought some hens: black and white Marrans, as recommended by our neighbouring farmer's wife, Mary Tancock. (She sent us a card for our diamond wedding anniversary – did I mention that? I do appreciate these long threads that run through lifetimes). We also, fairly soon, bought a pair of goats, a nanny and her kid. Sophie was the one who named our animals. This pair was called Nancy and Dusky. Nancy was fiendish to milk. It took two people: one to milk, the other to hold a hind leg which otherwise would have kicked everything within reach. In the meantime, Dusky would be looking for trouble in the yard, which we were in the process of clearing. Household and garden junk had amassed here, spilling down the open side of the yard to the stream. It seems that whenever we've moved (and we've done this a number of times) we've had mountains of a previous owner's junk to clear. It started with the front garden of 9 Westrow deep in empty wine and milk bottles.

In our three years at the Mill, we cleared the yard, created a vegetable garden in a quarter of one of the acres, and progressed from goats to a Dexter cow. Our friend Katharine Whitehorn wrote about the cow who came with

the name Morning Glory. She likened it to a small grand piano, by virtue of its short legs. The article was about self-sufficiency, as far as I remember. We were at the forefront of the living off the land movement. *Self-sufficiency* by John Seymour was our Bible. But we were not full-time smallholders. We had our own work. Peter's reputation had grown to the extent that he was working to deadlines all the time in the ready-made studio in the apex of the converted mill part of the house. Besides working on novels, I'd written a play for television, having become enamoured with the medium while watching programmes in the Montolieu Gardens playroom. The play, *The Portrait*, was produced by John Frankau at London Weekend television and directed by John Glenister. I was invited to the read-through and a rehearsal which fascinated me. The three parts were played by Annette Crosbie, Maurice Denham and Trevor Eve. "A masterly portrait" said James Thomas in the Daily Express review. "*Across the easel, the conversation between two very different people was not only witty but sad, as subject and artist start to examine each other in a way which neither had really bargained for.*"

The idea for the play had come to me while sitting for a portrait at the request of our friend Oliver Campion. Oliver needed an example of his work to show in the gallery which was the source of his portrait commissions. Being between novels, I was happy to sit for him and daydream. We were still living in London at the time. I wrote the 50 minute play in the spare bedroom at Montolieu Garden and it was accepted, thanks to Judy Daish, the film and television agent Toby had passed me onto. For the production a portrait of Maurice Denham had to be created. I recommended Oliver. Maurice and Oliver got on well as the work progressed, Oliver going down to Brighton, I think it was, over the course of some weeks. On screen, the stages in the painting process were evident and convincing. It was a portrait of a quality unusually high for a prop in a play. I wonder where it is now. The artwork Peter was doing around this time is popping up in auction houses, each time at a higher price. Perhaps Maurice Denham's portrait is doing the same.

I was so thrilled by seeing my play come alive that I resolved to write more for television. Somehow or other – I cannot remember the details of this – but I know Ken Loach came to visit me at the Mill to discuss an idea. Looking back, I see the start of one of the many paths not followed. In fact, I would never have become the kind of writer Loach was looking for. I was not hard-hitting enough. Another invitation appeared which entailed taking a train to Reading and meeting someone to discuss an idea he had in mind. At the time, I couldn't understand what he was talking about. It made no sense to me. Years later, when I heard about video games, I realised he was at the very start of their production. He needed subject matter. It was hard for him to explain what he was after when what he was after did not yet exist, either digitally or verbally. I doubt whether I would have been able to write the kind of stuff that makes a good video game, although I might have had a go if I'd understood what was wanted.

A path I was more likely to have followed began with a report in the Observer that caught my eye. A delivery man, failing to raise a response at a mid-Devon farmhouse, found the farmer, his younger brother and his sister in the vegetable garden, all three shot dead. The two brothers and a sister had lived all their lives on the family farm. The elder brother, unable to manage

Illustrations for La Nature,
published by Flammarion

the farm any longer, put it up for sale. He couldn't face the loss of the farm, nor the stress the prospect caused his brother and sister. He took the only course he felt left open to him.

I'd read and admired Truman Capote's *In Cold Blood*. Might I write a script for a dramatised documentary on the same lines? I began visiting Winkleigh and talking with the people who knew the Luxtons. The journalists the story attracted, locally and from London, were cold-shouldered, while I was taken into homes and given cups of tea and wonderful background information. As the weeks passed and my notebooks filled, I became more and more uneasy. Each time I visited, I had to pull into a lay-by on the way home to be copiously sick. I formed the notion that Frances, the sister, was sending me a firm message: **stay away**. But there was a powerful story to be told. What was I to do?

A journalist called John Cornwell had spotted me at the auction of farm goods and learnt that I was gathering material. Over several months he urged Toby to persuade me to give way to him and pass on my contacts and information. I took him up eventually, realising I did not have the attributes of a journalist. John went on to produce an excellent Capote-style book with the title "*Earth to Earth*".

I'd taken ten years to discover what sort of writing I could do, and what I couldn't. I don't suppose this is surprising. I returned to novels and, in the spare bedroom at the Mill overlooking the now cleared and tarmacadamed yard, I wrote *Private View*. I was also trying to give up smoking at this time, inspired by the wonderfully fresh air all around us. There was little traffic past the Mill. Save for tractors …

Peter who'd spent much of his young childhood in North Wales and adult years on Greek islands, held that *real* countryside should be silent, save for the sounds of nature. He began to count the number of tractors that passed the Mill in a day. On his drawing pad of paper, in the margin of his roughs, he kept a tractor count. He grew more irritable and depressed. Well, we could move! We'd find somewhere well away from a busy lane. In any case, our animal count was stretching the bounds of the Mill's acreage. We had several sheep, a cow and a calf, a couple of pigs, hens, ducks on the stream, two dogs and a cat. Sophie had named them all. Kojak was the ironical name for the ewe with a corkscrew of curls hanging over her forehead. The dogs were Pepper, a Lassie collie, and Charlie, a collie-spaniel cross, inherited from neighbours who no longer wanted him. The cat, which we thought was a ginger tom, turned out to be a ginger female. Tarzan became Tarzanna.

It would be sad to move away. Family and friends had visited and loved the place. The Wilkinson family stayed. Tarzanna inspired their long line of cats. Jim Liontos, a Greek-Canadian first met in the London advertising world and a friend of John Burge, stayed with his partner Lynn, They looked after things when we went to Amorgos for the summer holidays; as did Peter's sister Jennifer, now divorced and accompanied by her new man, Bill. (They didn't have to milk the cow, a paid task fulfilled by a helpful neighbour). Their stays at the Mill led them to buy a holiday cottage near Honiton. They moved there eventually, when Bill retired. R.I.P both of them. Another visitor, sent from London for a short week, was Bernard Lyall. Either his mother, Katharine Whitehorn, thought Bernard needed to

David Attenborough's Life on Earth, Alan Jenkin's A Countryman's Year, the Sunday Times colour magazine and its Book of the Countryside were among the many publications that Peter worked on, besides commissions from America including several series of porcelain plates for Franklin Mint

understand where milk came from, or she needed a break from sons. Maybe a bit of both. I'd love to be able to ask her but tragically, her mind has gone.

This morning I missed the video call that my brother-in-law, Peter, and I try to make each Friday at 11. In the background I see Jane, slumped in an armchair, with what was part of Downderry's garden visible through the window. A single apple tree survives from what was an orchard. Jane, lying almost prostrate in her chair, is a survivor, too, having suffered from a bad reaction to codeine five years ago. She waves a vague hand towards the tablet that Peter holds. It is so sad to see her like this, when she spent her life as a dynamo of action. The video call maintains a tenuous connection with her.

After my father's death, my mother had converted the stables at Downderry and she was living there in the 1970s, next door to Jane and Peter and their sons, who now numbered five, Christopher having been born in 1970. Jane was teaching Social Science students at Guildford technical college. Peter was a part-time Probation Officer in a London borough while training as a psychotherapist. Our mother helped by giving the boys a cooked Sunday breakfast so Jane and Peter could have a sleep-in. Someone else who helped Jane at times was Frances Mellersh, the wife of Clive, a second cousin of our mother's. Frances was originally from Devon and, when she moved back as a widow, we became good friends until her death last December.

Such byways keep tempting me away from my main path through our married life. I can't resist catching the threads between the past and present which make clear the intricate and invisible network of time, place, people and events that run through everybody's life. I want to pin them down in case they reveal their significance later.

This phenomenon was at work today. Peter and I spent an hour after lunch investigating a small wicker hamper which dates from my parents' Hong Kong days. It holds the surplus from the drawers of a previous, far bigger desk. Peter is sorting through hundreds of photographs, with illustrating this memoir in mind. I'm on a hunt for my first photograph album which I was sure I'd kept somewhere. But no, it's not in the attic, nor in my present desk's drawers, nor in the wicker hamper. I think I have to accept that, in a wild frenzy of clutter-clearing when moving from a larger house to a smaller house, I threw it out. How dangerous tidying can be.

But my hunt threw up a photograph of John Withington, a second or third cousin who we'd met several times in New Zealand. I'd just read an email from his wife Pamela telling me he had died the day before. The coincidence made me think of the invisible network underlying our lives. In the wicker basket were many New Zealand photographs, taken when visiting Ben, which will be described when I reach the turn of the century.

In the spring of 1976, we went to stay with my mother in Godalming. I can see her standing at the door of Markham. She'd given the name of our much-loved Tavistock home to Downderry's converted stables. She waved her stick in farewell as we drove away. She had needed a stick since having her hip replaced some years previously, one of the very first such operations in the UK. The other hip, even at that time, was well worn out. She'd been a good golfer and tennis player and bore her painful lameness stoically most of the time. But she'd never been her usual, cheerful, socialising self since

my father's death. During this visit, she told me how depressed she was. It wasn't only her depression that concerned me; it was that she'd made such an admission. I discussed the situation with Peter and we decided to invite her to live with us in Devon.

A Kentisbeare neighbour, Jo Allen, had told us that a friend of hers, Mrs Eley, wanted to find the right buyer for her house and 22 acres of land bordering the river Madford. Jo thought it might suit us with our expanding livestock. We went to see Mrs Eley and Madford House. Peter was impressed by the painting at the foot of the stairs. It was by Gainsborough. Several exclamation marks are called for. The property was more elaborate and more expensive than seemed possible for us but perhaps, if my mother wanted to take up our invitation, we could manage it.

The wicker hamper has provided me with a number of significant family letters. This one is from my mother written on June 1st 1977.

June 1st

Darling Sue

Ages since I wrote, many thanks for telephoning last week. I was so glad to hear you are getting things settled in Greece and I hope you may also get what you want in Devon. Not at all June-like here, such a cold wind this week again. No news of Uncle Dicky yet from S. of France, they are due back on 6th. Beryl phoned last night and has kindly invited me to lunch on Sunday, which is kind and very convenient as Owtrams all going out to a Jubilee lunch. I wonder what celebrations Kentisbeare has! Thank you for being so understanding about my refusal of your kind offer to have me – appreciated – but I am too old to move.

Poor Robert has had a nasty go of hay fever and was off school for a day or two. Michael had a cold, lost his voice completely, and Jane was very stiff after playing tennis for the first time this year. I expect S & B are looking forward to half term. Peter well, I hope, busy in his studio. Hope all livestock well.

I was at Arthur Welches on Sunday for Bridge, he always asks after you!

I think of you all so much, dears.

Must go to bath now

Very much love, Mummy

Two days after writing this letter she fell down in her kitchen with a massive brain stem stroke. When she was found by her helper, she was ambulanced to hospital and put on a ventilator. I drove up to Surrey at once and sat by her bed with Jane. It was clear to me that only the ventilator was keeping her tethered to earth. I drove home. She had always been a keen churchgoer and I knew she was convinced that my father would be waiting for her in the after-life. So I spent time in Kentisbeare church, with the idea she was more likely to gain sustenance from my presence there than in the hospital. On the fourth or fifth day when I returned to her bedside, Jane and I understood that it was up to us to make the decision to switch off the ventilator. It was not a hard decision to make. In my unmedical mind, she had obviously departed her body. June 3rd was her wedding anniversary. In her wedding photo taken on the lawn of Downderry, the roof of the stables is visible. This was where she ended her days.

Back in Devon, I found it hard to accustom myself to the loss. I grieved for both parents. They'd moved from Devon to be near their daughters. Jane fulfilled her role. I left my post and gadded off to live in Greece. Then, when back in England, I'd moved from London, a short distance from Liphook and Godalming, to Devon. Before motorways and dual carriage ways, it was a long and tedious drive. Trains were not direct. It was only much later, when I became a grandmother, that I looked at my record askance.

"I never loved her," Jane said at one point as we sat by her deathbed. I was shocked by this incredible confession and have not yet quite worked out the story behind it.

While we were still at the Mill, we spent the six weeks of the summer holidays on Amorgos. Sophie and Ben were happy to be back in the sea and the sun but Peter and I were not completely at ease. Being summer visitors did not suit us. We harked back to the wonderful year-round times when we'd been settled in a daily life that suited us. In short summer visits, we couldn't get down to any worthwhile painting or writing. Being there felt pointless.

We were there when an unusual number of planes flew across the sky, taking the route of the daily scheduled flight from Athens to Rhodes. We went over to Katapola to find out what was happening and were told that fighting had broken out on Cyprus. Sophie promptly made an emergency plan. I noted it down. "If those men come here," she said, "I will ask who is their leader. I'll say to him, come and have a drink. He'll come for a drink and then he'll blow on his whistle and tell his men not to fight and everything will be alright." Well planned, Sofe.

The war on Cyprus turned out to be the closing chapter of the Junta years.

When we arrived for the summer of 1976, we were warned on arrival that there had been an addition to the bay of Ta Nera. No-one would tell us what it was. We walked to the house. Nothing seemed changed. With the usual joy of home-coming we got the house straight and made the beds. As soon as it was dark, a colossal wailing erupted from the direction of the sea. What the hell? We rushed out onto the terrace and gazed down at the bay. Was it a passing boat belting out pop music? No, it was not passing. It was stationary. In a corner of the field just behind the tiny triangle of sand ("The Sandy Beach" we called it, giving it a grander name than it warranted), there was a searchlight. From here, the valley, the hillsides and the bay, the whole scene was shaking in the blast of the voice of Demis Roussos.

Ever and ever, Forever and ever you'll be my dream … forever and ever rainbow's end … the song I sing … my dream come true … forever and ever.

It certainly seemed to us that Demis Roussos would fill the valley with his yowling forever and ever.

Next day, first thing, we went into action. We had to put a stop to the ghastly plan of the misguided individual who hoped to create a disco in this corner of **Our** valley. There followed days of talk. The wailing went on regularly every night, although no-one came, either by foot or boat. We learnt much later that the disco was never attended and soon its thatched roof over the megaphone disappeared. We didn't wait for this to happen.

Vicky Wilkinson, now about eighteen, had arrived on Amorgos with friends and tents. We asked her if we could do a swap, their tents in exchange for a stay in our house. They wouldn't mind listening to Demis Rousos belting out the same song, night after night. Packing a few necessities into a couple of bags, off we went with two tents and four sleeping bags, taking

Goodiford Mill

Madford House

the very next *vapori* to Piraeus. We spent the rest of our holiday touring the Peloponnese in a hired car before flying back to London.

Before we left the Mill, we had the idea of pinning up Peter's artwork on the crumbly, red, cob walls of the barn at the entrance to the yard. It would be a way of explaining to the people in the neighbourhood what on earth Peter did for a living. (After the amazing film rights, I never made much from my writing). This home-based exhibition was the first of many, all of which were far more enjoyable – and simpler to organise- than the ones in galleries. In these years when we were settling with the children into English life, Peter was doing what may have been his finest work as a wildlife illustrator. Many of the original watercolours were sold but we kept the two illustrations he did for the Sunday Times colour supplement which later appeared in their Book of the Countryside – *Butterflies* and *Hedgerow*. They are hanging in their frames in the hall, the other side of the wall to the right of my desk. I often pause as I pass by to marvel at the way he could paint in intricate detail so many different creatures in one incredible but credible scene. His paintings invite us to stop for a minute and see what really does exist beneath and beside our hurrying feet.

The decision to bring the children up in England seemed to be worth the loss of our Greek life in terms of our careers and the children's lives, present and future. But it was evident that we were each floundering in our different ways; Peter with his deep depressions and I with my rebel streak. Although I knew I should give up smoking, the more Peter disapproved of the habit, justifiably finding it noxious and polluting, the more I wanted to smoke. I also took any excuse to catch the train to London and meet up with people I should not meet up with. I felt like one of those sparklers that light up easily only to fizzle out too soon. It was easy to regret the road not taken on the night of 1959's New Year's Eve party. My possible fellow traveller on that road similarly hankered. We'd both chosen wisely, marrying a firmly-rooted spouse. We both knew we'd made the right choice. Together, we'd have sparkled brilliantly and fizzled out too soon. Knowing this didn't make it any easier, particularly when our separate, married lives with our sensible other halves were not going well. There we were, on each other's horizons, representing what might have been, particularly when the going got tough.

Peter and I thought the move to Madford House would lift his depression. In fact, it was at Madford that our marriage nearly broke into smithereens.

In the autumn of 1976, on our first visit to the house, Mrs Eley told us that Diane would show us around the land when she got home from school. We must have looked baffled. Who was Diane? Mrs Eley was well into her 70s. A partial answer was given by Diane herself as she led us down to the river. "It's so nice and convenient here," she said, "My father lives over there." She waved a hand to her right. "And my mother lives over there." She waved a hand to the left.

Later, we learnt the story. Muriel was one of three, unmarried sisters living in a cottage some two hundred yards down the lane. Florrie was the eldest. Betty was the youngest. All three, over the years, had helped Mrs Eley with cooking, housework and the care of numberless cats, hens and other poultry. Muriel, some thirteen years previously, had been surprised in the lane by Jack who lived in a cottage at the crossroads, the beginning of the

no-through road that led to two farms. The baby that appeared nine months later caused Muriel even more surprise. Mrs Eley, a generous, kind and straightforward woman, brought Diane up and would take her to Norfolk. They would live in a wing of Mrs Eley's son's house. Ely Cartridges were the source of family money, I believe. Diane was a credit to Mrs Eley, negotiating her way gracefully between different social strata. She married a policeman who she brought down to Devon to meet Jack and Muriel.

Mrs Eley was a persuasive character, something of a grande dame. My mother would have either got on well with her or just the opposite; they might have seen themselves reflected too closely in each other. Mrs Eley looked at the Barretts and reckoned that I was the soft touch. When the sale was in the hands of solicitors and progressing smoothly, she invited me to tea. By the time I left, I'd promised to take on Betty as well as Muriel, all the cats and poultry, and to consider the purchase of her piano.

I didn't want a piano. The piano teacher at the R.S. was a little woman whose legs did not touch the floor when she sat beside me. She made me think of a gnome on a toadstool. Her hands were wider than they were long. With them, she could span more than an octave. She used to press her thumb between my fingers, trying to make my hands as like a duck's webbed feet as her own were. "If only you could play as well as your sister," she used to sigh. I gave up the piano as soon as I could. But here I was, however many years later, being persuaded into buying a piano. Mrs Eley wanted £200 for it. I didn't need a piano. When we moved in and found that the piano was still in the drawing-room, I felt obliged to produce £200 in one way or another. I persuaded Peter to agree to sending Mrs Eley one of his panoramas in lieu of cash. How weak I was.

It wasn't only the piano that was left behind the day we moved in. I'd arrived ahead of Peter and the removal vans. This was fortunate. Betty was sitting at the kitchen table – the Eley kitchen table. Her head was in her hands and she was moaning and rocking to and fro. No, she wasn't going to move. She had helped Mrs Eley for years and years and this was her kitchen, she could cook, she would cook. "Good," I said, "We can talk about that later but *right now*," I said in as firm a manner as I could, "our furniture is on its way and we've got a kitchen table and we don't need this one. Please help me move it into the yard." Moan, moan, rock, rock. I realised that Betty's state was rather worse than I had at first imagined. It took about an hour before Betty and I were on our feet, one on either side of the table. I felt as though I was urging someone away from a cliff edge. "That's it, Betty, that's wonderful. Just lift it up a little, it isn't heavy."

Crash! The table was so worm-eaten that the drawer had fallen out. Whisks, forks, tin openers, corkscrews, teaspoons, cotton reels, scissors, knives … The kitchen filled with a cacophony of sound as the contents of the drawer bounced in all directions.

"Ha!" Was that Betty's burst of laughter or mine? We became friends as we scooped up objects from all the corners of the kitchen.

But poor Betty was depressed, far more severely than a brief burst of laughter could cure. She needed medical help which she would receive in the future. When we were at Madford, she had recurring bouts of misery. "I'll put me 'ead in a bucket, I will. I'm no good for anything, I'll put me

Rooks and jays for Reader's Digest 'Birds of Britain'

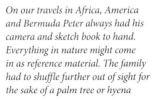

On our travels in Africa, America and Bermuda Peter always had his camera and sketch book to hand. Everything in nature might come in as reference material. The family had to shuffle further out of sight for the sake of a palm tree or hyena

'ead in a bucket and end it all." I was torn between concern for her, anxiety that I could not help her, and a strong desire to draw the cartoon I could see whenever she talked of the bucket. It sparked so many questions. Would it be large enough for Betty's head? Could one drown in a bucket? Had someone in Betty's life done this?

Talking of heads, Muriel always wrapped hers in a purple chiffon scarf. She arrived first thing in the morning, a scarlet gash of lipstick in the region of her mouth. Her job was to feed and let out of their many cages, the golden pheasants, the guinea fowl, the geese and the hens. And the cats. There was an uncountable number of cats, all in different stages of cancerous decay. They lay in mangey heaps on top of the boiler, jumping down every so often to crap on the shelves of the dresser and up the backstairs.

Jane came to stay early on. She was washing up in the scullery when one of the cats leapt from the draining board on one side of the sink to the other. Jane shrieked and stepped back. One foot landed in cat's mess. She shrieked again. "Susie! You simply must get rid of these ghastly animals!"

We did. Shush. My promise to care for everything Mrs Eley left behind flew out of the window. We shut all the cats in one of the sheds and called the vet.

The golden pheasants were dealt with in a different way. Our good friends, met and made that winter at a party given by Trevor and Jane Cox at Stentwood House on the far side of the river, caretook Madford when we went away that summer. The pheasants' cage was left open (thank you Tony and Lucy).

At the bottom of our home field, a white-painted metal gate opened onto a narrow bridge across the river. Madford House was originally the rectory for the church that lay in the ruins of a Cistercian Abbey on the far side of the river. The rector and his family had been friends with the Stentwood House family in the late 19th century and the bridge was often used. The bridge became used again when we became friends with the Sidery family who lived in the Old Schoohouse, one of the few houses in the hamlet known as Dunkeswell Abbey.

In our first week at Madford, Brian Sidery had walked with his dog Shona from Abbey, along the lane that bordered the river, across the road bridge to the crossroads and from there down the lane towards Lower, Middle and Higher Mackham Farm. He hoped to catch a glimpse of the new owners. Unfortunately for him, or fortunately, who knows, Shona got her head stuck (yes, I was talking of heads) in our white-painted, wrought iron, front gate. I happened to be outside at the time. Hearing the yelping of a dog, I went down the drive to investigate. Brian was apologetic, as though anxious that I'd suspect him of placing Shona's head in the gate with the sole aim of meeting us. I invited him in for a cup of tea.

"Sidery?" queried Peter. It turned out that he and Peter had been in the Scouts together at Dulwich. Another example of invisible threads.

Rachel and Ruth, Brian and Sue's daughters, were one year older and one year younger than Sophie. They are still good friends. Ben found a boy of his age to muck around with but in the snow that fell heavily that February he joined in happily with the girls, making elaborate igloos. The snow drifted to the tops of hedges. We tramped our way to the cowshed to milk our Jersey cow. After a week of being snowbound we ran out of cow nuts and borrowed from our nearest farmer.

With the spring we began work on the house, removing the back stairs to add a small bathroom to our bedroom. We redecorated. Elaborate William Morris designs in wall paper covered the walls. I scraped the dresser of cat crap, removed the varnish with sandpaper and burnished the pine to a fresh glow. Our most major task, the one we gave our builder, was to create a studio room on the top of the stable block.

In the summer of 1978 we had no desire to return to Amorgos. That wonderful phase of life was over. Instead we spent a wet week camping in Wales alongside the Owtram family. Peter, now at work again in the stable block studio, had been devastated to realise that Madford lay far too close to Dunkeswell aerodrome where the Marines came regularly to parachute. This entailed a plane's long slow climb with its heavy load, followed by a concentrated circling over our heads. The planes made a noise like a circular saw or an electric drill. The noise penetrated Peter's skull and stayed there. He talked, in lighter moods, of getting a ground-to-air missile. He constantly rang the aerodrome to complain. His childhood in Kent during the Battle of Britain had come back to haunt him.

I couldn't blame him at all for the return of his intense depression but I was not going to let it get me down. I let my interest wander away from home in a way that Peter would notice. It caused an upheaval in our lives that shook us to the core. Had we both been wiser, we'd have talked things out and over long before this. But we were inept. We hadn't learnt the way. A crash was necessary to bring us to our senses and start mending.

I need to ask Peter now which Mozart symphony we played continuously, while getting to know each other all over again.

The answer to that question was Symphony in G minor, number 40, Mozart's second to last symphony. I've been listening to it this morning but I'm not convinced this was the one we constantly listened to that week. Music is heard in ways that vary according to the listener's mood, age, and circumstances. I trust Peter's memory for facts. He's also helped by the diaries he has kept since 1978. He's brought into the study the very first and we are both surprised to see that it was I who began the habit. I clearly had become obsessive about noting down every detail of our move from the Mill to Madford and the work we did in that first year.

16th January Moving Day. Inherited from Mrs Eley four cats: Tango, Mary, Escargot, Venus– all incontinent and ugly

They had names! I'd forgotten this. It makes our invitation to the vet seem even more wicked.

Friday 20th – roof rentokilled
Saturday 21st – Jane, Francis, Jocelyn, Christopher arrived for lunch. Walked around the place in p.m.
Sunday 22nd – big housewarming party – 71 adults, 42 children, 11.30 – 6 pm. Then to John and Jo Allen to watch Nicole's film re otters and supper.

Party! 71 plus 42! I think this must have been the biggest party we ever gave. No, correction; not the biggest. For Sophie's wedding celebration in Greece in 1990 we invited two whole villages.

In the first few blank pages of this diary, I've listed the fruit we planted in the fruit cage we built, and the roses we introduced to the segmented rose bed above the tennis court. I clearly had hopes that Madford would be our home for many years. There was something about its ambience that caught me. I think it was the way it held echoes of my childhood. Mrs Eley might have been a Tavistock friend of my parents. The Victorian house reminded me of my grandparents' Downderry, and – only seen in photographs – Holloway Hill House and, even further back, my father's mother's Foxdenton Hall, where she and her 15 siblings grew up. Luckily, Madford was neither big nor grand – it just seemed so, in the way it sat on its grassy terrace, half way between the skyline at the top of its fields and the river at the bottom of those fields. The Scots pines that lined the drive – and in spring, the daffodils – made the entrance appear more imposing than its rutted, gravel surface merited.

Just one more snippet from the diary of 1978:

Livestock count 31st May

2 cows, 4 calves, 2 ewes, 21 lambs, 3 geese, 15 hens, 6 ducklings, 15 chicks, 3 guinea fowl, 2 pheasant.

The lambs did not all belong to the two ewes! They were bought in. Our ever-increasing number of animals was greedy for time, taking us away from our work. Yet it's evident we managed to carry on. I wrote *The Beacon,* a novel which featured a group campaigning against planes. Peter had some meaty commissions with trips to London and Paris. He did a series of stamps for the Post Office featuring dogs, which created a local stir. The landscape behind one of the dogs was based on the view from a local farm that belonged to John and Sally Donnithorne. Sally and I had been at the Royal School at the same time, and re-met in Kentisbeare.

I shall return the diary to join all the others in the studio, one for each year from 1978 to the present. I cannot let the plethora of details interfere with my own memories and sense of the past, the subliminal content that feeds my writing. Peter with that resource and his accurate memory can be my fact-checker.

In this period at the end of the 1970s we were adjusting to our life in England. London had been too great a contrast to Amorgos. Now we were trying the English countryside. The Mill had been our first attempt. There, we began learning how to care for animals and grow vegetables and fruit. Yet it hadn't been quite countryside enough. A mill was always on a road – of course it had to be. We fell for it, without realising that even country lanes can have traffic. We moved to Madford, only to find that noise could come from the sky.

In 1978 or maybe 79 Father Lorenz got in touch with us. Would we consider selling our house on Amorgos? We had not gone back since leaving the house so precipitously in 1976, handing the key over to Vicky Wilkinson in exchange for tents. She'd been there a week or two and then gave the key to Calliope and Yorgo, our best friends there. We had no idea what state it was in, but if the Dutch Ambassador to Greece wanted to have it as holiday home for himself and his family, why not sell it to him. Letting go of one thing so that something new could come in was always our way. We'd achieved the aim that had taken us to Greece in the first place. Sophie and Ben were at secondary school locally. We were both doing well in our work.

Nothing was, as Demis Rousos sang, *forever and ever.* We hardened our hearts and sold.

Suddenly, we were not bound to return for brief summer holidays to the island. We could go anywhere! We went with Peter on one of his work trips to America. Mike Brodie, Peter's agent, arranged for us to stay at the Plaza hotel New York. Red carpet led across the pavement from the taxi door to the hotel's entrance. Sophie and Ben watched colour television sitting up in bed for hours. Ben had chocolate waffles with his bacon and sausage-breakfast, as much as he could eat. We swam in the pool of a Ramada Inn in Philadelphia while Peter had meetings at Franklin Mint and did roughs of scenes which would later grace porcelain plates. Then we flew west to California, hired a car, bought tents and sleeping bags, and made a circular trip taking in the Grand Canyon, Yosemite and Stinson Beach. Sophie sat in the back of the car absorbed in reading "*The World According to Garp.*"

Another year we spent a month in Kenya, introduced to the Masai Mara river camp by someone Peter had met through his wildlife painting. A hippo clambered out of the river and up the bank where Ben was sitting, contemplating the view quietly. He scrambled away fast. In a hired car, a low-slung saloon unsuited to our demands, we followed hunting dogs; sat still and silently as a herd of elephants trundled past on either side; surprised a lion snoozing behind a rock; and returned the car in a wrecked state to the Nairobi hire firm. They accepted it without a murmur.

Another year we went to Bermuda at the invitation of the Wilkinsons who'd bought a beautiful house with a cascade of white roof and a swimming pool. Inside, the cool house smelt of cedar and a frightening English couple stood by, waiting for orders. A fast launch was moored off the private jetty. Ben and Marcus and another friend from the Lycee dived for the golf balls that had been driven from the 10th tee and failed to reach the green the far side of an inlet. Francis had made a great deal of money in selling his share of a part-work publishing venture he'd set up in the 1960s. He'd taken the family to live in France. Later they would go to live in San Francisco, where Ben was to visit them on his travels as a young man.

I see from our 1980 Diary that it was August 31st of that year we flew to Nairobi, the start of our Kenyan holiday. I also see that on September 26th John Knowlman (of Dobbs, Stagg and Knowlman) "rang re Luggs." On our return from Africa, we'd asked him to look out for a house with a smaller acreage than Madford's. Holidays can often have the effect of a life-review. When away from home, it's easier to see what has ceased to make sense.

On Monday 29th September Peter and I went to see Luggs. We visited again next day. On October 1st (Sue Sidery's birthday I noted) John Knowlman took particulars of Madford. (That evening we went to Exeter to hear Segovia play. What an amazing treat.) On October 3rd we took our builder, Dick, to give his opinion on Luggs. On the 5th we took Sophie and Ben there to learn their views. Diary note: *Family discussion. Verdict: we want Luggs.*

But I remember Sophie not being keen. In the end we promised she could have her bedroom painted whatever colour she wanted. She chose purple.

We moved from Madford to Luggs on December 1st 1980 and stayed there for 27 years.

THE 1980s

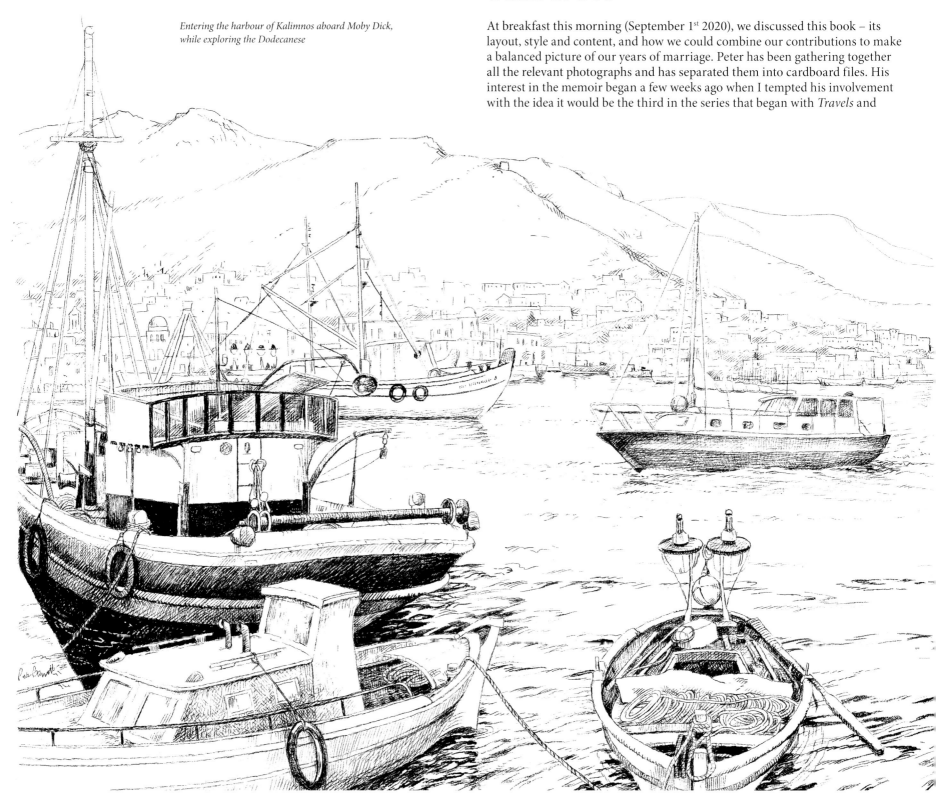

Entering the harbour of Kalimnos aboard Moby Dick, while exploring the Dodecanese

At breakfast this morning (September 1st 2020), we discussed this book – its layout, style and content, and how we could combine our contributions to make a balanced picture of our years of marriage. Peter has been gathering together all the relevant photographs and has separated them into cardboard files. His interest in the memoir began a few weeks ago when I tempted his involvement with the idea it would be the third in the series that began with *Travels* and continued with *The Garden*. In the last week or so, it was becoming clear that he was visualising fitting our memoir into the Garden's format. I was growing anxious. The memoir is text-heavy. It's a narrative and I want readers to read it, not flit from one illustrated page to the next. It's not driven, as the Garden was, by excellent black and white photographs taken at the time. The photographs we have are family snaps rather than aesthetic objects. They are of interest to no-one but our respective families. Another problematic question: how can we do justice to Peter's career when many of the original paintings and pieces of artwork have been sold?

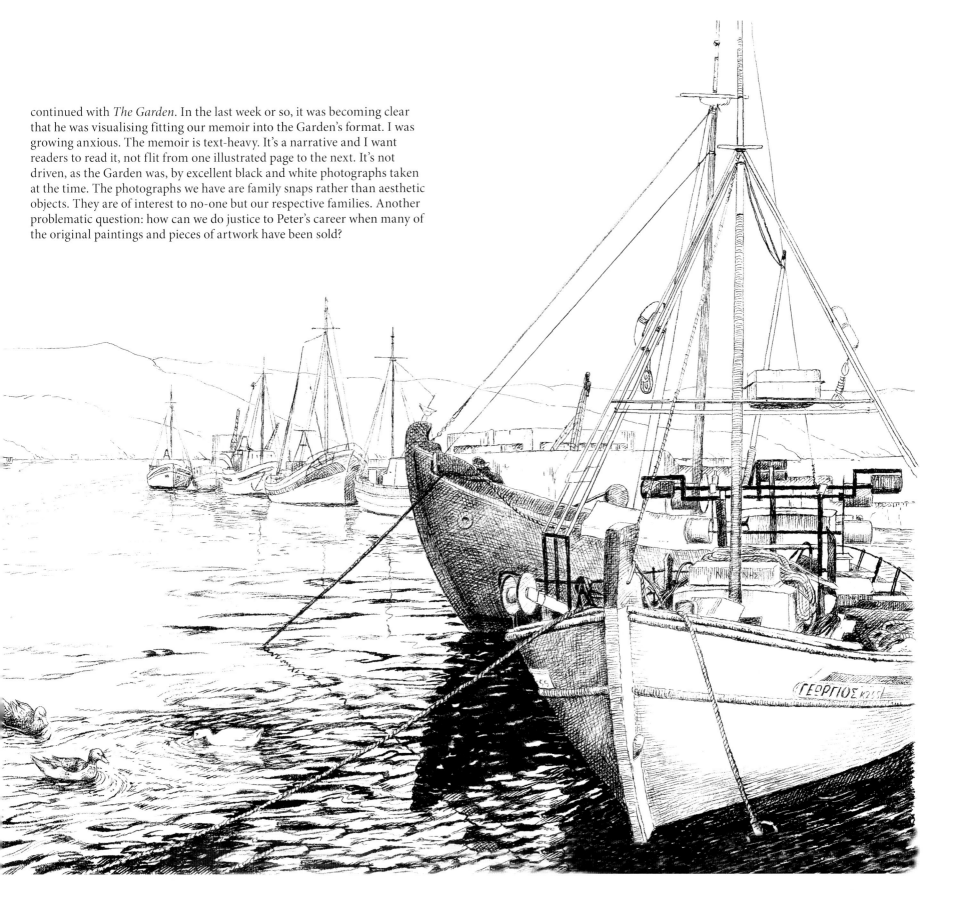

When I started writing this in April, I imagined him doing pen and ink drawings to illustrate the text. After this morning's discussion, he's going to come up with pictures that sum up each decade to introduce each section. He reads every page I write so that anything that appears in the final book will have been vetted by him. This is an example of what makes our marriage work. It's a balancing act between my flights of fancy and Peter's realism.

Luggs Cottage

A postscript added in December as we complete the book: Peter has fitted in about 360 illustrations of his published work as well as his paintings. His room is like a Russian doll. It conceals layer after layer of work of all kinds, which we've been scanning and photographing to make digital files in the hope we can afford a print run. If anyone other than ourselves holds in their hands a book with the title *So Far, So Good*, we'll have succeeded.

When I think of the 1980s I call up memories of the time we worked together on *Travels*. Bernard Higton of Bellew and Higton, met through the latest book Peter had illustrated: (*Birdwatcher's Diary* by Roger Lovegrove), introduced us to Gill Rowley of Columbus Books. The suggestion was that Peter and I should work together on a wildlife book, as writer and illustrator. What could it be about? What a wonderful question! As we were tied to England by children's schooling and smallholding, we suggested a book about British wildlife. Too hackneyed, said Gill. What about Greece?

This concentrated our minds on working out how this would be possible. Our way of life at Luggs was simpler than at Madford. But we still had two cows and some sheep, hens and pigs, two dogs and a cat. And two children, not yet at the age of independence.

We'd moved into Luggs at the tail end of 1980. We'd fallen for it on our first sighting. It just needed the car to bump over the cattle grid at the

entrance from the Culm Davy lane for us to feel – *this is it*! The long drive bordered a copse of hazel and sycamore clustered on the steep banks of a number of ponds. These were old marl pits, barely filled by a trickle of stream and rainwater. In the spring the slopes were covered in bluebells. Turning a corner after a hundred yards or so, one end of the thatched cottage came into view with a derelict barn standing at an angle to it. The wisteria that clambered up the cottage walls was bare of leaves but held the promise of pendants of pale purplish-blue flowers next summer. The branches wound around windows which, on the upstairs level, regarded the view under thatched eyebrows. At the back of the house, a never-ending stream of water flowed out of a pipe into an open tank. Very soon I'd tracked down the suggested origins of the name *Luggs*: it was Celtic for a stream of sparkling water.

On arrival with our retinue of animals, we immediately started work with our building team – Dick, Pete and Ernie – to bring the house from the previous owners' 1950s into the present day. This meant dividing the perishingly cold bathroom into two; uncovering the boxed-in beams and treating them as they deserved; discovering what lay behind a wall in the drawing room – an inglenook – and in the hall: a screen which dated the cottage to the late 13th century.

There were no ghosts at Luggs. Unlike the Mill whose creakings at night fed the imagination, particularly of Ben and myself, as well as alerting the greater sensibilities of the dogs. One early evening, while we were watching television, Pepper the rough collie and Charlie the collie-spaniel cross, were snoozing by the fireside. Something startled them to their feet. The hairs on their backs bristled. They fixed their eyes on the middle window of the three windows along one wall, which looked out to the front garden. In a low crouch they advanced towards that window and its wooden seat, softly growling. *There's nothing there*, I told them, more to reassure myself and the children than the dogs. After a moment or two, they reluctantly returned to the fireside. It seemed they still didn't entirely believe me. We learnt later that the middle window had replaced the original front door of the mill house. Another time Ben was convinced that his hand had been gripped in the night by something icy and evil. I thought, and told him at the time, that his arm had probably been lying outside his duvet on a very cold night.

The atmosphere at Luggs was tranquil. It gave us, up to a point, the peace and quiet that we'd loved on Amorgos. We want μοναξια κι ησυχια, isolation and peace, we'd explained to the Greek islanders who'd thought us weird to live so far from others.

Our English life had many advantages for this stage of our lives. Sophie and Ben were at Uffculme comprehensive school, catching the school bus from the end of our drive. Both of them made friends fast. The Visitors Book I started to keep in 1978 shows they often had friends to stay. Peter managed to work in the room which would become my study after the Barn was rebuilt to suit us. This meant first dismantling the metal caging for battery hens on one side of the Barn's upper floor, and knocking down the collapsing cob walls of the whole of the superstructure, including the corrugated iron roof. The diary entry for June 2nd tells me that Graham Whiteley drew plans to submit for the local authority. In August we went to Greece, hiring a car

to drive to the Mani for a week or so; then on August 20th to 25th we went to Amorgos for a quick, nostalgic visit. The four of us braved the walk to Ta Nera, answering all the questions on the way as best we could. *Why did we leave? Why did we sell the house?* There was no quick and comprehensible answer we could supply. On the terrace of the house the enormity of the loss of this home hit us and we stood there, each of us overflowing with tears.

The trip to Greece was prompted by the idea of doing a book together. Our minds were full of possibilities. We did a practice page or two for the proposed book. Peter has just found the mock-up produced by Bellew and Higton on the shelves in his room. It's full of blank pages save for a few at the start. On the fly leaf there's a pasted note. *THIS DUMMY IS THE PROPERTY OF BELLEW & HIGTON PUBLISHERS. If sending by post for any reason, please pack with extreme care, with several layers of strengthening material, because replacement would cost in the region of £500. Thank you.* The next page is the projected cover. BARRETT'S GREECE Peter and Susan Barret.

The image under the title is one of Peter's watercolours painted from a sketch he did in the Mani the summer of 1981. I like the look of this dummy. Its typeface and the layout of the few pages produced are classic. The eventual book, published by Columbus in 1986, had another layout but the same classic look and did Peter's work justice on its alternating colour and black and white pages.

There's a note in purple ink on Sunday April 19th in the 1981 Diary: *Observer review!* This was for my sixth novel, *The Beacon.* Peter had gone down to Hemyock for the paper, crisps and beer, as he still does from our present house. From the vantage point of 2020, we can look back nostalgically at those golden days in wildlife illustration and publishing. In the photograph on the book jacket, I'm at my typewriter (still the Olympia portable) in the dining room of Madford House. This is the only jacket that Peter didn't design for me. The art editor at Hamish Hamilton wanted

Charles Keeping to do the cover. A lithograph of his, showing a decrepit cart and a horse in an even more decrepit state, had been one of our first acquisitions, so I accepted their choice. I wasn't too happy with the way he visualised my main character. In his hands, she became a startled, and startling, redhead with freckles, not remotely like the person who'd existed in my imagination. I prefer the plain cover of the US edition, illustrated below.

I was with a new agent at this time, as Toby had gone to live and work in New York. Deborah Rogers appointed Nann du Sautoy to look after me. Nann was the most encouraging person I ever had in my writing career. She once told me that, whenever she read anything of mine, she just wanted to jump for joy. When I heard this, I too wanted to jump for joy. As it turned out, I only had one more novel to go while I was still with mainstream publishers. That was *Stephen and Violet,* published by Collins in 1988. Two years before that, *Travels with a Wildlife Artist* came out, published by Columbus.

With our summer holiday in the Mani in 1981 we started work on *Travels.* Sophie was by now a blonde, blue-eyed 15-year old who remembered a little Greek which she spoke in the beguiling tones of a small Amorgian schoolchild. In Agios Nicolaos, a small harbour village, she soon had a posse of lads in her wake. One of them who had gained, then lost, her attention threatened to drown himself in despair. When a large enough crowd had gathered, he jumped off the end of the harbour wall. It would have been dramatic had there been more than a metre of water at that point. His rival appeared at Athens airport to give

Sophie a gold necklace on our return to England. Ben made friends with some local tearaways. Motorbikes, drinking and discos were involved.

Both our children have always made friends easily and adapted quickly to wherever they have found themselves. But they were now teenagers and were on the look-out for reasons to be fed up with their parents. In adoption it's easy for both sides, parents and children, to blame genetic difference for problems on either side, even if this is not openly admitted. Teenage is the time when we sort out who we are, a combination of nature and nurture. It's hard enough for children who are brought up by their own parents. Much harder for those who've been adopted. Also, adoptive parents may sometimes think how much easier life might have been if their children were their own flesh and blood. Yet even in natural families, there are two sources of genes, so one can always blame the genes you did not contribute. So it goes …

From the beginning Peter and I were keen that our children should have the chance of meeting their natural parents one day, and Sophie and Ben knew this from the start of their lives. They understood how hard it had been for their mothers to give them up and how lucky we'd been to find them. Bedtime stories often included the word 'adoption'. Sophie, when she was very young, proudly told someone visiting us on Amorgos that she was published; she meant adopted. She was keen to meet her mother when she was mature enough and it was possible to arrange this. Knowledge in such matters is better than imagination and everyone involved benefited. When she was about 18, her natural parents were on holiday in the west country. We invited them to Sunday lunch. Sophie sat at the table with two complete sets of parents, surely a very rare occurrence in an adoptee's life. She's a credit to all four of her parents, a happy mix of genetic inheritance and environmental influence.

After this, we wished that Ben would have the same chance of meeting his natural mother. I had kept in touch with Diane, as I had with Mary. But Ben had never shown any interest in a future meeting. When I asked him after that Sunday lunch if he'd changed his mind, he said no firmly. Believing it to be a necessary step to take if at all possible, I persuaded him to let me try to find an address. I'd lost touch with her when she married. I knew that Diane's sister had married a pharmacist so I contacted the Pharmaceutical Association. Fortunately, I'd memorised her name and learnt she was living in New Zealand. I wrote a guarded letter, not giving away any facts. "*When your sister was a nurse, she was very helpful to my family and we'd like to thank her after all these years – seventeen now, I reckon.*" Or words to that effect. We had a phone call, almost at once. Vanessa had understood my coded message and was very happy to talk. It was a relief to hear from us, she said, and she thought Diane would feel the same. She was right. The outcome was that Ben and I went up to London and met Diane and her husband Ken at the arranged rendez-vous at the foot of the Albert Memorial.

The four of us went to the Serpentine café. It was obvious from the start that Diane and Ben were kith and kin. They both had thick, dark hair with startlingly blue eyes, a typical Irish characteristic. Ken was an understanding man and accepted Diane's newfound son. He and Diane had been married

some time and had two children. It was a relief that the meeting which Ben had not really wanted had worked out so well. Diane wrote that she felt a burden had been lifted from her shoulders.

Ben went to stay with them. If he hadn't been going through a patch of difficult behaviour at home, we might have been anxious that we'd lose him. That is the fear of adoptive parents. It has probably prevented many an adoptive parent from encouraging a meeting. But however difficult Ben has been, our bond has never shattered. After his first stay with Diane and Ken, he expressed astonishment that anyone could drink and smoke so much and never clear up. We smiled. A short while previously, we'd let him move out of his bedroom and into the big barn room, the twin of Peter's studio. There was one condition: I wouldn't clean the room or scoop up clothes for washing. The room was now knee-deep in beer cans, fag ends and discarded clothes.

I have one of Ben's letters beside me, kept over the years in a box file of precious papers among them the last letters of each of my parents, the last letter from Pete Rose who died in Australia soon after his Australian wife June's death; the children's drawings, Sophie's and Ben's, our grandchildren's too;, mother's day cards, school reports, I can't resist preserving some of these now in this memoir.

A Mother's Day card from Ben:
Dear Mummy
I hope you will have a Happy Mothers Day I have loved you for 8 years and a ½ and 28999 years and I love you Mummy.

This was before America influenced British manufacturers to foster spending on cards and gifts with the creation of a Father's Day. Peter received his own accolades in different ways. And shared all letters.

Dear Mum and Dad
I'm very sorry if I seem a bit miserable at the moment. Its got nothing to do with the bike or money. Its lonleyness. The trouble with being really lonely is not so much being alone as you now Im used to being alone its more to do with what goes on in ones head when your alone, you have constant conversations and arguments in your head all the time and some times I feel like Im going slightly mad. Always these arguments and problems in my head with no one to talk to or sought ones problems out with. I end up talking to your or arguing with you both. I am sorry and will try to realise when it is happening so as not to take it out on you the two people in the world that do care about me and worry about me when things aren't going quite right.

I find it difficult to say what I realy feel to your faces. I've never been very good at showing my real feelings.

I just want to say I love you both very much and I am very grateful for the help you have given me not just in the last two years but throughout my life you are the only people I can depend on. And I do love you both very much for it. Love Ben.

This undated letter probably dates from the beginnings of his travels but it gives a good picture of his lifelong problems and endearing character. We thought meeting his natural mother might help him understand himself, but the one person who would have filled in the genetic map was absent: his father. He had not featured in Diane's life except for a brief time around

COMMONWEALTH OF DOMINICA — BREADFRUIT VAMPIRE — 15c

COMMONWEALTH OF DOMINICA — SOURSOP CORASSOL — 35c

COMMONWEALTH OF DOMINICA — HELICONIA LOBSTER CLAW — $5

COMMONWEALTH OF DOMINICA — ANTHURIUM — 45c

COMMONWEALTH OF DOMINICA — PASSION FRUIT — 10c

40c — BLUE-HOODED EUPHONIA — COMMONWEALTH OF DOMINICA

20c — FOREST THRUSH — COMMONWEALTH OF DOMINICA

$5·00 — LESSER ANTILLEAN PEWEE — COMMONWEALTH OF DOMINICA

*Commissions included
paintings for stamps
and prints*

9P

10½P

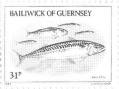

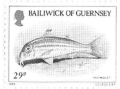

BAILIWICK OF GUERNSEY — 31P — MACKEREL

BAILIWICK OF GUERNSEY — 9P — CUCKOO WRASSE

BAILIWICK OF GUERNSEY — 29P — RED MULLET

BAILIWICK OF GUERNSEY — 34P — SUNFISH

11P

13P

Ben's creation. We think he must have had similar problems to Ben. Diane could not or did not want to give Ben any more information than that at one time she knew he was in prison. We were always worried that Ben's wild behaviour could lead him down the same path. It's to his great credit that he has only spent a couple of nights locked up, once in California and once in New Zealand.

Environmental influences? Bad as well as good, no doubt. We moved the children around a lot, only giving them a more settled life when we moved to Luggs in 1980. Settled? Hardly. We soon got going on Travels, fitting in trips to Greece as best we could. After the family holiday in 1981 in the Mani and Amorgos, we returned to Ayios Nicolaos in 1982 with the Sidery family. Brian, having been in the Classics stream at Dulwich, was keen to learn about modern Greece, the language, people and scenery. This holiday led them to plan to spend time in Greece, teaching English. In fact, they spent a year in northern Greece in Xanthi and another year in Volos. Rachel and Ruth had much the same experience as Sophie and Ben, with parents taking leave of absence from parenthood during their teenage years.

Somehow we managed to find people to stay at different times to be the Resident Adult. Others appeared when needed to look after the smallholding. Luggs in any case was a magnet. The Visitors Book is jampacked with recurring names of grateful people. Jane and a selection of Owtram boys, Elizabeth Dun, Oliver Campion, Graham Fawcett, Virginia Edwards, Ma and Pa Barrett, Jennifer and Bill. Luggs provided a haven of peace and quiet and nourishment for city-dwelling adults. For the young, it was a magnet. The Barn provided a communal space. At that time, nothing like that existed in the village. It was a place of freedom for the lads could play loud music, drink beer, smoke pot, dismantle bikes, and ogle Ben's sister. Sophie joined in some wild escapades on bikes. She had a moped and when she'd passed her driving test, she had a mini with fluffy beige seat covers. As in many aspects of our lives, we were confident the everything would be alright, even if the passage was turbulent

From the start of Ben's school life, I was writing excuse notes of an increasingly creative nature. Starting with the Maths teacher at Kentisbeare, then Hemyock primary school, we progressed through the years at Uffculme until there came the point of no return. The event which went beyond my ability to explain and excuse happened on September 14th 1983 (Peter's 48th birthday). Ben was sent home from school with a letter threatening expulsion. He'd taken strong exception to what his art teacher was telling him to do. He'd picked her up and sat her down on the work bench. After a meeting with Mr Corke, the school's head, and the art teacher, Mrs Snow, we all decided that it would be better for everyone involved if Ben had tutors until the following summer's exams. From that moment, Ben was taught English by Tony Anderson and Art by Lucy Willis. They were life-savers for Ben and for us. An essential part of Tony's teaching technique was to make Ben laugh. An occasional bout of wrestling on the floor broke up the tension of learning. Lucy was one of the very rare adults Ben would listen to. If he was going to be inspired by anyone outside the family, it was by her. He has earned money from his artwork ever since.

Nature and nurture working well together? Ben, as a child, stood beside Peter, watching him work through all the stages of producing a picture. He was obviously very interested. He must have had some innate ability and he learnt a lot from Peter as well as Lucy. When as a young adult he began to get commissions, Peter stood beside him, metaphorically and sometimes literally. Peter had the car with its engine running, waiting for Ben to put the last brush strokes to a picture for the Somerset Country Cricket Club. I'm afraid Ben didn't imitate Peter's self-discipline.

God and the Devil by Ben Barrett, aged 16

Concern for the environment, however, he developed young and it has stayed with him. When he was seven he was desperate to save the Amazon rainforest and wrote a letter to tell the United Nations to do something about it. On a more realistic level, he was instrumental in saving a patch of native woodland at the top of the hill behind Luggs. This is the story.

Walking down the drive from the school bus – this was at the end of June, 1983, before he was expelled – he heard the persistent buzzing of chainsaws. On the third day of asking us if we knew what was going on, we were infected by the same need to know. We went up to the wood. What we discovered there led to days of phoning, gaining information and alerting the authorities. A Doctor Smith from London had hired three young men from the Job Centre to clear-fell as much of the 22-acre wood, known as Clements Common, as they could in a week. They'd never used chain saws before. Dr Smith had not obtained permission from the Forestry Commission to fell a single tree. The local council's planning department had no idea about it. Neither did the true owner of the wood. It didn't belong to Smith at all. He was negotiating to buy it from someone who'd bought it

The trees in our 22-acre wood which we saved from felling
have provided Peter with endless subjects for painting

originally with the idea of having a caravan there, but who now needed the cash from the sale.

Clements Common is an area of mixed woodland surrounded on nearly every side by conifer plantation. We regularly walked there with the dogs and up to that moment thought it belonged to the Forestry Commission. Dr Smith must have been confident that no-one would bother about his plan to fell the 22-acre wood, return it to pasture and claim the grant for doing so. Standing in the wood, it's easy to think you are alone in an empty world. But Smith had now learnt that just a few hundred yards down the hill lived people called Barrett who did bother.

He invited us to lunch at the Castle Hotel, Taunton. Over Dover sole and a good white wine, he told us he was an environmentalist. We listened, while enjoying the fish and the wine, which he'd hoped would stop us country bumpkins in our tracks. We'd learnt by then the illegality of his plan and knew the expensive meal was not going to make any difference to the process which was on track. In the end the lunch bill was the most he had to pay. He was taken to court but the magistrate didn't want the recently-qualified doctor to have anything untoward on his record. The small fine was waived.

Meanwhile, we had thought of creating a local consortium to buy the wood. The vendor wanted £15,000. We invited local people to coffee. We hoped to gather 15 around the Luggs dining table. Seven came. All left, commending our plan to buy the wood but with their cheque books firmly closed. We couldn't blame them; only one of them lived on the spot. That was the local farmer's wife and she was only there to learn what was going on. The wood might have gone to another clear-feller, one who had the relevant permissions. Not that hard in those days. Fortunately (how often do I begin sentences in this memoir of our marriage with that word?), fortunately, my mother's cousin Beryl had left me some money. It was going to pay off our overdraft. We went and talked with our bank manager. Roger Williams of Cullompton Lloyds heard our plan. He got to his feet, shook our hands with a smile and said, "Go for it."

We still own Clements Common. We have a garden shed hidden among the Scots pines, birch and rowan where we can stay the night, watch badgers, charcoal grill a meal. Last year we climbed the steep hill and arrived outside the hut with the same idea at the forefront of our minds. When we'd caught our breaths, we exchanged our thoughts. Now we have a Polaris, a two-seater all-terrain vehicle which gets us up to the hut with no panting at all, carrying gear in its truck and bringing down logs, chainsawed by Peter on the spot. We've funded Mark, Sophie's son, for a chainsaw course. We are happy to help, glad to have both funds and family.

September 6th 2020. Olivia, Sophie's daughter, visited today with Bertie to show us her engagement ring. They were on their way to visit Dean, Sophie's first husband and Olivia's father, before going to lunch with Sophie and Nick. Dean, having moved away when he and Sophie split, is now back in the village with his new partner. The local nature of the Bradbeer extended family may have been a good part of the attraction for Sophie when she first got together with Dean. She'd experienced the attractions of a tightly-knit community on Amorgos. Mary and John and Arthur and Di came from much the same social background, even though in different parts of the country. We've benefited, too, from the effects of her genetic inheritance: stability, practicality, and a cohesive family.

When we started work on the Greek book, she was on the cusp of deciding where she would position herself in her adult life. One idea was to ask Peter's agent in New York to take her on. She would have done very well as an artist's agent. That would have been following the path opened up by nurture. Instead, she chose safety. After secretarial training, she joined the staff of the local insurance brokers. This didn't suit her so she did a beauty therapy course and worked briefly in Taunton. (My nails have never been so well filed). But being a freelance therapist was too unpredictable and she joined the Department of Work and Pensions, as it's now called. She's found enough variety within the department to keep her interested most of the time. She has moved up the rungs in the office, working on different projects, travelling around the country, wearing power suits and staying nights away. During Covid, she has been responsible for keeping her team safe in the office she's worked in nearly all her career. She's been a steady counterbalance to the life Peter and I have led and makes sure we are safe, too.

The diaries for 1981–1985 are so full of activity, that I've been having sleepless nights trying to work out how to deal with these years. Peter has made notes of the main movements for me. It's too easy to get bogged down in detail. Yet without some detail the intense flavour of the time is lost.

Jan 18th 1983 S stopped smoking
29th to London, Gavin and Kath Lyall's 25th wedding anniversary
Feb 5th sausage and brawn making
Skittles
S decorating Barn workshop
P teaching Art School
24th March Jane Dorgan arrived by moped to caretake
26th March leave for Greece, three weeks in Crete with Sophie and Ben
June 1st, S. started smoking again.
Mid July P, S and Ben to Greece. A week later, Sophie joined us in Vassiliki, Lefkadha, travelling out with Jane and Robert. Jane had hired a car in Athens. Driving out of Athens stretched her nerves to the limit. They were with us for a week. Ben went home in early August, we stayed on until 19th August.

We certainly couldn't do a book like Travels at our age. Building on all the explorations we did in our early years, we travelled back to the same places as well as new ones, recording what we experienced in our different ways.

Ours is not a guide book, I wrote in the Introduction, *it is a personal selection of places seen with the eyes of an artist interested in nature and a novelist interested in everything.*

I want to add a sentence from Gerald Durrell's Foreword.

"It is rare that you get a married couple who complement each other as well as Susan and Peter Barrett do, for her magical prose complements his delicate and lovely pictures so well and his pictures add a new dimension to the prose."

Thank you, G.D. May this present book repeat something of the quality he found in Travels.

Travelling with Ben in the summer of 1984 (Sophie and Dean had been

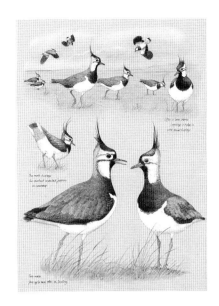

Illustratons for posters and calendars

with us in Kassiopi, Corfu), we came across an old wooden caique pulled up on a beach on Lefkadha. The three of us became excited. The owner of the boatyard told us it was for sale. It belonged to an Italian who had converted it from a Sicilian fishing boat and named it Moby Dick. We clambered all over it, tried out its six unmattressed bunks, peered into the dark and inexplicable recesses of its engine, ran fingers over its flaking varnish. It would need a lot of work. *It*? Yes, we've always referred to Moby as 'it', finding this a more realistic gender for wide-beamed and engine-driven Moby than the conventional 'she' for yachts and other, smarter, sea-going vessels.

We immediately found out how we could buy it. It would give us a travelling home base as we filled in our knowledge of the islands of the Ionian, Cyclades, and Dodecanese. The owner, Signor Rossi, a consultant surgeon, lived near Milan. We visited him by car in April 1985. We have vivid memories of snails gathered from a fenced enclosure in the Rossi garden for a delicious meal, a trip to Chioggia near Venice to sign papers, the bright, red yachting shoes that the solicitor tried to sell us, a second trip later in the summer to collect Moby's paraphernalia – plates, cutlery, orange, towelling mattress covers and mattresses, ropes, sails, anchors, and god know what else – followed by long days in the boatyard, waiting for engine parts, the mechanic, carpenters …

On 27th July Moby was launched. The next day we moved on board.

The thrilling launch was followed by days of difficulty. On August 1st the fuel tank started leaking. On August 3rd we met Ben at Igoumenitsa – he'd flown to Corfu. On August 4th we took the tank out. On the 5th Nikos Saxonis arrived from Athens for his holiday with us, kitted out in white yachting clothes. We were covering the tank with glass fibre at the time. However, on the 7th we were ready to invite Kiriakos, the boatyard owner, and Panos, the mechanic, on board for champagne. The next day we chugged off to Meganisi, a small island close to Lefkadha. The steering cable broke on the way home and the ignition failed. Peter tried to solve these problems but I climbed onto the cabin roof at once, where I waved a towel at passing boats. We were towed back, ignominiously, to the boatyard. We felt sorry for Nikos. He sensibly left next day.

We managed a trip to Sivota, Ithaki and Vassiliki with Ben before driving him back to Igoumenitsa for the plane from Corfu.

On August 17th we had engine trouble. Panos the mechanic advised us to change the oil. We discovered that we needed to replace the oil filter seals. Having done this we managed to reach Sivota once more. On the 20th the loo broke and the cooking stove's gas bottle ran out. Without those two modern conveniences, and with limited time for our trip in mind, we sailed on to Skala in Kefallonia. On the night of 21st we anchored off Porto Mundi beach to join James Sutherland and his turtle watching team. The book was about nature, after all, rather than engines. After Zakinthos town we went on to Laguna where we grounded on a reef. This was quite alarming. We were pulled off. From there we sailed on to Katakolon on the Pelopponese where we managed to find a plumber to mend the loo and buy a new gas bottle.

On August 25th we had a wonderful day's trip from Katakalon to Methoni, eight hours of calm and glorious weather. But Peter developed severe flu while we anchored in the harbour of Methoni. A very strong wind got up

and the anchor dragged. With Peter in his bunk and in need of medication, I rowed the dinghy ashore. This was one of the severest trials of my life. The wind was immensely strong and the waves heavy. I had to fight to make headway. The wind wanted to sweep me and the rubber dinghy out to sea. I remembered complaining bitterly as I rowed; in fact, I was whimpering with exhaustion, self-pity and the temptation to give up, my hysterical side coming to the fore. As this writing proves, I made it, someone helped me anchor more firmly in the harbour, and in a few days Peter recovered.

On 31st August, the steering broke while we were crossing the gulf to Kalamata. We managed to get ourselves into the harbour at Kalamata where a new cable was fitted on August 2nd. On the 3rd we had a glorious passage to Porto Kaio and from there next day to Monemvasia. From Monemvasia we intended to reach Milos but another storm brewed soon after we left the harbour.

The *meltemi* wind rose quickly. The waves mounted. Peter was amazingly unconcerned. I was convinced that Moby would break up and we would face death by drowning. The sea was a vast expanse of wild emptiness. Steering through and over the waves was hard. We rose up, the wheel swivelled, down we went the other side, to find ourselves off course, heading for Crete. All other vessels must have stayed safely in harbours. A rocky islet appeared on the horizon. *Please, please, let's head for that.* But Peter still seemed unworried and he, on Moby, was most definitely captain.

Thank heavens, Poseidon and Peter's judgment, we headed for the rock. A fishing caique had anchored before us in the only slight inlet on the rock. How relieved I was to hear the anchor rattle down and find its grip on the sea floor.

Falconera – we later learnt the rock's name – gave us a good page in the eventual book. Eleanora's falcons were patrolling the cliffs, in wait for passing birds. A dove found sanctuary in Moby's rigging, perching in the decorative life belt, and stayed with us until the wind abated two days later.

For the rest of the trip to the Dodecanese I will leave *Travels* to tell the tale. I want to bring in northern Greece and the ruin we rebuilt in the Pindos mountains.

We'd drawn the boat up in a Patmos boatyard for the winter and took a plane from Samos back to Athens. From there we went by bus to pick up our car which we'd left outside the Lefkas boatyard over the summer months. Our plan was to explore parts of the mainland which were unknown to us. We drove beyond Ioannina (visited in our very first winter), skirted the feet of mount Kipseli, drove past the turning to Albania and under the hill with the word Οχι (No!) picked out in white stones. This commemorates the way the Greeks fought the Italians in deep snow for six long winter months, the prime minister having said No to their invasion. Beyond Kalpaki where a road leads north to the border with Albania, we turned off the main road to follow a winding road, which would become familiar in years to come.

Imagine listening to a fairly humdrum passage of a symphony, which goes on and on, deferring the promised arrival of something unknown, yet more exciting. Perhaps, we thought, as we drove through a nondescript village called Mesovouni (Middle Mountain) – perhaps a disappointment awaits

A few watercolours from Travels with a Wildlife Artist, our first major collaboration, commissioned by Bellew and Higton and published by Columbus Books in 1986

us. Years before, Nikos Saxonis had mentioned to Peter, over a drawing pad in the Alpha magazine offices, the name of a village that was really worth a visit. *Papingo*. We'd never made it yet. There were so many other places to visit. For Nikos, too. Until then, he had never returned.

On we drove, higher and higher. Turning a corner, we sensed a sudden opening in the landscape, below and ahead of us. We pulled in to the side of the road where the land fell sharply away. Ahead of us, a vast display of mountainside was revealed. The far slopes which rose in columns to the sky, seemed covered in a pale gauze, a lilac-coloured light coming from another world. If we could have heard the sight, not only seen it, we would have heard a crashing chord from a full orchestra. It overwhelmed us into silence while we took in the detail of the view. At this point, the 11-kilometre Vikos gorge reaches the deep valley below the peaks of Astraka. A corkscrew of road can be seen winding up the far side of the blue river. This road leads in tight zigzags to the village of Papingo, divided into two communities – Megalo (Big) and Mikro (Small).

In the extraordinary way life has of springing unlikely chances on us, Nikos Saxonis happened to be visiting Papingo, carrying out his twenty-year old intention to visit again. He'd been to Prespes and had thought of Peter, prompted by all the birds seen on the lakes. He'd pinned a ridiculous note to us on a telegraph pole, in the million to one chance that Peter would turn up to read it. He had no idea whether we were in Greece, were due to come to Greece, or had left Greece; but he knew we had a book on Greece in mind. The year before, we'd called on him in his Athens office as head of McCann-Erickson. He'd probably advised Peter to research the Prespes lakes and visit Papingo. By being there himself at that time, he was taking a long chance that we'd meet.

We'd been in Papingo several days and were about to leave when to our surprise and pleasure we came across the familiar figure of Nikos, back straight and head up, at a turning in Mikro Papingo. We were coming down from what would in the future be our house, although we had no idea of this at the time. With Nikos was Polly, his new love after the break-up with Oliga, our friend from Athens days. We decided to stay another night. In those days the only place to stay was in the rooms above the shop. It belonged to Koulis. There was one room with four beds, reminiscent of a mountain hostel. Laughter and chatter went on late. The nature of the Saxonis-Barrett friendship is that great chunks of time can slide past without a sighting. As soon as we get together again, it's as though no time has passed.

That was our first visit to Papingo. While working on *Travels* our habitual pattern was to turn up for a night or two at the next place, go out onto the mountainside and find the right spot. Peter would sit down and sketch. I would sit a distance away and scribble in my notebook. This was an enjoyable activity and nowhere did it cause us any difficulty – until we reached Papingo. We had to leave, unsatisfied with our work. Both of us felt we had not caught the magnificence of the place. We had not nearly done it justice. "You should come back and buy one of our many ruins," we were told. No, we replied. We owned a house in Greece once and we don't want to own another. Our thought, not expressed, was that we didn't want to fall for another place, only to see it change too much, too fast.

We heard the same refrain on our next visit. In my memory we returned three times before we agreed to buy a ruin in Mikro Papingo.

In the spring of 1985 Moby Dick was still sitting, propped up on wooden columns in the Patmos boatyard. We decided it would be an excellent idea to take Ben with us to sail back to Lefkatha and that his best schoolfriend Grant should come too. Grant's parents readily agreed. They, like us, were battling problems though not quite in the same way. Grant had actually been appointed head boy – Mr. Corke's plan for achieving a complete turn-around. Both Ben and Grant had long, dark, straggling hair kept off the forehead by a red and white kerchief, worn low. It was known as a doss rag. They were equally tall and heavy. They wore tattered jeans and heavy boots, called Doc Martens. Ben and Grant were wedded to bikes but were willing to do without them for this trip.

The father and son owners of the Patmos boatyard had proved rather prickly before this, but on launching they became actively bad-tempered. Perhaps the audience of four foreigners unnerved them. There was a slow build up while they argued among themselves about the right way to get Moby onto the cradle by knocking away the supports. Things did not look promising. Moby faltered on its cradle, wobbled for a moment before toppling sideways. There was the distressing sound of splintering wood. The head of one of the supports had pierced Moby's side. Blame was placed on the audience. We disappeared while they did the carpentry necessary to fill the gaping wound. When this was completed, we were in such a hurry to get away from the brooding tempers that we set off too soon. A wooden boat, after months out of the water, opens up. It needs to sit at anchor, taking in water which swells its timbers and seals them tight.

I remember the consternation of opening up the hatch over the propeller shaft with Peter and seeing what looked like the inner workings of an

Lesser kestrel, Pindos mountains

88

Peter enjoyed illustrating 'My Family and Other Animals' by Gerald Durrell and James Herriot's 'Moses the Kitten' and 'Only One Woof'

industrial-sized washing machine. The amount of water being tossed around was slowing down the propeller. The hand bilge bump came to the fore. We were well out to sea by now and we were not going to turn back to face our boatyard chums. The wind was rising and the boys were growing hungry. We'd not stocked up with food as we had assumed we'd reach our next port of call before supper time.

The next port of call was not a port at all. It was the sheltered inlet on Levitha, last visited when the only child on the island mistook Sophie for a doll. The family had left the island. A fishing boat was anchored in the bay and the fisherman donated an onion. Ben jumped into the water with his gun and emerged almost at once with an octopus. We had octopus stew for a few days.

On a bright moonlight night, not far to the north-east of Amorgos, I was steering us westwards in a mild swell. The gentle movement through the waves was wonderfully soothing. Up we rose, down and forward; up, down and forward. Ben emerged from a deep sleep in the cabin. "Mum! Rocks!" It wasn't only the nearby rocks that presented danger. We worked out I was steering us back towards Patmos.

It remined me of Sophie's alarm call in Kenya. "Mum!" She didn't take the time to shout more. She simply pointed behind me as I took a gentle pee. I leapt into the car, my pants around my ankles, imagining a lion about to pounce. The animal that was loping towards me was only a hyena. However, I was glad to be in the car with Peter, Sophie and Ben and with the windows wound up.

A few days later we shouted down to the cabin: "The Corinth Canal!" This was something really worth seeing. Ben was thrilled, especially when a large steamer entered the Canal behind us and began inexorably bearing down on us, looking bigger and bigger as it drew nearer. Would we reach the end of the Canal before it mowed us down? We encouraged Moby to do her utmost. If we'd had spurs and whips we wouldn't have hesitated to use them on her. (You see that I have to use the feminine in this case, breaking our rule of "it"). Grant emerged from the cabin, took a brief glance around, and went down to his bunk again. He was reading a really exciting novel. We kept trying to get him on deck to see a number of views – "Grant! Kefallonia!" "Grant! Ithaki!" "Grant! Lefkadha!" – but he only came on deck when we'd reached the boatyard.

His disinterest in gorgeous views puzzled us. But perhaps being on deck made him feel queasy? "I'll go inside now," said three-year old Olivia, when we were bobbing at anchor. The boat would stop rocking when she was in the cabin. All very logical, if you think of houses.

Another thought. Teenagers are not interested in views. Sophie also read a novel while we drove through California.

If one of our decades was ever fuller and more productive than another, then it would have been the 1980s. I feel exhausted whenever I dare glimpse at the diaries to check on a date and a happening. All those friends to stay! Names recur. Jane and a varying number of sons, in Devon and Greece. Elizabeth Dun, first met on Hydra in 1962, then a faithful visitor to us on Amorgos, in Devon and on Moby. Martin Young, friend since our first year in Athens, then – what a renegade – moving to Spain to find plentiful

water to create a garden. He came to Lefkadha to find us on Moby, bringing with him by car from Malaga a ham and a cheese. Imagine its transit in the summer heat. Not a practical man. I wrote the one-page Ham and Cheese Story, which made me – and others, I hope – laugh weakly. Continuing the list, there's Graham Fawcett, a fount of literary knowledge and poetry, now a lecturer, met through Elizabeth in her flat in Royal Crescent. He came to pick up a typewriter while I was staying, Elizabeth having gone to work. (An engineered meeting, I later suspected). Oliver Campion, another introduction by Elizabeth and a very favourite visitor wherever we were. We liked and admired the way he painted, and tried to attend his rare exhibitions. We appointed him Ben's godfather and he left Ben a painting. Jennifer and Bill, Peter's sister and her partner, stayed often, later following us to live in Devon. The list goes on. Ma and Pa, who found our life a constant source of interest. After Ma's death in 1985 Pa was

Peter had fun illustrating The Wind in the Willows for an American publisher. The commission gave him the freedom to exercise his imagination

with us regularly. An Edith appeared, a girl friend from his youth. But she disappeared after a trial weekend in Bath. "She talks too much," said Pa. Jennie Tierney, originally on Amorgos with us, then a regular visitor and frequently a caretaker. Virginia Edwards with Rod in London and on Amorgos, and then by herself, for many a visit to all our homes with the exception of Moby Dick. I rang Virginia the other day, concerned after our last stumbling conversation and realising that we had no mutual friends to ask how she is. Luckily, the phone was answered by someone who lives in the flat above. Vera was making sure Ginny was eating her evening meal. She's been in hospital and has a touch of dementia. We work out that she must be 93. So it goes …

Vera is living in the flat below the one where John and Claire Burge lived. John, soon after returning from his year in Greece, married Claire, a judge's daughter from the north. John would have liked to be a judge himself. He was the sort of paterfamilias who would stand in front of the fire, his hands linked behind his back, and pontificate. Claire and their four children could argue but only if they did it briefly. Pete Rose and Peter, in their early pub days with John, created an expression: a place could get Burged. John would draw himself together in his chair, swivel around to beckon a waiter, his bald head shining ominously. We'd hold our breath. *My good man, you may have spent many years providing your customers with forks as deeply mired as these in what I can only imagine is pig's swill but it is not the forks that overly concern me it is the FOOD we are waiting to put on these bloody forks.* Most of the time, we just let John have the floor. But very occasionally I take exception to someone's remark and feel the need to refute the case. This will happen when everyone else has fallen into silence with their mouths full. I have no idea what sort of disagreement I voiced with John, but he looked down the long family table with surprise, sprang out of his lair and stung me to the quick. The gist of what he said was that I talk too much. Stupidly, I burst into tears. It seemed so unfair. How many times had I listened to John holding forth, and how seldom did I talk for any length of time?

Perhaps he was diabetic. I came to this conclusion after two Burged occasions. The first was when John and Claire visited us in Papingo and we were waiting for food in Alexandria's cafe in Aristi. Alexandria always generously treated us to her home-made cheese pie. She never moved fast. John grew noisily cross as she padded around, gathering supplies for us. We were acutely embarrassed. The other occasion was when the Burges were visiting us in Devon and we were waiting to be served in a Dartmoor pub. John became sarcastically impatient with the landlord. *So that's it*, I thought, when I re-ran these events in my mind. *John's blood sugar level drops and drives him mad.*

In June 1985 we were at Luggs for our silver wedding anniversary. Claire Burge's handwriting is the first in the Visitors Book. "*A wonderful day with mayhem (and murder) and one relic of the original feast.*" She's referring to John who was one of the ushers at our wedding. They and a number of friends stayed overnight and I got them to play a Murder game I'd written, the characters tailored specifically to suit each of them. I remember Oliver lurking in the greenhouse, being the murderer. It was an elaborate game in which all valiantly took part, save for Brian Sidery who hid in my study. We danced on the lawn. A photo reminds me that I wore a dress made out of Liberty fabric by Di.

Kath Lyall wrote: Heaven. Can't wait 25 years for the next.

Gavin Lyall: Even the weather was superb.

Nann du Sautoy: Fabulous!! Perhaps see you in Greece/?

Vicky Burge: Thank you Peter and Susie for brilliant feasts, complicated games, nice chats and sunshine!x

Jon B. (Vicky's boyfriend from Bristol university): Best Game Best Wishes Nice Time.

Virginia: (no words in the book, a picture sent later)

Oliver: Marvellous. Thank you.

Jennie Tierney: A lovely dream. Congratulations, love and thanks.

Frank and Rosie: A pleasure and an inspiration. Can't wait to get back. I'm sure I'll find an excuse soon (as if one were necessary!)

The last two were friends of Ben's. We always get on well with Ben's friends. We went to see Frank, an amazing dancer, perform in Exeter a short time later.

Other parties happened in the mid-80s at the various exhibitions of Peter's work. The original paintings and drawings for *Travels* were exhibited at the Illustrators Gallery, London, at Otterton Mill, Devon, and (later in the 90s) at Chris Beetles Gallery in London. In Greece, we had a wonderful party at the British Council to open the exhibition of the Greek book paintings there, as well as selling copies of the book. Various young environmentalists became fans of Peter's. Peter Brousellas of the Hellenic Society for the Preservation of Nature appreciated the boost our book gave the fragile movement. In general, Greeks were happier shooting birds than studying them.

The lawn in front of the Barn at Luggs was the setting for several wonderful parties. One was for our Silver Wedding in 1985. Another was for Susie's 60th birthday in 1998

On December 15th 1986 Peter was interviewed for the Greek language broadcast from BBC Radio about our life in Greece and *Travels*. He spoke well, fluently and clearly. I was relieved but he didn't seem nervous at all. Unlike me when we were both interviewed for Woman's Hour. We were sitting on a deep sofa in the Illustrators Gallery. When I heard the re-play, I thought I sounded as though I was just about to fall asleep; either that or just about to wake up. I hadn't arrived satisfactorily at either state.

Another time I made a poor subject for interview was with Radio Devon. I agreed to the interview because the novel that had just been published could not be found in any bookshop in the west country. "I can't think why I bother to write," I told the interview crossly. At the end of the interview, he pulled the strands together. "Well, Susan Barrett, you don't know why you write and your book's not available in west country bookshops. Thanks for coming in." Shot out of the water!

The book was probably my best to date: *Stephen and Violet,* a novel fed by our journeys by car between Greece and England. I'd taken in Gavin Lyall's technique. Kath would sit in the passenger's seat with a notebook and tape recorder while Gavin drove through the landscapes he would describe in his latest thriller: Germany, the Netherlands, Belgium, I used a tape recorder on one journey from Athens to England. Paying close attention to everything we passed, and finding the words and phrases to describe it, was a wonderful way to pass a journey which had become commonplace. A review on publication described the novel as being as authentic as the stamp in a passport. This was before Britain joined the EU when passports ceased to be stamped at borders. Now we are about to crash out.

I used to say I couldn't have written *Stephen and Violet* if I hadn't lived with a teenage son. But Ben was not the Stephen of the title. If I'd set out to write a true-to-life picture of Ben, I would never have finished the novel. He lurched from one disaster to the next, one bike crash to another, one brief job to another. He was staying with Diane in Rochester, driving a fish delivery van around Kent in the hurricane of 1987. Branches whirled around the van. It wasn't until a large oak tree crashed in front of him that he thought he should give up and go back to base. There was a short period when he was a motorcycle dispatch rider in London. Every so often he came home to patch up the latest bike and catch up on sleep He was chased by the police in and out of Cullompton, on and off the motorway, and finally caught. A court case followed.

A peak in my writing life was the party Toby held for me to launch *Stephen and Violet.* I was flattered beyond belief, not just by the number of friends who came but by the Names that were there; in particular, Sebastian Faulks and Jonathan Raban. For them, it was all part of the job as a known writer: when in London, keep visible. If we'd stayed in

Putney – that's often a thought. But after the thought has been sent on its way, I breathe a sigh of relief at the life we've led, at our own pace, in our own way.

The latter half of the 80s were the years when Sophie and Ben were beginning to leave home. Sophie came with us to Greece one year on her own, perhaps hoping for something or someone to happen, as an alternative to what lay ahead in England. It was not to be. Sophie and Dean moved into their first house in Wellington and joined us in Greece on holidays. Ben, after a number of girlfriends, met Monika, an Austrian air hostess. She contacted me on Facebook this spring, asking for Ben's address. She's still with Austrian Airlines, a record surely. Forty years and more ago, her parents were not thrilled with Ben. In fact, it would have been hard for Monika to find anyone more unlikely to be approved of than Ben Barrett.

At different times the two couples joined us in Greece. Ben and Monika slept in a tent in the paved entrance to the ruin which the Sarakatstan cousins, Nikos and Dias, were to rebuild as a hotel after they finished carting stones up the hill for our house in Mikro Papingo. This is a whole new chapter of our lives, if I let it be. But I have never wanted to write a book describing the rebuilding of the ruin we bought in the mountain village, or the building of our first house in Greece on Amorgos. Or details of the renovations in Putney, in Kentisbeare, at Madford and at Luggs. (There are two more moves to come, fair warning.) My reluctance was compounded by meeting Peter Mayle and his wife before they moved to France. We'd read his book, *A Year in Provence*. A whole rash of such books followed, some as competently written. It's a tried and trusted formula in which the hapless owners of a ruin employ local builders who are either amusingly eccentric or lovable rogues. A number of ghastly accidents occur. Disastrous faults are put right. Everyone loves each other in the end. They toast each other's health at a final, all night party.

Real life experience has informed my writing in different ways. It's mangled and transformed into fiction. It has fed the text of *Travels*, which was more a nature guide book than a personal saga. Our Greek life in the 1960s provided the verbal descriptions to go alongside the photographs in *The Garden*. Our long periods in Mikro Papingo inspired the background to my 11th novel, *Greek Gold*. In none of those did I feel I was writing a year in Provence style of book.

Is this present book dangerously close to the pit I wish to avoid? Could it become a "we rebuilt a ruin"? No, it has a much broader and far more difficult a sweep. It deals with two people's lifetimes from birth to present date. I must avoid looking down from the tightrope but simply do what I can, when I can.

Moments can never be totally recaptured but the diaries and the Visitors Book have helped my memory. They've also threatened to drown me in detail. Without letting the day-to-day events and people entangle me, I shall call up pictures of our life in the 1980s. Peter is working in his room above our bedroom in Mikro Papingo. Rain is hammering away on the stone roofs of the neighbouring houses, gushing down the alleyway outside the roofed entrance to our courtyard, dripping off the leaves of the elderbushes. Heavy clouds have removed the rest of our world from view, hiding the distant lines of mountain ridges that lead into Albania. We've walked many kilometres up and over our local mountain, visited on foot far villages, seen the fresh pad marks of bears, heard wolves, surprised a chamois in a pass. We've tramped up and down the gorge, and along the river to its opening onto the plain where we've eaten many a trout. Peter has illustrated, in the last years of the decade, a number of children's books for America. He's illustrated *The Wind in the Willows* for an American publisher. We've divided the year between Papingo, Moby Dick and Luggs.

Peter is still extremely fit. He can haul up anchors and dive for fish. He can climb to the green belts on the Towers of Papingo to find the red lily and other rare plants. I no longer follow because I am beginning to limp. Pa Barrett is now living in a bungalow in Hemyock and is quite content, walking to the Post Office to buy the Daily Telegraph from Dean's aunty Margaret, before going on for a pint and a sandwich at the Catherine Wheel. Sophie and Dean have moved into a two-bedroom terraced house in Wellington, their first home together. Ben has left for Australia where he will meet some of Diane's relations. He's already met an uncle in England. Diane's brother Gerard is just a year or two older than Ben and almost a twin. He came to stay with us at Luggs, arriving late because he'd crashed his bike on the way. A shared gene?

Fortunately (that word again) we didn't know that Ben was caught in a current off a beach on Lombok and wasn't able to swim back to shore. He was saved from drowning by four lifeguards. We had a good long letter from him months later, describing this fright. Most of the time on his early travels we had no idea where he was or what he was doing. Only when he turned up to stay briefly with our old friend Pete Rose in Brisbane did we know he was safe and well.

The last few years of the 1980s were times of intense activity and movement for all four of us. Our settled life as a young family on Amorgos acted like a lode star. That time could not be repeated, yet it informed our movements. Peter and I, having come upon Papingo, wanted to recreate a Greek home, without giving up our ties to England. Sophie had her own dreams, wishes and realities in both countries. Ben longed to be away from wherever he was at the time and regularly gravitated back to us, more often in Greece than in England. He came and went, sometimes picking up work in England for a few weeks – nights at the local St Ivel milk factory, working for a table mat manufacturer and getting one design accepted followed by a short stint with a furniture maker until sawdust aggravated his asthma. He helped Peter by chain sawing, stockpiling wood for the winter. In Greece, he lived for a while on the boat, ostensibly to scrape the varnish off the interior's mahogany, having crossed Europe on his bike with a friend. That must have

Poster for the National History Museum. Illustrations for children's books on animals and prehistory

been the summer when he set himself up on Nidri quay, drawing portraits. We came down from Papingo to spend time on Moby and took Ben out for a meal. When the bill came, he told Peter to put away his wallet. He unrolled a thick bundle of notes and peeled off a few, tossing them onto the table with casual abandon. This was a triumph.

In this period we always managed to make arrangements to be away from our complicated life at Luggs, for six months at a time. Each year someone would turn up who wanted accommodation in exchange for caretaking. Ruth Sidery was one such person, with her man of the time, Paul. One year it was Sophie and Dean who stayed in the barn while the house was let for the months we were away. Dean managed to help one of the cows produce twins but I think we must have had someone else to do the daily livestock care. What about milking? Ever since Mill days I had a few customers for clotted cream and sometimes butter. This was unlikely to be taken over by someone else. Before settling into this division of the year between Greece and England, we'd given up smallholding and arranged for a farming friend to graze his sheep on our two acre field. David and Meg Palmer farmed Lower Mackham Farm which is where we first met them. Meg's mother Evelyn lived with them; she'd known my sister Jane in Godalming.

I'm constantly brough up short by such coincidences. You could almost believe that we are being played like a game. What under the table manipulations are going on as we move around the board, thinking we are in control? Never believe that this person you briefly met today won't turn up, twenty, thirty years hence, in a key role? The moral is: take care in all your dealings. When I was going through a deeply religious phase as a schoolgirl, I was struck by the lines my godmother penned in the prayerbook she gave me for my confirmation. "*Any good thing may I do it now for I may not pass this way again.*" The reverse is as true. "*Any bad thing may I* **not** *do it now for I may pass this way again.*"

Wherever we live, we draw inspiration from our environment, the landscape and its people. On the right is a painting of a courtyard in Mikro Papingo, the village in the Zagori where we rebuilt a ruin. Elenitsa was always ready to invite us in for a glass of tsipouro. We lived here, painting and writing for long periods from 1985 to 2001. The Vikos gorge and surrounding mountains were a constant inspiration for Peter and provided me with the background to fictionalise in a recent novel, Greek Gold

Scenes for RSPB calendars

Rebuilding the ruin in Papingo

Paintings around Papingo

THE 1990s

On September 14th this year, 2020, Peter was 85. When Covid did away with our diamond wedding anniversary party in June, I wanted to put in place something for his September birthday instead. This was a gamble. It seemed foolhardy to make plans during a pandemic, yet I went ahead with bookings for a family get together. Half the plan worked out. On Sunday 13th the family met for a pub lunch in north Devon. We were eight adults sitting at two socially distanced tables: Sophie and Nick, Mark and Rio at one, Olivia and Bertie and ourselves at the other. Davinia, five months old, slept in her carrycot, and Brinley, at 2 years and 8 months, ran around in circles when he wasn't lying on the floor next to Rufus the dachshund. With Mark and his family staying in a holiday let in Mortehoe and ourselves in a hotel nearby, we had two sun-filled days on beaches, exchanging satisfied smiles with Davinia and well-washed pebbles with Brinley, until sea mist came down and sent us home early. The children weren't sleeping well. For the very young and the very old, being away can be disturbing. Peter and I wanted to get back to our accustomed bed and our big bath, our own cooking, our own view, chairs, books and, most of all, our present work together – this memoir. Ironically, it describes the years we've spent constantly moving away from one home or another. On reflection, though, we are never away because our home is wherever we can settle down to painting and writing.

The Voidomatis river emerges from the Vikos gorge below the Towers of Papingo, an inspiring setting for long periods of painting and writing

Taking this long, hard look back at our life, it continually strikes me how fortunate we've been. The decisions we've made have turned out well. We have a family, thanks to the decision we made to adopt. And thanks to Sophie and her decision to live in Hemyock, we don't have to go away to see them. If we had no children, we would be in the unenviable situation of two of our very good friends, Virginia and Christine. Virginia has been a friend since the 1960s when the Burges came to live in the flat above hers in Regents Park Road. She'd got to know them when she had a sucking pig laid out on her kitchen table. It wouldn't fit in her oven. She mounted the stairs and knocked on the Burges' door. Imagine her Australian voice. "I need a saw to cut the legs off a pig." Through the Burges, Virginia became an essential part of our lives. She was a very good illustrator – Peter knew her as Virginia Smith before we met her. A serious car accident demolished her ability to work. After this, she suffered from recurrent and deep depressions. Rod, her jewellery-making husband, was a drinker; he became worse; eventually they split up, he went back to Australia, gave up alcohol, met someone else, and died. Virginia is now 93 and alone. Luckily, she has a very caring neighbour in what was the Burges' flat.

Christine is in a worse state, or at least in a different situation. She was diagnosed with Korsakoff's syndrome and placed in a specialist care home in Weston-super-Mare. Before the pandemic, we were able to take her out to lunch. She seems perfectly well as long as we stay in the moment with her but without a short-term memory it is impossible to live normally. A court case was necessary to get her into the care home in the first place, and this was reviewed in July. At the hearing, the judge determined that she could go home for a month's trial. No money and no alcohol would be allowed. She's now been home for two and a half weeks. How this is going it's difficult to discover. At my first phone call, she sounded panick-stricken; there was someone at the door, she couldn't find her keys, she would ring later. Of course, she didn't. I've just tried again. I'm in two minds about the wisdom of trying to connect. It's like trying to hold a handful of water. Yet she is glad to hear a familiar voice, so it's worth it.

Other friends whose names recurred frequently in our Visitors Book were also single. I'm remembering a weekend when Graham Fawcett and Martin Young coincided at Luggs. This would not have been by design. On the contrary. Each of them needed the stage to themselves, or so I was thinking as the meal progressed at Luggs dining room table. Peter and I listened with interest tinged with apprehension as Graham and Martin began to spar. Small arms at first. A little skirmish here and there as the battleground was set. A sharper rattle, the crack of a pistol shot, followed by a gradual crescendo until all guns were blazing either side of the ground on which plates of venison stew cooled. Sweat broke out on brows. Veins pulsed. Mouths spluttered. Suddenly Martin flung down his napkin and stood up. Graham pushed back his chair and stood, too. "Never," he managed to say in a clear, loud voice, "never did I imagine that I would meet at this table a ----." He drew in his breath for a final volley. "A thapkin-numper!"

A second's silence followed as we worked out what on earth he'd wanted to say; then each of us, including Graham, folded over in helpless laughter. After this, thapkin-numper was a surefire way to bring smiles to the face of either visitor. Graham is still around. Martin, very sadly, died not long after we visited him in his Spanish house and garden near Ronda. He liked conversations with Peter about rare plants. He'd written guide books to Corfu and the Cyclades, published by Collins. He'd visited us on Amorgos for a chapter on the island. He'd cast his scholarly eye over the text of our first Greek book before publication, removing or maybe adding a blizzard of commas. He would have liked to have written such a book himself and hoped that Peter would collaborate with him on something in the future. He had a big leather-bound visitor's book which lay open on our last morning in Ronda. I picked up the pen that lay across the page. "No!" His sharp command startled me. "Only Peter!" he said, taking the pen from my hand.

It's possible – a re-appraising thought – that he wanted only Peter's handwriting in the book, expecting that Peter would write both our names. At the time I assumed he didn't want my name at all. Whatever Martin's intention, Peter wouldn't think of including my name with his, so I just seethed quietly away at what I imagined an intentional put-down.

This is just one of those unverified assumptions and misunderstandings we leave in our wake, tiny pinpricks that can fester unless straightened out at the time. I remind myself that I have something to thank Martin for: his introduction to Patrick Leigh Fermor. Through Martin I sent P.L.F a copy of *Stephen and Violet,* my seventh novel. He responded kindly with a good quote that the publisher used on the book jacket. "*A psychological itinerary movingly traced with great insight and skill.*" We nearly visited the Leigh Fermors, through Martin's introduction, when we were sailing from the Ionian to the Dodecanese. We'd planned to anchor off Kardamili but the wind got up as we were heading up the gulf and we turned tail so that we could reach the haven of Monemvasia that evening.

Settling back to work after our brief time away this September, Peter has begun the drawing which will introduce the 1980s, when that big trip on Moby Dick took place. He's sketched out a harbour scene. Meanwhile, I'm in the 1990s, a doppelganger with today's 2020s. I've just received an email out of the blue from someone called Kalliope Stara, reminding me of Rodoula in Papingo.

Rodoula? The name is familiar but who exactly was she? I rack my brains, bringing a number of black-clad widows sitting in Papingo doorways to mind. Mousso, Stavroula, Elenitsa, Despina. But Rodoula? A blank.

I do better with Kalliope's surname, Stara. I was actually recalling Klearchos Stara the other day. He was a ferocious old man who chastised me for stubbing out a cigarette with my heel on the *kalderimi* that led up to our house. Nowadays I'd share his loathing for fag ends on the cobbled path – for smoking in general, in that clear, clean, fresh mountain air. How Peter put up with my nicotine addition, I cannot imagine. I'd started to smoke tentatively on a bench halfway down Royal Parade, Plymouth, in bored lunch hours from the Tech. I was not a committed smoker and had given up entirely when Pete Rose encouraged me to start again, much to Peter's disgust. His disapproval was evident and fed the determination which I distributed evenly between the desire to stop and the wish to continue. I tried hypnotherapy several times. Each time it worked, in so far as I gave up smoking. But I always took up something else. When the addiction was

peanuts, I grew enormously fat. Another time I found I couldn't write. I was halfway through a novel and it got stuck. This upset me so much I lit up and continued with ease. But the novel had suffered from the break and never really healed. This became the point when I lost all interest in fiction, both reading it and writing it. As for smoking, I gave it up for ever in response to Ben who told me, one evening in Luggs kitchen, that he couldn't give up because he'd been smoking for too long. "I've been smoking for twenty years," I said. "If I can give up right now, so can you." We both stubbed out our fags on the spot. Ben lit up again within a week. I promised myself I could smoke again when I was 70. That seemed sufficiently far ahead, yet at such an advanced age that I'd have no health to damage. I safely passed my 70th birthday twelve years ago and I still have no wish to light up.

When I was stubbing out fag ends on the cobbles of Papingo's *kalderimia*, I was interested in learning all I could about our new home. Klearchos Stara was an interesting old man, an authority on the local flora and fauna. He had created a three-dimensional model of the mountain and gorge which made the complicated shapes of the landscape clear in a way that contour maps and actual presence could not supply.

Kalliope's email began: *"I wish you are fine and you remember us from Mikro Papingo. I am Kalliope Stara, Rodoula's daughter and Rigas my husband and we had visited you together a long-long time ago."*

Rodoula? The name brought no picture with it. Perhaps North Devon sea mist had befuddled my brain. It was hard to get myself back to our Papingo years. But, on following through with her request for photographs of Peter's drawings of birds in the Vikos gorge, another email from Kalliope attached a photo of her mother. Of course! That's Rodoula! The daughter of Sofia, our next door neighbour. Sofia was old and, as we remember, mostly bedridden. Rodoula would appear regularly to open up the guesthouse on the far side of her mother's house. It was called the Agnanti, translatable as The Prospect. Sometimes Athenian visitors would stay here and stand on the threshing floor terrace. They would declaim at the tremendous view in voices that ricocheted

Photos taken on long mountain walks

off the mountainside. We in our nearby eyrie chafed at the disturbance. Now Rodoula's daughter, our neighbour Sofia's granddaughter, was a professor at the University of Ioannina, as was her husband Rigas. They were both writing chapters for a book on Aristi, the village on the far side of the river.

"Rigas would like to include one, two or more of Peter's wonderful drawings of the area, e.g. the Egyptian Vultures in Voidomatos gorge, the Kingfisher in Vikos river, the golden eagles on Astraka."

Kalliope explained that Klearchos was her uncle, as was the other Staras we remember well, Pyros. Pyros and his wife Despoina lived in Ioannina but came up to Papingo every so often to air their house, directly below ours. Pyros must have been in his 90s. When he was a boy, he told us, he'd walked to Ioannina to demand an audience with Ali Pasha. Epirus was still part of the Ottoman Empire at the time and the Turks were in control of everything, including, of course, education. Pyros was indignant that his school had no exercise books. How could he learn if he couldn't write anything down? The Pasha listened to him and agreed. Pyros walked the 30 kilometres home with exercise books for the whole school.

Pyros was a living link back to Papingo's subjugated past. He'd experienced life under the Ottomans and the liberation of northern Greece in 1917. He'd lived through the Italian invasion, the German occupation, and the years of the civil war. Memories of these times were still fresh in old people's minds when we arrived in the village as eager listeners. We were there on the cusp between the Old Days and the New Days to come. We weren't the first newcomers. Before us two couples from Athens had rebuilt derelict houses in Megalo Papingo. One of the four, Yorgos, had been a child in northern Epirus during the war. Another, John Demos of a Greek family from Thessaloniki, had spent his childhood in America. He was a very good photographer. We'd first noticed his fair-haired, Dutch wife Bernadine at Big Papingo's church festival. More of them later.

Kalliope continued her first email. *"These gorgeous drawings are so important for conservation too. E.g. the Egyptian Vulture does not anymore breed in the area, it is threatened with extinction in Greece and it remains only as a memory."*

This we find shocking. The Egyptian vultures were a familiar sight, circling over the high plain where the Sarakatsan graze their sheep in the summer months. Peter delved into the stockpiles of pictures in the studio and photographed some to send Kalliope. The list below gives an idea of the sort of subjects he was painting in those years, some of which were for local calendars, exhibited and sold.

Chamois and Alpine swifts, Karteros Pass – oil painting
Egyptian vultures and Lesser kestrel sketches – pencil
Golden eagle over Vikos Gorge – oil
Golden eagle within Vikos Gorge – oil
Lesser kestrel, Lapatos – watercolour
Partridges, Zonaria – watercolour
Peony study – watercolour

I say years, but in fact we were only there for half-years, in the months from April to September or October. Winter life in the village was traditionally to be avoided if at all possible. Papingo could be snow and ice-bound for weeks, cut off from the rest of the world as an island can be in storms. Nearly all families had a flat in Ioannina and a granny in the village who could be brought down to the town before the worst of the winter. The Sarakatsan shepherds spent the winter months with their flocks in the plains near Igoumenitsa, driving them on foot in years past, latterly in lorries, between the high mountain pastures and the sea level plains twice a year, in spring and autumn. The few permanent inhabitants of the villages, Big and Small Papingo, owned goats. The herd's return in the evening and its exit to the mountainside each morning timetabled the day with a cascade of sound, the goats' hooves on the cobbles and the jangling music of the bells around their necks. In Big Papingo there were a few Jersey cows, tended by Vlassos whose manner was as gentle as the eyes of his cows. The first time we joined the walkers of the village on an expedition I found I could slot in comfortably behind Vlassos. His steady pace, geared to allow for his asthma, provided me with a helpful slipstream.

We usually walked on our own but we did join the Papingo Mountain Club which was gradually coming into existence, or being revived, encouraged by clubs in other parts of mainland Greece. Koulis, who was the mainspring of life in the community, and Thannos, one of his brothers, had begun opening up old paths, painting red spots at intervals along the way. One particularly memorable walk was a circuit of Astraka to include the Megalakka, the Big Ravine. We knew it from the map; a gash with a modest start behind the peak of Astraka, widening and dropping steeply over a distance to meet the bed of the Vikos gorge at a roughly midway point. We knew it would take a whole day but we had no idea just how long a day it would be nor how difficult a walk. Koulis and Thannos were equally innocent. They hadn't been this way since their schooldays.

It was an unusually big party that we joined at the first spring, having taken the back way from our house, setting off at six in the morning. Members of the Mountain Walking Club of Grevena – or some such place – were taking part, too. Their difference to the locals began to show very soon. They took the longest to reach each spring and voiced more complaints. After three hours we'd left behind the hostel on its ridge and were heading across boulder-strewn terrain on the further flank of Astraka. The gap between the last of the Papingiots and the first of the Grevenistas had grown wider. We, in the middle of the Papingiot bunch, were more concerned than anyone else with the increasing gap, foreseeing that the Grevenistas would get entirely lost. Shouldn't we wait for them? we asked diffidently. But we were the real foreigners. It was up to the Papingiots to look after their guests.

It was at this moment that a disagreement broke out between Koulis and Thannos. The line of walkers faltered. Some sat down. The Grevenistas caught up. The argument continued. Then Thannos set off in one direction and Koulis in another. Which leader to choose, now that we had two? The whole party came adrift as we entered the ravine. There were occasional halloos from strange directions and long silences. Figures appeared, disappeared. Peter and I were working from visual memories of the map and some sense of responsibility to others. I gazed down from a platform between two sheer slabs of rock, fearing there would come a point where, if I dropped down to the next level, I'd be faced with a precipice I couldn't descend and a rock face behind me which I couldn't ascend. Peter wasn't worried. This was one of those moments when the way he doesn't imagine what I'm imagining has its benefits. On we went together, alone in the landscape, an eerie silence all around us. Eventually, we reached the point where the ravine entered the dried watercourse at the bottom of the gorge. My legs went into spasm and the experience went into *Greek Gold,* the novel I brought out in 2019. I enjoyed putting my main character into a fictitious version of the Megalakka. He had concussion, after landing badly by parachute, whereas we only had sore feet. We were home by 10.30 p.m. Yes, it had been a long day.

We were living in Papingo at the cusp of change. Old ways were being lost or transformed into new ways. The change that was taking place was dramatically apparent in the physical appearance of one of our first friends. Nikos Tsoumanis was a good-looking young lad with a head of thick, curly, brown hair. On one of our first hikes up the mountain we'd met his father, Michaelis, one of the Sarakatsan shepherds. Michaelis was worried, like all the Sarakatsan. Their sons did not want to take over the flocks. Michaelis understood their reasons. The way of life was hard. If Nikos could earn money another way, then that was his good fortune. At the same time, he found it tragic and extremely depressing that their centuries' old way of life might be coming to an end. Not long after we met him, he got cancer and died. Nikos lost his entire head of hair within a matter of weeks.

Nikos and his two cousins, Costas and Tassos, were on hand when we were succumbing to the suggestion we should buy a particular ruin at the top of Small Papingo. We were part of the new way of earning money. They used their mules, which up to then had carried sheep's milk down the mountain, to carry stone and other building material up to the house. Then Costas (nicknamed Dias, that is, Zeus) and Tassos bought a ruin for themselves and rebuilt it as a guesthouse. Nikos, sometime later, did the same in Big Papingo. All three of them found wonderful wives to help them run increasingly flourishing concerns.

The perennial puzzle of finding wives in small rural communities was solved by the sudden availability of young women from communist countries, in particular from Northern Epirus where Greek families had been sealed within Albania. After the fall of the Berlin wall in 1990, Albanians were walking over the mountains to find work in Greece. Stavroula found three hungry men with bleeding feet wrapped in tattered black plastic by the first spring and took them in. These three became Papingo's first Albanian workmen: Sotiris, Thanasis and Christos.

We employed them when we decided to extend the house with a covered veranda. This was to provide us with extra room but it was also to shield us from sight and sound of anyone in the Mayor's house, in whose shadow our re-built ruin sat. I'd become fascinated by a previous inhabitant of this house, a Michael Anagnostopoulos who in the 1800s had gone to America, become involved with an institute for teaching deaf and dumb children, among them the famous Helen Keller. I learnt about him from the lawyer who helped us buy our ruin. Yannis Papaioanou was a local historian. I enjoyed reading and translating his books as an exercise in Greek. Navsika, the wife of the mayor, Odysseas Skourtis, was a descendant of

Anagnostopoulos and owned the house where Michael had grown up. It had been empty for years but she liked to grow onions and greens in the patch of earth behind her courtyard's retaining wall, which formed the boundary with our garden. Whether she had done this before we came to live there or not, I have no idea. But she – without demanding our attention – often engaged us in conversation, a trowel in her hand. It was as though she was standing on our shoulders.

We weren't upset by Navsika. We liked her. It was the way that, one summer, she let an English couple rent her house that ruffled our feathers. It was clear that Fran and Peter Annear, who went on to rebuild a ruin themselves and are still faithful Papingiots, had no idea what effect they might have on the English couple in the house at their feet. They must have thought, we'd be glad to have compatriots next door and listen to guitar-playing and singing in the evening. We very quickly took avoiding action. We went down to Moby Dick. We also took the opportunity to explore places as yet unknown to us. First we visited the Agrapha. This is a region in the south eastern corner of the mainland which the Ottomans left 'agrapha' – unrecorded – as it was so far removed from administrative centres. We went on from there to two attractive stone-built villages in the southern Pindos, Syrakos and Kalaoritis, where cloth was made for the French navy or was it Napoleon's army – this is from memory and unchecked.

We returned after 10 days and found all was safe and peaceful again. Our upset reminded us of the difficulty we had to adjust to neighbours on Amorgos. However much we tell ourselves we shouldn't feel this way, we will always be jealous of our privacy in what is no doubt an exaggerated and unreasonable manner.

At the same time, we like letting down our drawbridge on occasions. After *Travels* was published in 1986 and an exhibition of the

Oil painting of a Golden eagle over the Vikos gorge

original paintings held at the British Council in Athens, young Greek environmentalists wanted to meet Peter. Dias and Tassos had a copy of the book in their café. Through the book, several visitors to Papingo came to find us, among them Ken and Gillian Clarke. Never before or since have we had politicians as friends. Even more surprising is that this politician was, and still is, a Tory grandee. In fact, he is now Lord Clarke of Nottingham and a member of the House of Lords.

Ken and Gillian were easy to like; it was their interest in flora and fauna that brought them to our door. Ken and Peter could talk habitats and species. Gillian was a skilled quilt-maker and somewhere in a chest I have the quilt she designed and made for Peter's birthday. While Ken was Chancellor of the Exchequer, they invited us to stay with them at number 11. I asked Gillian if I could bring anything from Devon in the way of food, having learnt that it wasn't easy to shop for food from that address. We turned up at the guarded gates with a heavy plastic bag. The policeman on duty inspected its contents: a frozen leg of lamb. This led to jokes about the murder weapon in a Roald Dahl story.

Ron Hall and Christine Walker were other visitors to Papingo who tracked us down by virtue of *Travels*. Ron, who'd been the editor of the Sunday Times Book of the Countryside, knew of Peter's work We also had a mutual friend in Polly Hope, who we'd first met through Raleigh Trevelyan of Michael Joseph. At this stage we didn't know Polly at all well. Polly's Greek house was on Lindos in Rhodes and our English lives did not overlap until we coincided at a small wedding reception in a London flat. Martin Young had sprung a great surprise and announced his wedding to Carlotta, someone he'd loved as a young man. She'd married someone else but was widowed young. After the Registry Office formality, we were among the few guests at the reception and so was Polly. I suppose it wasn't all that strange that Martin turned out to be a mutual friend; we had Greece in common. But we felt slightly alarmed, knowing we might be swept up by Polly, a tidal wave of a personality as daunting as she was generous. She was a great collector of people and organiser of parties. She'd told her friend Ron Hall to look out for us in Papingo. We'd be able to help him with the background for the article he was to write for Conde Nast's magazine, *Traveller*.

We remember the spot in Small Papingo where we first met the Halls. They were climbing the steep path to our house. We were on our way down to visit someone. Christine retains a memory of someone somewhere pointing Peter out the day before, as he strode past the café where the Halls were sitting. That must have been in Big Papingo. Fortunately a good sense of direction is not a qualifying attribute for a travel editor. Christine held the Sunday Times travel section together for a striking number of years without ever being aware of where she was in relation to anywhere else.

Ron was in Papingo to research an article about the Greek National Tourist Board Organisation's scheme for the conservation of what they called traditional settlements, Papingo being one of the villages that had been selected as the inauguration of the scheme. This was in 1987. When the proposed article was to be written and finalised, he returned with a photographer. We became Ron's gofers and translators. Beside me on my desk I have the Conde Nast Traveller magazine open at Ron's article. It appeared in the July 1992 issue. "Criminal!" says Peter today, looking at the photographs. The classic view of the two villages merging into the grey rock of the mountain with the distinctive skyline formed by the pinnacles of rock known as the Towers of Papingo – well, where was this iconic and unimprovable vista? Instead, an indistinct photograph presented us with a vague line of black smudges hidden by a close-up of waving, orange-coloured grasses. They could be beside a railway track in Oklahoma. Another photograph shows us a glass of retsina in focus against a blur impossible to recognise, tinged with the same orange glow. Worst of all is the yet again orange-tinged image of a shepherd perched on top of a spectacularly sharp and slender outcrop of rock, jutting over the gorge, taken with a dark lens to – one suspects – heighten the drama. I was present at the time, translating between the photographer and the daredevil 'shepherd for an hour'. When you are actually there, the overwhelming grandeur of the gorge comes from the glinting lightness of the vacant space held between seemingly bottomless precipices on either side. Ron's text, describing his vertigo on a narrow ledge in the gorge-walls, captured this. The dark image destroyed it.

At the time we met the Halls, we were exercised by the threat of untrammelled tourist development, the fear of which had sent us away from Amorgos. There were those long absent who had now returned with dollar signs glinting in their eyes. They imagined Papingo becoming a kind of Alpine resort. Let's have a funicular up the mountain! What about running a road through the gorge, wouldn't that be magnificent! People will come from the whole world to see the landscape. This was the talk heard from the men who began to populate the increasing number of cafes. One such owned a prime site just above the road, which was now asphalted and led to the space where there might be a car park one day. Without much warning the shape of a building appeared among the houses, pushing a cluster of cement columns above the rooftops. Papacostas' hotel! We joined the chorus of dismay. It was out of all proportion to the village. It was not being built in a traditional style with traditional materials. It should be stopped! The village was divided into factions, more often along the lines of rivalries than aesthetics. I sat down and wrote down our thoughts and warning, with the hope of swaying opinion towards the importance of not destroying the very thing that would attract discerning tourists with money to spend. Quality not quantity should be Papingo's unique selling proposition (McCanns training to the fore). I wrote my version of the classic golden goose cautionary tale in English on my wonderful new Amstrad with its green winking lights, then translated it into Greek. The chairman of the village's Amenity Society, who was very much On the Right Side, let me use the computer in his shop in Ioannina to type the final version. I sat at the back of the shop, learning how to use a Greek word processing system while customers came in for car parts and tyres. Nikos Saxonis checked the speech, making sure it was correct and would read well. He had by now bought and restored two traditional houses in Big Papingo and had opened a pleasant place to stay for Athenian and foreign visitors. The Halls stayed there. Nikos was on the brink of retiring from his position as head of McCann-Erickson, Greece, this McCanns connection being one of life's strange threads.

There was a meeting in Big Papingo's central courtyard at which Peter read our speech. It was considered a strong weapon in the anti-Papacostas armoury that Papingo's own foreigners didn't want the sort of development that the pro-Papacostas faction thought foreigners wanted. Whatever the persuasive forces turned out to be, the outcome was that development in Papingo has not been as untrammelled as it otherwise might have been. A large number of hotels have been built, which although out of scale, are not quite as huge as Papacostas' threatened to be. Their concrete block walls are faced with stone. The roofs are made of overlapping stone slabs in the traditional manner even when their framework sits on an untraditional waterproofed ceiling. In our house we were always listening out for the drip of water in the bowls we put in the roof space.

Here I will follow one of the threads that run through our lives and story. Peter read our speech in the village's central church square. This was where we had first met Bernadine, the Dutch wife of the photographer John Demos. John, besides producing his own books of photographs, sometimes provided news agencies with images. He was due to return to Kosovo where he planned to record the tribulations of the Albanians under strict Serbian rule. He wanted a writer to go with him. Would I be interested?

I don't have easy access to a No. However frightening I found the experience, I didn't regret the time I spent with John in Kosovo. It was an intense week of seeing history in the making. We careered from place to place in John's van, following leads. We started in a village where two young Albanians had been shot. While John moved around silently like a ghost, I talked with the grief-stricken women. As in my sallies' forth in Winkleigh with the triple death of the Luxtons, I make a useless journalist. I wasn't actually sick in Kosovo. In fact, during the day we were arrested by the police and were sealed in a prison yard, I was in a better state than John. He had greater knowledge of the dangers we faced and all the responsibility for getting the film out of the country to be published. I was in a confident 'I'm British' frame of mind. All would be alright in the end. I just needed to last without food and water until we were released which I was almost certain would be very soon. It was dusk when the gates were unlocked for us. John was incapable of driving. I sat in the van's high seat and gazed at the controls. I couldn't make out at first what was what; starter, lights, brake, accelerator. The day spent as a prisoner had blurred the connection between my eyes and brain. But we had to get away. It was up to me. We kangaroo-ed out of the prison yard.

I knew we were being followed. My aim was to find some quiet country lane to park in for the night. Up to then I'd spent each night in a hotel but tonight I would stay in the van, no doubt about that at all. No supper, no police, just a parked-up van and a good night's rest.

The lights of the car behind followed us out of town, left, right, left. We were among fields of maize. I saw a track into a field and plunged down it. A good way into the field I stopped the van. No lights behind. I'd thrown our pursuers off the trail. I dared have a pee and so did John. We settled in the back of the van, all in silence. Safe at last! And then headlights appeared again, turning into the field at the start of the track. Whatever vehicle it was stopped and glared across the maize at us. No rabbit was ever as rigid as I

was in those lights. All the terror held at bay until that moment came at me with full force. After several minutes which felt like hours the lights wavered sideways and juddered away lighting up the hills behind. We watched them disappear eventually into the black landscape. Safe?

Yes, we were. Unlike the Kosovan Albanians.

When I think of Kosovo, I see the group of village women and children in one of the settlements behind a high stone wall. "Tell President Bush," they urged me. "Tell the president what's happening here." I took the request to heart. When we were back in England, I made a trip to London to see Ron and Christine, taking with me a manila A4 envelope which held the account I'd written of the week in Kosovo and what I'd learnt of the atrocities being committed there by the Serbs on the majority population, the Albanians. Ron and Christine invited me to supper. I think I stayed with Polly. In the Halls' Hampstead home, I was regaled with lots of wine and good food. Another couple had been invited, I've no idea who they were because all my attention was focused on the envelope laid at my feet. How was I to introduce the subject of persecution and killings? Here's another proof of my uselessness at being the sort of writer who can manage such things. Many years later I put the Albanian women into a novel I called 'Making a Difference'. The way I couldn't make any difference to their miserable lives, which were about to become far worse, inspired the compensatory story.

In the spring of 1990 Sophie and Dean planned to marry. Dean was set against any sort of wedding ceremony. He would wear a suit, Sophie could wear a wedding dress; they would go to Taunton Registry Office and afterwards have a pub lunch, followed by an evening disco. Sophie agreed to let Dean have his way, so long as she could also have a traditional Greek wedding in a Greek orthodox church in Greece. We were happy with the Registry Office and the pub lunch, and this took place in April. Pa Barrett was there, as was Ben, Mary and John, Di and Arthur Bradbeer, Dean's sister Debbie with her daughter Lucy who was Sophie's bridesmaid. There was a matron of honour, too, a good friend of Sophie's from work. The pub lunch was fine but we found the disco a bit of a challenge. However, we took up her request for a Greek wedding with enthusiasm. This would be a new experience.

We didn't have any idea how to go about it. In fact, it was one of those occasions which you don't know how to do until you've done it – maybe like life itself! We had lots of guidance, mainly from Tasso. It was a fantastic event, not just for us but for Papingo, too. The two neighbourhoods, Big and Small, came together. People said, and continued to say, that they hadn't had such a reason or willingness to unite for very many years – perhaps since before the Italian invasion, said one old man. There'd been the regular church festivals but these were attended mainly by those loyal to a particular saint and church. For Sophie and Dean's wedding, the celebration was open to all and all came. We'd had notices printed in Ioannina, working under direction. The wording had to be correct; it was the religious blessing of a wedding rather than an Orthodox marriage service. Tasso booked the musicians, although it's possible we did this ourselves. We were known at the Glass Café where the gypsy musicians gathered. Tasso told us how much to order of everything – bread, potatoes, meat, salad, tomatoes, wine – and

which women to ask to cook the many pans of stew in their own ovens. We were to peel the potatoes and, thank heavens, the Siderys arrived for the wedding in time to help with this.

I reminded Sue of this when she was here the other day on her way home to Nether Sowey where she now lives. She often calls in after seeing to a holiday change-over as the cottage she made in a corner of their field at Dunkeswell Abbey. When the Siderys lived in the Old School House and we were across the river at Madford House, the dark shed at one end of their neighbour's barn was where we once helped Brian extract a dead lamb from the womb of one of their ewes. So much life we've shared, we said, as Sue looked at Peter's diamond wedding anniversary picture. I'm often conscious of our different fortunes. She's been a widow for 26 years.

Brian died suddenly in the spring of 1994. It was a Sunday morning. Sue was upstairs dealing with a social work backlog. She'd been the breadwinner of the family for some years, with Brian as house-husband and vegetable-grower. He used to like coming for a coffee. He'd sit in the Windsor chair in the corner of our kitchen, first at Madford, then at Luggs, and talk in his mournful, self-deprecating and meandering way about – what? Life in general, life as lived by us in Devon, by the Siderys in Edinburgh. On Sunday morning, March 27th 1994, Brian was downstairs in the schoolroom, their living room. Sue, later, wasn't sure if she'd heard anything or not – perhaps the scuffling of feet on the varnished pine floorboards, perhaps nothing. It may have been a while before she happened to go downstairs and found Brian lying on the floor, comatose. She rang for an ambulance and then called me. I dropped everything and drove fast from Culm Davy down and over the intervening hills to Abbey.

The ambulance men were there when I arrived. I sat and watched in stunned disbelief, as they tried to revive him. After a while, they left. I remember little of the immediate aftermath except that the Sidery cat (called Mish or some name like that) sat a short distance from my feet and stared at me intently, without moving. I got the fanciful idea that Brian's soul had entered the cat and he was telling me through the cat's eyes to take care of his family for him.

I did. For the next few weeks, the Sidery family was top of my list of people to look out for. They are still on the list.

Ruth was living in Hemyock at the time with her chap, Paul. She had his support. Rachel, on the other hand, was in wild disarray. She'd spent many years as a member of the Orange People, the Bhagwan's sect, in various ashrams in different countries – the last being India. She'd had a psychotic episode after crashing out of a whirling ritual dance and her parents had been summoned to take her home. Brian was the parent who went; not only had he been a Bhagwan follower briefly but Sue had her work commitments. Brian had always avoided planes. He was terrified. He flew out and back again with Rachel, having persuaded her with enormous difficulty to come home with him. This had happened just a month before his heart attack. All too easy to imagine the turmoil of emotions in each member of the family that this history added to the mix.

This was a period when we were able to be the good friends that people need at such times. Sue was out of her mind from shock. She had the fixed idea that she must get to Marks and Spencer to change a skirt the day after Brian died. This was something she'd planned to do that day and she wouldn't be persuaded against it. So we went to Marks and changed the skirt. Surreal therapy. The evening before I'd taken Rachel home to stay with us. And for the next week, Rachel spent the nights at Luggs. I remained in position as chief supporter, helping to get the funeral organised and held, and continuing to be present until the date of our departure for Greece on April 24th. Before leaving, we put in place a plan for Rachel and Sue to fly out to join us for a restorative time on Moby Dick. Whether this really was restorative or simply an added strain, I'm not sure. They did manage to arrive in Corfu after an 8-hour delay at Bristol; not a promising start. We got them on board Moby where they had no decisions to make, no meals to cook and a gentle sea to rock them to sleep. From Corfu we sailed for Paxos, which

Illustrations for children's books

became shrouded in mist as we headed in that direction. The wind got up. By the time we were in the wind-tunnel of Lakka harbour, the sea was heaving. Moby swung and tossed at anchor. Sue and Rachel were horribly seasick. Not such a brilliant recovery package. Next day was calm and we went on to Gaios, the other harbour on Paxos. We went ashore for a meal, with Sue and Rachel in a better state. The following day we were swimming off the beach at Antipaxos. We had a night in Parga on the mainland and Petriti on Corfu before getting them to the airport for their flight home a week after their arrival. Perhaps it was as reasonable a way to spend the aftermath of trauma as any other. Time has to pass.

Sue often remembers that I appointed Di Whiteley as supporter-in-chief in my absence. This was the time they got to know each other better. I couldn't imagine a better companion than Di if ever I was in need. But she is no longer available. A month and a year ago, on August 23rd 2019, I was holding her hand as she herself was slipping away. I never thought she'd leave the Culm Valley before me.

In 1994 we returned to England during the last week of June because Sophie was expecting her second child. Olivia was born on July 13th, weighing 6 lb 12 oz. Have I included the birth of Mark, our first grandchild? That was on May 7th 1992.

The diaries are full of details with dates and numbers as important as these and as insignificant as the quantity of gooseberries going into the freezer. I'm drowning in a seething mass of comings and goings, births and deaths, books and paintings. When Olivia was born, Peter was working for Franklin Mint painting scenes to be printed on porcelain plates.

I had sent off to Toby a novel called "The View from Here." I can't even remember what it was about. I know it got nowhere and I lost interest in fiction, both writing it and reading it. After Kosovo, it seemed pointless. *I myself* was pointless. The feeling was dragging me down until one day I was sitting in the back seat of the car, listening to my sister and husband discuss the question I'd posed; what on earth could I do, instead of write books?

The answer they came up with took me by complete surprise. I should become a psychotherapist. I don't know which of the two thought of it first but they were in unison. This was astounding. Did Jane really think I could become such a thing? I thought she still viewed me as the troublesome younger sister who needed a warning from our parents to pull her socks up. (She'd written home along these lines from the R.S.) As for Peter, it was perhaps more puzzling. He knew that Jane's husband was in therapy as part of his training as a psychotherapist. He'd been dismissive of this as a career choice in relation to Peter. I was surprised he thought it a good course of action for me. Yet both of them sounded as though they'd found the perfect answer.

As for me, I heard their words as though they were coins spilling pell mell from the pay-out mouth of a Las Vegas slot machine. Of course! That's exactly what I could do! I looked into the various ways and means of becoming the sort of psychotherapist I'd like to be. I dismissed any Freudian slants. I considered a Jungian approach. I'd been introduced to Jung's writing by Nancy, the wife of Kevin Andrews, in Athens. But I veered towards an approach which I learnt was called humanistic, not because it has anything to do with Humanism with a capital H but rather as a description of the belief that human nature is fundamentally good rather than evil and has an inbuilt tendency to heal. I signed on first for a few months' introductory course in counselling, which led to a two-year diploma course. After that, I trained in Gestalt therapy for a year, and wound up taking an 18-month course with an American trainer called Miriam Dror. By the mid-1990s I was practising as a therapist with a list of clients with whom I worked in ways that sprang from my understanding of the person, the moment, the circumstances and the relationship we'd created between us, all founded on what I'd learnt through training, reading and experience.

My growing understanding of my own nature – characteristics, quirks, weak points, strong points – was a central part of the process of learning. One of the key times that deepened this understanding was a 36-hour long vigil in our wood. Miriam had worked with Native Americans and liked to incorporate in her courses elements of their cultural traditions and beliefs. We were due to go on a Vision Quest in a wood near Exeter. The owner of the wood withdrew permission at the last moment. "Does anyone know of a wood we could borrow?" asked Miriam.

We'd rescued Clements Common from clear felling in 1983. Its 22 acres of bracken, Scots pine, birch and rowan, holly and beech provided ideal Vision Quest territory. Eight people would easily find their own secluded spot, out of sight and sound of the others while remaining within their own prescribed circle, eight feet in diameter, until Miriam let us know the time was up, some 30 hours later. Easily, I say – but was it?

In the late afternoon, we walked up to the wood from the Barn where we'd been primed about the rules. No food. No drink. No shelter. No sound. We each chose a spot, with Miriam taking note of each location. She would quietly do the rounds at intervals to check (silently) all was well. Otherwise, she'd be in the Barn. Anyone who panicked could find her there.

One of us did panic. Jaki, a particular friend of mine in the group as we had adoption in common (she as an adoptee), was not a country-dweller. She'd grown up in Birmingham. She found the creakings and whisperings of the black wood at night as horrifying as a Dracula movie. Heart in mouth, she fled the wood at midnight to spend her Vision Quest in the Barn. It probably took more courage to give up than to stay.

The rest of us got through the hours as best we could in our different ways. My way was to add an umbrella to our permitted equipment of one sleeping bag. I felt perfectly happy so long as my head was shielded from potential spiders and rain. Entertaining myself with uninterrupted thoughts was a lazy holiday from daily life. On the last morning I did reach out from my invisible circle to pick a succulent blackberry I'd been eyeing. I hadn't been conscious of hunger or thirst (we must have been allowed a bottle of water) but we all fell on the waffles and syrup breakfast Miriam made for us in the Barn as though we hadn't eaten for a month.

Lovely supper. Susie was sick.

That's the diary entry for July 1992 when we were on one of our many journeys to Greece, taking in Simandre at the southern edge of the Jura, a pretty area off the main route. I must have succumbed as usual to Madame Tissot's menu and her exquisite cooking of the best quality food, much of

We collaborated on a number of children's books for American publishers

109

it home-grown. I'd probably started with snails, not modestly with *les six* but, with unbridled greed, *les douze*, floating in a tureen of golden butter generously laced with fat cloves of garlic. This was probably followed by the most tender fillet steak and, finally, a concoction of fresh fruit from the garden, heaped with meringue and thick cream. Then came the stagger up the narrow staircase to the usual bedroom where a high bed waited for us under its square, puffed-up, white lace-covered duvet, looking like another kind of meringue.

We'd fallen by chance on Simandre on our first cross-Europe by car. This was after several years of van travel: the red Thames van with just the two of us to start with, then with Sophie in her Moses basket placed on the engine cover between driver and passenger seat. After Ben's arrival, the van was still a Thames but now it was dark green, with sorbo mattresses laid in the back and nappies drying on a line strung overhead. With our first au pair, Stephanie, we did the journey by train all the way. *Heraus! Heraus!* The shouts at some unscheduled stop in the night took us straight back to the horrors of war films. We managed to go to Munich zoo during one expected stop. Otherwise, it was a long, slow, clanking journey with puzzling waits in the heat along the way until at last we pulled into Athens station.

Now in the 1990s our usual route was by car, crossing the Channel overnight from Portsmouth, arriving in Simandre after an early start, in time for a rest before the eagerly anticipated meal. Sometimes Madame Tissot had no room. Ville La Reversure was another good overnight stop in the same area. On one such occasion it happened that Ben and his Austrian friend Monika were with us. It was Peter's birthday, September 14th. We managed to smuggle cards and parcels onto the table in the restaurant.

Peter took no notice of them until our hints grew so heavy that he turned his attention to the table. He was quite taken aback as well as pleased. He'd forgotten it was his birthday. We all got quite drunk. After the meal, we needed fresh air. Peter wandered around the silent village hugging his pillow from the car, looking for a bench to lie down on. He never believed a hotel pillow would be comfortable enough for a vital, good night's sleep.

Over the years, with new roads and improvements, the journey took less time and we overshot the stops near the Jura. We reached the Alps where we found a lovely hotel near St Gervais. The distinctive feature of this hotel, besides the grassy terrace with the view of Mont Blanc, was the music that accompanied our chilled glass of Kir on arrival. Each time we turned up Madame was playing the same piece on her piano in an unseen room. Beethoven's Waldstein spilled forth into the crisp air with wonderful verve – until one particular bar was reached. It was one of those obstacles which, once they have occurred, stick for ever in the channel between brain and fingers. Over the several years we stayed in St Gervais we knew exactly where the obstacle was lodged. We ceased to enjoy the gay abandon of the first quarter of the piece. Instead, we were on tenterhooks for the moment when the rippling notes would suddenly falter and halt in a jarring cluster, to be repeated only to stick again. *Give it up!* we silently pleaded. She never did. She'd always start the piece with the gusto of innocence, as though she never expected any difficulty.

I suppose we did the same, with our arrivals at the boatyard. Like Madame St Gervais we constantly hit difficulties. Ours were of many varieties and lengths but, like hers, were interspersed with passages of such pleasure and ease that we always returned to begin again.

Three of the illustrations for Desmond Morris's 'World of Animals', Jonathan Cape, 1993

Important in our lives have been the good friends with whom we share our love of Greece and Greeks as well as words and pictures: writer Tony Anderson, artist Lucy Willis, yachtsman and artist Julian Marshall and master printmaker Hilary Adair. Peter learnt how to etch from Hilary. He produced several series of etchings which proved popular in exhibitions but finally the lengthy and laborious process became to great a strain on his patience

Our journeys by road across Europe provided the stepping stone between our English and Greek lives. It was the time to go over what had been happening in one home and preparing ourselves for what was to come in the other. What was to come was usually a period of rescuing property from the effects of absence. Moby was particularly prone to problems. Peter has made a list of troubles with their dates. Oil leaks feature frequently. We eventually found the right-sized seals. The list covers three sides of A4 paper. "Actually," he says, "I thought it would be worse."

Moby was not a sensible purchase in the first place. It was an old wooden boat which had been virtually abandoned by its owner. Its engine was old. Neither Peter nor I were, are, or ever will be, mechanics. Peter hides when an engine fails, although if no help is at hand he will battle for hours. With an engineer for a father, I think I may have gained some slight mechanical sense through watching him go about practical things. I sometimes say "try that knob" which may lead, with a large dose of luck, to a surprising breakthrough. Moby's engine had troubles far beyond a knob-tightening remedy. We only once found a mechanic who knew what he was doing. What we should have bought – and we knew this perfectly well – was one of those white, glass fibre yachts that sail blithely and form flotillas. But we loved Moby. It was our floating, comfortable and spacious country cottage.

Over the years we'd had some idyllic times pottering about the islands near Lefkadha, anchoring in hidden coves, sometimes giving friends time on board, too. Polly and her second husband Theo Crosby spent days with us. Elizabeth Dun was with us for a week which was good because she was going to succumb to cancer in 1995. Sue and Rachel Sidery, post-Brian's death, were with us. Moby provided Ben with a base when he spent a summer drawing portraits on Nidri quay. The rapid increase in tourism suited him. He was licensed to sit for an hour examining intently one long-haired blonde after another, and be paid for the pleasure. It didn't suit us. The number of flotillas increased exponentially. Coves were no longer secret. Now that I was involved in training courses, there was less time for Greece. Did I mention the Montessori correspondence course I took on before all the counselling courses? Peter had to fly out on his own in the spring to get Moby painted and launched and the house in Papingo freshened up after the winter. This would take two- or three-weeks' hard labour. Then back he came to Luggs for hedging and ditching, strimming and drain-clearing. Besides this, he was working on publishers' commissions. At this time, he was illustrating *The World of Animals*" by Desmond Morris, besides doing children's books for America.

As though all this wasn't enough, we fell for a holiday house in Cornwall. Perhaps we were prompted by the way our attention was increasingly focused on England rather than Greece. We'd been staying for a couple of nights in the Old Schoolhouse in Port Isaac. Directly across the harbour we were attracted by the look of a long, low, white-painted cottage with a tower at one end. It sat rather like a white-coated seal on a narrow shelf in the cliff beyond the fish sheds with steps down to the harbour. The steps were underwater when the tide was in. The FOR SALE sign tacked to the gate at the top of the steps was irresistible.

Like the half-timbered Morris Traveller of Goodiford Mill days and Moby

Dick, it would be an attractive but not entirely sensible purchase. However, it was temptingly possible. We could buy it with a mortgage. Holiday letting would fund the repayments. In the way of all the things we go in for, Halwyn House took a tremendous amount of work to bring up to date. Besides complete redecoration inside and out which we could do ourselves, the roof needed attention so we hired a local builder, Trevor Grylls. Trevor became a founder member of the group of Port Isaac singers, the Fishermen's Friends. Some years later, we heard on the national television news that he'd been killed in a tragic accident while on tour with the group. Like a terrorist act, an extraordinary event that demolishes an ordinary life adds to the shock, whether there's personal involvement with the victim or not.

Halwyn House provided us with great deal of fun with family and friends. There was a secret passage that had been used as a dumping ground. A trapdoor in the floor of the lower room in the tower opened onto a dark space, down and into the cliff – or would have done originally for the smuggling of brandy from ships. Now it was chock-full of rubbish and rubbles a kind of landfill site which we cleared with the help of Ben and his old schoolfriend Grant.

We had thought we might make Halwyn our old age home. The few years we owned it were an enjoyable experiment in retirement living. We stayed there between holiday lets, loving the crab from the fish shed next door, the friendly atmosphere in the pub, the walks along- – no, not along, but steeply up and down the spectacular cliffs, and living within the ever-changing sight and sound of the sea. There was a substantial list on the credit side of the balance sheet. I used to keep myself awake so that I could listen to the waves lapping at the terrace wall, lulled by the ceaseless rhythm of the sea. On the debit side, in wild weather, with waves crashing over the terrace with enormous force, we thought of rising sea levels besides the obvious negatives: the summer crowds, the constant traffic jams, the lack of parking space, and the grandstand position. We might have a wonderful view from our waterside seat but we were part of other people's wonderful view. People would, naturally enough, lean on our wall, calling to each other in loud voices. We were as much part of the scenery as the boats moored in the harbour. It was Navsika and her onions all over again. These aspects of the place would not be supportable. All the same, we drew endless plans in an attempt to solve two of the problems; the lack of studio and car space.

In 1998 a couple, leaning on our wall, called down to us as we sat on the terrace at sunset. Would we consider selling the house? We invited them in to discuss this and they ended up buyng Halwyn. Not long after this, Port Isaac became the setting for the filming of Doc Martin. The house itself featured, we were told. We never watched the programme, preferring the life we'd imagined for ourselves over someone else's fantasy.

At the beginning of the 1990s I was beginning to find walking painful. One of the last treks I enjoyed was the round trip from our house in Mikro Papingo, up and over the mountain to the village of Tsepelovo and back next day through the gorge. This was when we met William and Jill Fell, the only other walkers of the Vikos gorge that day. Another of my last big treks was over the mountain to the Aoos gorge. Peter has a painting hanging on the wall in his studio which reminds me of the moment when I threw down my haversack and refused to go another inch. We were just about to reach a high and remote pass on the far flank of Gamila, on our way to Vrissohori where we'd stay with Stavroula's daughter. The ground was steep and stony; not an ideal spot for a slippery sleeping bag, but probably better than what we might find the far side of Karteros Pass. Next morning what we found at the pass was a chamois. This was a thrill. They are rare and elusive. It looked at us in surprise before skittering away over the boulders and out of sight. The descent the far side was precipitous.

I shouldn't have been surprised to need a hip replacement. My mother underwent one of the first such operations. Jane, too, had her right hip replaced a few years before I started limping from the pain in mine. I remember hobbling along the road that leads from Hyde Park Corner to Knightsbridge, fighting my way through the agony to the Montessori Institute for something to do with the correspondence course I was taking. This was after the trouble was diagnosed as osteoarthritis, something I'd refused to believe for a good year. In England I tried various strange cures. The most memorable was conducted by someone who lay me down on her couch and pulled my hair. She told me I had the wrong balance of salts in my system, or something on those lines. My right leg did jerk when she yanked a handful of hair on my crown but this was no cure. Later, in Greece, I grew more depressed at my immobility. A Greek doctor was visiting Papingo.

He asked me to lie down on our wooden seating boxes (replicas of our Amorgos ones). "Lift your right leg," he ordered. I couldn't. He told me I had osteoarthritis in my hip and would need an operation. He scribbled a note which we took next day to the medical centre in Delvinaki, a town near the Albanian border. We came home with a big envelope of x-rays which I took to a consultant in Ioannina who said he could give me a new hip. I would have gone this route – so quick and easy – had I not read the wording of one of the framed certificates on his wall. It announced that he'd been awarded a Diploma in Micro-Surgery by Correspondence by an American institute. I might trust myself as an assistant teacher of four-year olds after my Montessori correspondence course, but a surgeon qualified in micro-surgery by correspondence? I was not going to put myself in his hands. We returned to England and I had the operation in the brand-new Chelsea and Westminster hospital in April. Ron Hall brought me a specially put-together tape of Verdi arias which helped me through, as did the opium on tap. I planned to take Lily, who lay in the next bed, on a world tour. I would write her life story as we travelled. She thought it a jolly good idea. Six weeks later we drove back to Greece. I was a little anxious about climbing on board Moby from the rubber dinghy but having managed it once, I was fine. In Papingo I walked up the hill to our house with a beaming smile on my face and I made the climb up the mountain refuge in under three hours before the summer was over.

That was in 1991, the year Pa Barrett died. We let Ben have his car. He was home after spending six months in the States, where he was rescued from various crises by Francis and Diny Wilkinson who were living in California. After a few weeks of driving Pa's car around the lanes, catching up with friends, Ben had a crash driving into Hemyock. He wasn't hurt but the car was a write-off. What is it with Ben and vehicles? Only recently have I learnt that this is a characteristic typical of people with what's called borderline personality disorder. Does a diagnosis help? It did for me, in relation to osteoarthritis. If we and Ben had known from his childhood that there was a name for his pattern of behaviour, we might have looked for help and support. On the other hand, the act of singling him out in this way, labelling him as someone with something wrong, might have worked against his well-being. As it was, he's managed well enough. He's had wonderful girlfriends.

From quick pencil portraits on the quay in Nidri, Lefkadha, to huge murals in the Bay of Islands, New Zealand, Ben takes on challenges as an artist

He paints amazing pictures. On Saturday I was showing Sue Sidery images of his paintings, which he'd sent to us on a memory stick. It includes work in progress on his 40-foot long wooden yacht, *Reremoana,* as well as photos of a huge mural he's working on for a Waitangi hotel. He can be a perfectionist as well as a wrecker. I often remind myself of the motor bike he dismantled into piles of metal and screws and then re-assembled to make a roadworthy vehicle. He manages his life, so long as he has regular injections of funds from our bank balance. He's been worth it. Without him we would have had a far duller life. But here's a thought. From our perspective, anyone who can produce their own healthy offspring should understand their extreme good fortune.

Sophie and Dean who had married in 1990 now had two children, Mark born in 1992 and Olivia in 1994. We became active grandparents, taking our turn with Dean's mother in looking after the children while Sophie returned to work at the Department of Work and Pensions. They have been a vital part of our lives ever since. Our good fortune, thanks to Sophie.

I'll talk of one more wedding before I end this section with Ben's wedding.

In the summer of 1995 Sotiris invited us to his wedding in Albania. We understood his ulterior motive: he'd get a lift back to his village in our car. But I think he genuinely wanted us to see his bride, his family, his home, and a traditional wedding. For us, it was a great privilege. The border was still not fully open. A hefty pair of metal gates was opened a crack to let through one or two people at a time from the huge crowd surging on the hillside all around: a Biblical scene out of a Hollywood epic. Sotiris, in a brand new, dazzlingly white T-shirt and stiff jeans, went through on his own, saying he'd find us on the other side. We, in one of the few wheeled vehicles, waved our British passports and were given special treatment. Even so, it took a long time to get through. A distance further on, Sotiris appeared and jumped in swiftly. Go, go, go! he urged. It was as though he doubted we had really got past the guards. There were pistol-wielding police at regular intervals along the way, signalling us to stop. Each time Sotiris peeled off a note from a wad he held under his T-shirt and folded it into the policeman's waiting hand. His nervous excitement was infectious and it was a relief to arrive at the village where we would meet up with his bride.

Mules and horses stood waiting the length of the dusty street, tethered to wooden poles. Sotiris ushered us into a café where we were offered refreshments – water? Coffee? Orangeade? I don't remember what exactly but I do know we'd realised the need for extreme frugality on our part. Sotiris, proud of his position as host, would not, could not let us pay. Along the street, people squatted behind a piece of cloth spread on the ground. On this they'd arranged whatever they had to sell: two or three LPs, a water melon, a bracelet, a kitchen tap, a single shoe …

Sotiris's bride appeared. She was wearing a kind of short, white ballet dress covered in tulle, with a sparkly top. She was very young and very shy. Sotiris's face went pink. After a long interval – I think we'd been waiting for the sun to lose its strength – the mule train set off. Peter would walk but I was offered a mule which I accepted. There was no knowing how long it would take to get to wherever it was we were going. We crossed a large plain and then began an ascent into a series of brown hills. It took a couple of hours to wind up into the mountain range, the one that Sotiris, Thanasis and Christos had walked over to find its sister range in Greece before the border was opened.

We knew we were approaching the village because several highly excited children appeared from behind bushes and stone walls. They scampered around our line of mules and walkers and rushed ahead calling out in high-pitched voices. They were the advance guard of the welcome committee. The last time a stranger had visited the village, we were told, was in 1940 when the Italians were about to invade Greece.

It's a sobering thought that events in the past are as much part of the present as present events are. Equally so are future events, because in the present we create the future. This thought has been inspired by watching Peter read the report sent by Rigas, the husband of Kalliope Stara, the daughter of Rodhoula and granddaughter of our nextdoor neighbour Sofia in Papingo. It reminds Peter of the times he sat and sketched by the Voidomatis river – the river that springs into being in the final stretch of the Vikos gorge. He remembers an occasion when he watched a snake slither up a slender tree to polish off the entire contents of a blackbird's nest. When Rodhoula used to come to Papingo to look after anyone who had booked a night or two at the Agnanti, Peter was being visited by young environmentalists. He was painting local scenes to be reproduced on calendars. Most of the originals were sold at exhibitions in Greece or London and these are now re-appearing in American auctions. The past keeps popping up in our present. "That's what happens if you live long enough," says Peter.

The report Rigas has written describes the decline in the flora and fauna in the Zagori, which has happened in parallel with the decline in the population. That's a counter-intuitive idea. At least I for one thought that nature creeps back as humans leave the countryside for cities. Not so, says Rigas. Nature benefits from a human population. I haven't read his article for myself. It would take too long, with a dictionary to hand. My Greek is rusty through lack of use.

At the time of his wedding, Sotiris was struggling to learn the language of his forefathers. The Greek population of Northern Epirus had been forbidden to speak or learn Greek after the break-up of the Ottoman Empire and the start of the communist era in Albania, the country of which it had become part. Perhaps the Celts felt equally resentful of losing their language when the Romans took over their country. Language defines a place and a people in ways easily overlooked. I often wonder what misapprehensions occur at international level due to overliteral translation. Here's a thought about character and language. Peter, who always spoke Greek more fluently than I did, is a more loquacious character in Greece than he is in England. I don't think I'm different. When living there, I worked hard at writing Greek, imitating the handwriting I admired and trying to discover an individual writing style – but failing. Greek is so exact, while English allows me more freedom. If ever I try to be colourful in Greek, people regard me with blank faces. I shouldn't attempt something that is beyond my capabilities.

The 1990s was perhaps our fullest decade with the most people and possessions in our lives. If I had trouble getting to sleep, I didn't count sheep, I counted frying pans. I pictured them in my mind, the bigger and the smaller ones, the non-stick, the tried and trusted, the thin and tinny; the one in Luggs kitchen, in the Barn, in Papingo, on Moby Dick, in Halwyn House – five! So much to look after! It was a repeat of our Madford era, when the rapid multiplication in livestock numbers had kept us from our work.

Such busy-ness was not possible to sustain. The first possession to go was the last we acquired: Halwyn. Our possessions in Greece were next in our sights.

By the last few years of the 1990s our grip on our Greek life was loosening. Moby was an increasing burden. Papingo was changing fast. No longer could you smell wood smoke as you climbed the zigzag road approaching the village. Diesel tankers arrived to send fat hoses snaking up the *kalderimia*, delivering fuel to heat the houses. This meant year-round tourism. Papingo had become a smart place to visit at any time of year. Guest houses and eating places sprang up. But the major factor in our decision to sell the house was Ben's wedding in 1998 in New Zealand.

After a series of short-lived jobs back home, he planned to return to Australia where he'd had some good times and luck with his artwork. He decided to get back into the country via New Zealand. He was hitch-hiking around North Island in the few weeks he had before continuing to Australia when he was given a lift by an attractive young woman with a mass of blonde, ringletted hair called Miriam. She offered him a place to stay the night in exchange for a couple of odd jobs, and he stayed and stayed as the list of jobs grew longer.

We had a phone call in early 1998. He was getting married. Oh? When? Any day now. We said we'd come out for the wedding but he musn't make our visit dependent on a wedding. We'd come anyway. We'd been Ben's parents long enough not to take any plan as definite and we didn't want him getting married in order to see us.

A few weeks after that phone call, we were on a beach near New Plymouth in Taranaki, waiting for Ben's bride's arrival. We'd spent a couple of days getting their home base ready. They were living in a bach (short for bachelor pad, a wooden chalet) on Miriam's mother's land, by the side of a deep, brown river. All kinds of jobs had become instantaneously imperative, among them steps in the river bank which Peter dug with the help of Tim and Anaru, Miriam's teenage sons by her first husband. We could see the atavistic attraction for Ben. Violet, Miriam's mother, came from an Irish family. Ben, with his dark hair and blue eyes from his Irish mother, shared Celtic roots. Violet stood short and square in wellington boots and was the matriarch of a large family. Miriam looked like a member of that dance group who stamp and prance in a line to the music of a captivating Irish jig. She asked me – and I was flattered – to gather flowers on the morning of the wedding and make her a wreath to wear in her long, pre-Raphaelite hair.

On a low cliff by some kind of club building, we waited for the bride with Ben, all washed and brushed up in clothes chosen by Miriam. He looked like the hero in a Western. A helicopter approached. It had been lent by someone who usually used it for crop-spraying. Today it unloaded Miriam at the back of the beach. As the helicopter departed, strains of music could be heard coming from a distant point at the water's edge. Shapes that we'd thought were boulders stirred and became languidly writhing maidens. An

arch of people formed and Miriam and her bridesmaids walked down it to where Ben had been directed to stand. We all then trooped to another part of the beach where fir branches had been stuck in the sand to make a kind of altar for the ceremony. The service was conducted by a priest in their Seventh Day Adventist church. The wedding was a wonderful mixture of planned event choreographed by Miriam and informal happening. We were full of hope for Ben's future in New Zealand.

With our daughter living a mile away from us in England and a son on the other side of the world, we decided to sell our house in Papingo. John and Bernadine Demos wanted to buy it. They were interested, too, in Moby Dick but, fortunately for them, decided against it. Poor Moby was soon to rot away and be burnt by the boatyard owner to free up space.

That was the end of our second phase of Greek life.

In the 1990s the Cornish coast attracted Peter's attention as well as a particular inland Devon habitat known as Culm Grasslands. Over a year he recorded the natural life in these boggy areas for the Devon Wildlife Trust

THE 2000s

When Ben married, our attention moved from Greece to New Zealand. One evening we were sitting on our Papingo veranda with a glass of *tsipouro,* watching the sun sink towards the Albanian mountains. What are we doing here, we asked ourselves, with a daughter living near us in England and a son on the other side of the world? The decision to adjust to our new circumstances was made before we finished our drinks. Very soon we'd sold the Papingo house to John and Bernadine, who wanted it for their New York theatre director daughter Ianthe to use as a base for summer workshops.

   After their wedding, Ben and Miriam led us on a short tour in the old car we'd bought them to replace one that had broken down. John and Pamela Withington had invited the four of us to stay in Wellington. They'd come to the wedding. It was the first time

Visiting our son Ben in New Zealand, we tramped through
many miles of native forest in both North and South Island

we'd met. John was a second cousin on my father's side and he was glad of the connection to his English family, having lived in New Zealand all his married life. I have a clear memory of Pamela sitting on a straw bale in Violet's field while Miriam's family and friends milled around the *hangi*. She was doing her best to appear comfortable while emphasising her difference with wry smiles. The smiles disappeared when the four of us stayed with them in their lovely house on one of Wellington's hills. It was as though we'd brought people without defined edges into a household where everything and everyone was clearcut.

Back in Miriam's home territory we met a few of her many brothers and sisters who lived in the area around New Plymouth. There was something reassuring about the echoes in names. I was born in Plymouth, so we could see it as a good omen that Ben was going to make his home near the city's namesake. On the ferry across the Straits between North and South Islands, we sat in the Barrett saloon. Barrett was a famous 19th century settler. Violet, Miriam's mum, was pleased when we talked of *gumboots*, rather than Wellingtons. It was a word that reminded her of her forebears. Violet herself reminded me of my Irish nanny. We felt optimistic about the marriage and very willing to help with anything that was needed. Miriam had quite a list of such things. She was full of ideas about ways to make money, from jewellery and candle-making to flotation tanks, all needing an initial outlay. At the end of our three weeks' holiday, we promised we'd be back soon. Besides wanting to bolster Ben's marriage, New Zealand was the place that would give us a new injection of material for painting and writing.

Christine had given me the chance to write a piece for the Sunday Times Travel section with the sub title: *Susan Barrett and artist Peter Barrett do New Zealand in three weeks – and find it perfectly natural.* I have it beside me now. ONLY NATURAL INGREDIENTS is the headline over the double page spread. The text is illustrated by Peter's watercolour paintings of seals, tree ferns and dolphins. There's a short section headed *Watching and Waiting for Whales* with the classic view of a diving sperm whale, its distinctive forked umbrella tail above the surface, dripping water. The section begins:

Half a mile of Pacific Ocean below the boat, a pair of sperm whales were engaged in eating whatever quantity of fish a sperm whale needs for breakfast.

Having written fiction most of my life to date, I found it exciting to write fact, especially as I had Christine as back stop, a wonderful, confidence-inspiring and painstaking editor. With this first New Zealand article she became the person I would trust with anything I wrote, to give me her seal of approval. The saddest thing is that, although she's alive, she can no longer do this. If you are incapable of remembering the beginning of a paragraph when you reach its end, you can have no idea what it's about. Fortunately for her, I think she constantly forgets her forgetfulness. I will note here that she's now back in the care home, having come to the end – or nearly the end – of her 4 weeks' trial of home living. Although I don't know the details, I think it became obvious to the care package organiser very early on in the month's trial that home-living was not something Christine could manage. We don't think she should have been subjected to such a confusing interlude. All the same, we know how easily she could persuade a judge that she is perfectly capable because, in her own mind, she is.

The next Sunday Times article I've kept is dated September 8th 2002. LACE UP FOR KIWI COUNTRY. Subhead: *Susan Barrett strode 600 spectacular miles to find the star treks of New Zealand's North and South Islands.* The headline shows Christine's editorial hand.

Oh! What a magnificent six months that was. And there I was, *striding*! I'd had my second hip replacement operation in April 2000 (this time my left hip) and we arrived in Auckland in September to begin the walking research, starting in the very north of North Island and slowly working our way down to the very south of South Island, doing the major treks on the way, as well as shorter day walks. By the end we felt we knew New Zealand as well as we knew Greece, and far better than we know Britain. I kept a notebook which, as far as I remember, described in almost step-by-step detail all the walks we did. It was agony having to condense it all into an article for the Sunday Times. The same feeling of thwarted desire recurs today as I speed past the six months of walks in this memoir, leaving even the most spectacular – the Tongariro Crossing with its acid, aquamarine pools on steep lava slopes, the utterly perfect Alabaster Lake lying like a moonstone on the Hollyford track, the seals, dolphins, whales, albatross and even the kiwi we met on Stewart island – all undescribed.

Mixed in with these fantastic experiences in the wild interior, we regularly met up with Ben and Miriam. On arrival, we'd bought a van which we kitted out with sorbo-rubber mattresses, sleeping bags, a box of cooking gear and supplies. I remember sewing curtains. It made a comfortable and totally independent home, essential for our peace of mind. However, we spent Christmas with Ben, Miriam and her two sons in Kaikoura. They'd rented a two-storey house for a family get together. The boys, Tim and Anaru, slept downstairs in a dark room with teenage clothes draped on every surface. A local friend of Miriam's supplied the household with crayfish, the most delicious we are ever likely to eat. Ben and Peter dived with the seals off a rocky point and each of them later painted pictures of what they'd seen. It is extraordinary the way Ben paints so well, in a style not that different from Peter's. How can nurture produce characteristics that are more usually inherited through nature? That's a constant puzzle not just to us but to everyone who sees Ben's work. What Ben doesn't have is Peter's single-minded application. He also has a behaviour pattern that, thank goodness, Peter doesn't have.

While we were with them in Kaikoura, all seemed well. Ben taught me how to make sushi when it was our turn to cook supper for us all. Then one day, out of the blue, I found myself in the path of an explosion. As I write, I can see Ben's towering rage blazing from his eyes. I backed away down the steps that led from the top storey to the ground. I wanted to jump into our van and escape but managed to stay for a few more days. Somehow, we negotiated our way through these rapids. It was not for the first time, nor would it be the last. But it was a relief when we left to continue with our scheduled walks.

The best of times and the worst of times – life with Ben reflects Dickens' words that open *The Tale of Two Cities*. Towards the end of our six months, we had put the worst of times to the back of our minds. One of the best of times was about to begin. Ben and Miriam, towing the dinghy, had come to

New Zealand scenes

join us. We were driving along an inlet in Queen Charlotte Sound when we came across The Folly. A sign to the side of the narrow road made us stop. *Gardens open*, it announced. Intrigued, we turned in.

A short length of drive curved around shrubs to land us in front of an attractive single-storey house. The drive led on and down through trees towards, we presumed, an inlet of the Sounds. First, it passed two extensive glass houses full of plants. Miriam was bewitched at once. We continued on and down, the drive winding through extensive bush. We came across glades of mown grass and eventually the water's edge. Back at the house, we wandered around the surrounding garden of lawn, flowering bushes and borders. On a grassy terrace by the full-length windows of the house, there was something that looked like a stone tomb within wrought-iron railings. There were two names inscribed on it and unreadable dates. Previous owners perhaps; except the house was modern and the tomb looked Victorian. Altogether, the atmosphere of the place made me think of Daphne du Maurier's *Rebecca*. It held a mysterious, slightly ominous attraction.

We learnt The Folly was up for sale and there was a caretaker in residence who was having to go away for a while. We'd be welcome to take her place for a few weeks. What an offer! We grabbed it. The house was comfortably furnished. It had two wings either side of the main kitchen-living room. Ben and Miriam took one wing; ourselves the other. Besides our bedroom there was a room where Peter could spread his sketch books and paints. Ben might also do some work in it, if so inclined. Floor to ceiling windows looked over the surrounding garden and the tomb. Miriam pottered about among the plants in the greenhouses. I liked driving the sit-on mower and kept a check on the grass, besides finding my way along the many paths that threaded their way through the treed and hilly terrain. Roxy, Miriam's dog, a large, immensely powerful and unpredictable Malamute, patrolled the grounds at night. We could hear her catching possums which she would crunch up noisily, leaving hardly a trace for us to find in the morning.

The romance of the place, coupled with the attractions of sharing with Ben and Miriam tempted us to put in an offer. Our time together had gone smoothly and overrode any lingering memory of the Christmastime explosion. Ben's dinghy was moored in the inlet and we could sail and fish with rods whenever we wanted. It was easy to imagine a life divided between Luggs and The Folly, six months here, six months there, as we had done during our Papingo years. The money from selling Papingo would cover the purchase price of The Folly. Letting Luggs would again give us an income to live in the cheaper country. We could see New Zealand providing us with masses of new material for painting and writing. The plan would provide Ben and Miriam with a home of their own. It seemed to us an exciting idea which we followed through until the owner of The Folly asked for proof that we had the money to buy it. Well, we couldn't produce proof quickly. Ben and Miriam were convinced that a scheme Miriam's brother Don was running would cover it for us, if we were to invest with him. This was, of course, too vague, and we probably came across as too unconventional, for The Folly's owner. Instead, she passed us on to friends selling their house along the coast.

This was another property we were saved from buying, although we drew close to signing the contract. Before the sale was finalised, we had to leave for home, leaving matters in Ben's hands, giving him power of attorney. He was convinced that the house would slip into the sea at any moment. He could have been right. The land was notoriously unstable and he sensibly didn't sign.

While we were away, the dot com bubble burst. We'd had some money in ethical investments which had lost all their value. We were told this on our return by our financial adviser who had failed to get in touch with us when we were away, although well supplied with the means for contacting us. It probably wouldn't have made much difference if we had sold our shares at the start of the crisis. In the meantime, Ben and Miriam had been encouraging us to invest with Don, who was dealing with the whole family's finances. By all accounts, everyone was doing very well. The brothers and sisters and their families were full of good cheer and driving new cars. Ben had persuaded us to give Don a small sum as a trial, and this had produced a good return; in fact, such a good return that cannier people than ourselves would have stopped to question. We didn't. We invested more. Sometime later, we heard that Don's scheme was being investigated. It took many months to unravel. Eventually, a court case was scheduled. The day before the trial, Don was discovered dead in his hotel room. We felt sorry for Violet, but she didn't seem unduly affected by the loss of her son or her money. She continued to drive the school bus and stump around her land in her gumboots. Ben was convinced that Don had fled to a Caribbean island, having arranged for someone to fake a death certificate. He has held more absurd conspiracy theories than this.

Some money was recovered and we put ours into an Icelandic savings bank. Don't laugh; all was lost once more in the financial crash of 2008. At this second loss we had a saviour in Alistair Darling, the chancellor of the exchequer, who came to the rescue of losers like us. Now, with Covid, how much will the economy have lost and how much will the government have paid out in support when the pandemic is over?

After our wonderful six months' walking experience in New Zealand, I'd proposed to Christine an article describing all the things you can do on water in New Zealand. She backed me in this which meant we could arrange various trips at discounted rates, on the strength of the publicity an article in the Sunday Times would give the firms organising them. This trip undertaken in 2002/3 included some of our best times – for instance, a day on White Island, the volcanic island where we stood on the rim of the active volcano. It erupted in earnest on December 9th 2019, an event which shocked us; it was like a near miss even though there was a gap of 16 years between our visit and its eruption. More safely, we – or rather, Peter – scuba-dived off Poor Knights island. We sailed with Ben in the Bay of Islands. He came north on his own with the dinghy on its trailer and we drove in convoy to Opua where we'd arranged the hire of a small yacht. Every so often we glanced in our rear view mirror to check that all was well with Ben. At a roundabout near Whanganui the dinghy came unstuck from the trailer. We could see a queue of vehicles mounting up behind Ben.

Having lived through so many accidents, Ben deals them with an impressive cool. It's the minor mishaps that he can't handle. I often think how lucky he and we have been compared with his two close school friends and their families. Grant and his girl-friend Tam had their right legs sliced off (and, in Grant's case, his right arm too) by the tail bar of an agricultural vehicle he was overtaking on his motor bike. Worse than this was what happened to Martin Shepherd. Martin had hung around Madford hoping to catch a glimpse of Sophie while becoming a pal of Ben's. In 1999 he was in Australia, on his way to catch up with Ben in New Zealand. Taking photographs of a sink hole on a cliff, he lost his footing and fell into the waves crashing around the enclosed circle of rock far below. His body came back for burial in Hemyock. It's wise to take note of reminders like these; there's only a hair's breadth between an ordinary day and death.

Before we started to research for this third Sunday Times article, we stayed with Ben and Miriam in the wooden lodge they were renting up a long farm track in the hinterland behind Onaero River Road. It was two years after our time with them at The Folly. Miriam was not happy. She was tight-lipped and silent. We could see that Ben was in a bad state, hyped up and ranting. I spent some hours listening to him, hoping to find a way to help him admit he needed help. I looked up medical, psychological books in the library in New Plymouth and read mental health leaflets in doctors' surgeries. At three o'clock on one of our nightly sessions, he said something that sounded hopeful. He'd consult a doctor. We left next day to continue our Things to Do on Water in NZ article.

We learnt later that Miriam and members of her Seventh Day Adventist family had arranged an exorcism for Ben, which took place on open ground outside the lodge as soon as we left. Ben went along with it. He has had faith, ever since, in the power of certain incantations to rid a person of the devil. He can cast out devils himself, he says. Sadly, his own devil remained in place. It has had outings on every occasion we've spent time with Ben At each explosion I've tried to remind myself that his state is a malady and a handicap worthy of our sympathy and patience, as it would if he lacked an

arm. But receiving the force of an explosion, always without warning, leaves little room for rational excuses.

However, we could see that Miriam, too, was not at all an easy person to live with. Perhaps they were too alike. They parted company after her brother's scam was brought to light. Ben was furious at the deceptions he – and we – had fallen for. He was on his own for several years, save for a

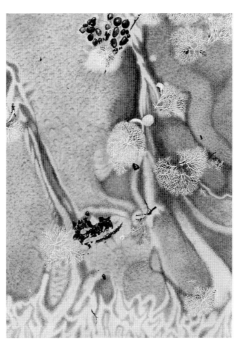
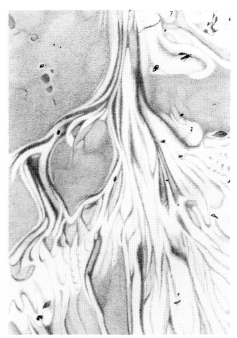

Patterns in nature seen in close-up

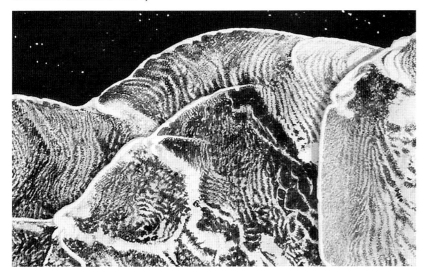

young dog he adopted. Major, a gentle, ugly, bull terrier, was Ben's faithful companion for a good 12 years.

In the aftermath of the Don episode, we thought seriously of moving to a smaller, easier to maintain property. We found somewhere that we thought would do. Looking back, it wouldn't have done at all. One wall teetered on the edge of a quarry. The neighbouring house was so close it all but shared the same breath. The only option for a studio would be a shed in the garden. It's astounding how I can convince myself against all evidence that something is possible. In the end we were saved from a bad mistake by the buyer of Luggs – yes, we'd got that far. She withdrew her offer. She'd found a better place for herself in the house belonging to new friends of ours, Robin and Sue Hicks.

The Hicks had been introduced to us by a phone call from Derek Robinson, our friend from McCann-Erickson copywriting days, who now lived with his wife Sheila in Bristol, his home town. Derek told me that his friends the Hicks had moved to a house near Madford. He'd met Robin through BBC Radio Bristol. Robin was head. Derek was doing a regular programme, having gained a reputation on radio with a series called 'Disgusted Tunbridge Wells.'. I followed up Derek's phone call at once, knowing if I didn't do so immediately, I might never do it at all. I invited the Hicks over and they came next day. We got on well at first meeting. They are a couple who live in delicate and negotiated balance with each other. Robin is always fizzing over with excitement, ideas and talk; Sue intervenes as necessary with a quiet, pragmatic word or two. Robin and I start laughing at the first exchange. Sue and Peter look on, waiting for a moment to bring us down to earth. It works. On reflection, we all laugh at what's just happened between us.

From the time we first met, their names featured frequently in our diaries. But Devon was not the answer to Robin's recurring depressions and they decided to try Spain once their house was sold. When our Luggs buyer decided to go for the Hicks's house, they visited at once to commiserate – or maybe they felt guilty? Not that there was any reason for guilt. A house-owner can't be held responsible if a house-buyer chooses their house over one belonging to someone else. And the loss was certainly to our benefit. We dug in once more to Luggs, with a new plan – or, rather, a resurrected one.

Over the years since leaving home, Sophie had occasionally thought of sharing a house with us. We liked the idea. Luggs and the Barn would provide the most obvious way to do this, but we'd also looked at other options; a house with a barn down by the river attracted us for a while. There was a lot going for the plan. We were active grandparents in any case, having shared in the care of Mark and Olivia with Granny Di Bradbeer when Sophie was working. The children often stayed the night with us when Sophie and Dean had an evening out. Sophie had looked after our correspondence in our frequent absences. It would give Dean and Sophie a larger house and garden in the years they needed it. It would provide us with care as we grew older. We could all visualise it working out as a feasible way of life. In the early 2000s we looked into the possibility with the planners. We would live in the Barn and Sophie and Dean would be in the house.

As a result of these thoughts, we continued to make the Barn a more comfortable place to live. We added a bath to the shower room upstairs,

and Chris, the husband of Barbie who'd helped with the wood rescue, turned the kitchen downstairs into an attractive kitchen/dining room. At the same time, I was developing the Barn as a centre for workshops. I called it the Calyx Centre, and designed a symbol and a letterhead. It was a smaller version of the Beacon Centre where I'd gone for all my various trainings. Wendy, who owned the Beacon Centre, was my therapist during my counselling training. I may have been imitating her – but I don't think so. I wasn't going to make a full-time business of the Calyx Centre, and we were not similar in character or fate. I didn't realise it at the time – I thought it was a disadvantage – but it was actually an advantage that I was older than everyone else I came across at that time. It was striking how many marriages hit the rocks as students, and leaders, reappraised their lives. Peter and I had done this ten, or was it twenty, years before and survived. The breakdown that I found most disturbing was that of Miriam and her husband Richard. Even if they did have an open marriage – they'd chosen the mutual surname of Dror, meaning freedom – I know Miriam was shaken to her foundations by the way Wendy, a student on one of her courses (I was on the same one,) got together with Richard. They continue to be together, as far as I know. Miriam turned to me as the provider of a venue. I'm still in touch with her. If I'm any good as a therapist, it's because of Miriam. Apart from anything else, we see the same funny moments that take you by surprise in daily life. I like drawing these and Miriam liked my drawings.

Today is October 3rd. Sue Sidery was going to look in for a cup of tea but rang to put this off. She has a chest infection. Whenever someone has a sniffle or a cough we all nervously think "Covid?" President Trump has developed it. It's hard not to wish he has it extremely badly. I was going to make a cake for Sue as it was her 80th birthday on October 1st and Terry was going to call in, too. He came on the scene in Sue's life some years ago. I feel I owe him several slices of cake, in thanks for the car-parking help he gave us when we did our talk and slide presentation on *The Garden* at Tony Anderson's Ebeneezer meeting room. That was two years ago, so it's high time I said thank you in cake.

Cooking for people was something I used to enjoy. In the years of the Calyx Centre, I took this characteristic to absurd degrees (there's probably a cartoon to be drawn here). I provided board and lodging for the leaders as well as any non-local group members who needed to stay. I found myself providing emergency psychological first aid, too. There was something about the groups – whether writing-based or therapy – that brought any shakiness in people to the surface. I dealt with my own shakiness (am I up to this as writer and therapist?) by providing delicious food. *At least I can cook*, I was saying to myself.

My confidence had taken a battering when I wrote several novels that Toby couldn't place. In 2002 I decided I should take a refresher course. Literary tastes had changed. I should learn what young writers were writing. I applied to join an MA course in creative writing at Bath Spa university. *Travels with a Wildlife Artist* was my passport to entry. I'd decided to keep my track record as a novelist under wraps, thinking it would work against me. Was I right to do that? I'm still undecided. I was selected by the Environmental Writing tutor, the head of the department, on the

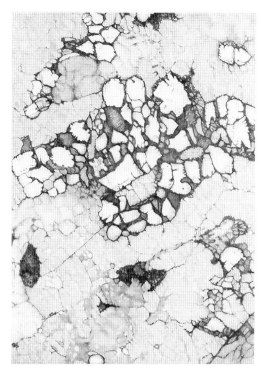

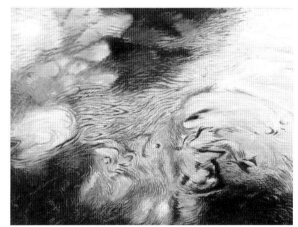

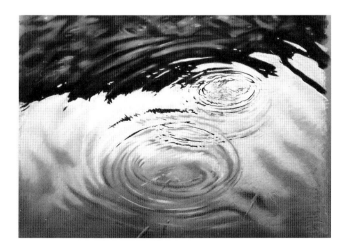

As interested in the patterns in sand as the looming figure of an elephant, Peter spent a period painting a series he called 'Natural Abstracts'

123

strength of *Travels*. In the non-fiction module I began to write *A Wildlife Together* which was the starting point of this memoir. I also signed on for the fiction module and began writing a novel with the title *Play It Again,* finally self-published with the title *Making a Difference.* I had several complicated plot ideas in mind. Past Life regression therapy was something I'd come across. I also wanted to work my Kosovo experience into fiction. The tutor, a novelist, took against me. During the term I was with him, I was miserable and confused. In my life, I've been taken by surprise by a few men who seem to need to attack me. John Burge was the first. Another was a fellow member of a therapy group. The tutor of another marked me down in a way that I knew was unfair. Years later, his supervisor told me how angry he was at the tutor's behaviour. Each time I've been left trying to work out what has hit me. *Projection* was one explanation someone came up with. I'm willing to admit to all kinds of faults and inadequacies. It's when the attack comes out of the blue and is clearly unjustified that it puzzles and hurts. *You have to provide a suitable screen for projection.* That makes sense. If I'm demonstrating cleverness, then someone with the same kind of cleverness in a position of seniority over me strikes out. John was a typical attacker; he was the old friend of my husband, pre-dating me in Peter's life; he was the first to Greece, the first to write a novel; worse still, I had mine published while he did not. For him I was 'an upstart crow.'

If I'd opted to major in fiction, I might have had Tessa Hadley as tutor. I am sure we would have got on well and I would have learnt from her. More roads not taken. Whether I would then have got back into the hands of publishers is unknowable.

While I was attending Bath Spa two days a week, I spent the intervening night with Benedicta in Bath. I'd visited her in Malta when I was 17. She was now a widow. Her family had been friends with my mother's cousin Beryl. Apart from that connection we had adoption in common. Benedicta and Ronnie had been childless for years and adopted, first Sally, then twins. When those three were all still under three, Benedict became pregnant. She had a boy they called Mungo (christened Simon, I think) and then Kate who is in public relations. We are in infrequent touch; latterly through Benedicta's death at the age of 100. Benedicta introduced me to mangoes. She was a wonderfully relaxed and interesting person to stay with. Her flat was in the building opposite the Abbey that had been the Admiralty during the war. There was a parking area for visitors, a great benefit, with a system of bollards that could be raised or lowered by an electric switch. On one occasion Benedicta came with me to help with this manoeuvre. She waved me forward, inadvertently raising the bollard at the same time. My car was skewered like a barbecued sausage. This was doubly unfortunate; the car was the replacement for the one that had broken down on the motorway the previous week.

In these early years of the 2000s Peter was doing a lot of work for a publisher whose offices happened to be in Bath, which was convenient for the occasional pick-up or delivery. The work was run-of-the-mill illustration for a number of nature books. Digital reproduction was replacing litho and publishers wanted exaggeratedly vivid illustrations. Peter's strength was in realistic and delicate watercolours. He found Anness work more of a chore than a pleasure. He began to dream up a project of his own, in which he'd be able to do exactly what he wanted. He imagined a series of paintings that would run on from one to the next, telling the story of evolution through time from the earliest life forms to the present day.

This was the beginning of what became his major work. His agent Virgil Pomfret, who'd returned to the scene at the millennium after an absence of

Paintings of Culm Grasslands for the Devon Wildlife Trust

some years, placed the idea with Mitchell Beazley, a publisher Peter had done a lot of work for in the past. Mitchell Beazley chose a paleontologist called Douglas Palmer to work with Peter and write the text. Douglas came to stay at Luggs to map out the book. They laid the content out as separate pages around two table tennis tables, ours and a borrowed one, in the Barn room. This was the start of several years of intense work for Peter. He painted the course of evolution through time, double page by double page in a continuing progression, 100 separate watercolours in all. The book came out in 2009, to coincide with the 150th anniversary of the publication of Darwin's *Origin of Species*. It was also published by the University of California Press. Sales were not as good as had been hoped. A chef (not that well known) was bringing out his cookery book at the same time and the advertising budget was directed towards that. Despite the disappointment in sales, Peter considers the book his best work. Another satisfactory outcome was that the complete artwork was sold at auction as a single item at Christies.

Talking of table tennis, we used to enjoy games with Mark, who was a natural, and Olivia who wasn't. Liv's shots ping-ponged around the walls and ceiling of the room, seldom hitting the table itself. Other uses for the table were meals. Sophie's 40th birthday party was one of these occasions. 28 gathered for supper at tables covered with damask cloths. She and I cooked vast quantities of *boeuf bourguignon* ahead of time. We served it in the brass cauldron inherited from Cousin Beryl, heated up on Peter's etching plate.

Another use for the Barn room was to assemble the Millennium screen. This was the idea of the Hemyock doctor at the time, Jonathan Meads and Christine, his wife. Taking the Ordnance Survey map of the area as model, five large screens would be made up, each composed of sections of the Culm Valley portrayed in textiles sewn onto pieces of fabric by willing inhabitants

of the valley's five villages. Woolly sheep, fluffy trees, thatched houses, streams and fields would give a picture of the life as lived in the valley at the end of the 20th century. It was a magnificent idea. Di encouraged me to take part, so I sewed a representative collage on the dog-leg shape of the area around Luggs. This – with my thumping great stitches – slotted in above Di's exquisitely stitched Whitehall section. ('Exquisite' was one of Di's favourite words). The Barn room was the place where the five screens were finally assembled. Meanwhile I'd decided to film the process. Sophie had a video camera which I borrowed. I was not in the least practised at this but I got something together and, with a technician who could join the short pieces of film and attach music, we produced something just about watchable.

In another lifetime I would enjoy doing more video work. I like capturing overheard dialogue and narratives told in the language of film. So far, I haven't pursued this, although I might have done something along these lines at the time when Ken Loach came to talk with me at Goodiford Mill. Carpentry is something else I took up briefly. In our cow-milking days, I sometimes made butter from the clotted cream skimmed from the top of a pan of milk placed overnight on a corner of the Aga. Wanting to learn something new, I joined an evening class in woodwork and made a wooden mould for butter: a round hole in a wooden hexagon shape into which fitted a plunger with a decorative stamp. I carved the name Luggs in mirror writing on the stamp. The hole could be filled with freshly made butter, pressed down with the plunger. Hey presto! It came out as a round half-pound with Luggs proudly written on its head. In Madford days, Di was one of my first customers and I was one of hers. She and three friends had started a dress-making business. Very few wardrobes in the Culm Valley did not contain a garment made to measure in Liberty fabric by the Square One

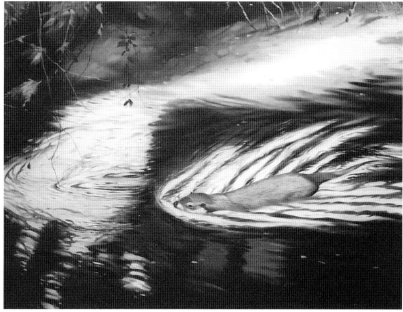

friends. They were thrilled when one of their dresses was worn on television by Katharine Whitehorn, thanks to my introduction.

We had many marvellous times as a result of our friendship with Gavin and Kath Lyall. One time we were Gavin's guests at a Crime Writers dinner; the other diners had names we were in awe of. Another time, we were Kath's guests at a meal for the Any Questions panel – an impressive and entertaining collection of people, one of whom was to become the focus of a notorious scandal. On one London visit, Kath invited me to lunch at her club; that was when she was having trouble with Gavin's drinking. She'd gone to see a counsellor and was left seething with anger. She thought counsellors should give advice, and bared her teeth at me when I said that wasn't our remit. In counselling sessions, you learn about yourself and your own ways out of problems. I realised later that I should have approached her antagonism linguistically. The term is likely to mislead because the first meaning of 'counsel' is advice. Counselling is something of a misnomer. That explanation might have satisfied her.

I find it very hard to be reminded, as I write, of Kath's present state. I only hope that she has lost all understanding of her situation. Graham Whiteley, Di's husband, is also in a care home with dementia. I believe he's perfectly happy because it was always his ambition, ever since he was looked after by hospital nurses when he had his tonsils out as a teenager, to be looked after, when adult, in much the same way. Di grew exhausted having to stand in for those nurses most of their married life. The third friend in similar circumstances but with a particular syndrome is Christine. I telephoned her yesterday, October 4th, having put the call off for too long. Yet it was an easier call than I thought it would be. The thing is to keep myself in the present with her. We can enjoy hearing each other's voice. We may repeat ourselves but we can do that ad infinitum. It doesn't matter. Phoning her is something that is difficult only in prospect.

Even at the best of times, I have never liked the phone. I sometimes explain my phone phobia by blaming my mother's endless phone conversations in Markham's dining room. I can bring to mind the look of the phone: its black Bakelite receiver with nicely rounded ends, one for your ear, one for your mouth, which would – after the call – fit snugly on its holder. I can see the holder's disc which announced our number – Tavistock 206 at a guess – and the long squiggle of brown and black flex which dangled between receiver and holder and always needed untangling. I know the table the phone stood on and the hazel trees in the part of the garden that my mother looked out on as she talked and talked and talked. I expect I hung around the hall to listen, consumed by curiosity. How good it is to have memories when and if you've had good times to remember. Nostalgia! An 18th century philosopher called Herder, as Simon Schama told us from the television set the other evening, considered nostalgia to be a physical illness, sometimes severe enough to cause death. I find this a very interesting concept. Of course, thoughts and feelings are intertwined and held in the body. That's not so surprising; the brain is part of our physical body. I used to feel sick pain in the pit of my stomach on returning to Tavistock as an adult. This was Herder's nostalgia. After re-visiting my childhood's location a number of times, I thought I was now immune. Not completely, I realised last week. I've pinned to my noticeboard a print of a photo of Markham's roof as seen from the moor outside the garden's high hedge, one of the photographs we took last week. Peter is in the frame, marking the present against the past. I was in such a state of sick excitement that I could hardly speak. *Aren't you interested?* I asked. *That's the window I used to climb out of, onto the verandah's roof.*

Evolution by Douglas Palmer published by Mitchell Beazley in 2009   *Life between 461 and 455 million years ago*

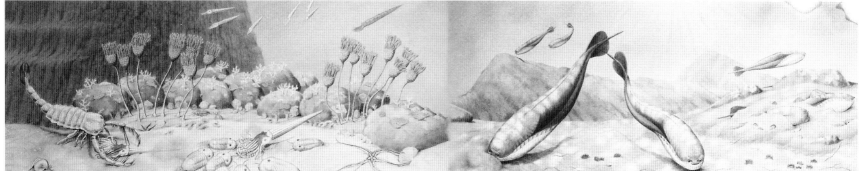

Life between 520 and 510 million years ago

We'd gone to Dartmoor, looking for a view that Peter could use to illustrate my childhood. We found it, just where I thought it might be. The spot is on the edge of Cox Tor where the moor dives down into the fields that lead to the distant dell that holds the town of Tavistock. It's a relief that the dell can still hold the whole town; it's like a bowl of barely visible, tiny, grey, sugar lumps. This view catches my heart in a way that Herder would recognise. Brent Tor is a distinctive part of this view, too. I am pleased beyond belief by the drawing Peter has done from the photographs we took. And – bonus – he has included some Dartmoor ponies. I used to say I had legs like a Dartmoor pony's.

I'd been bracing myself for the changes that Peter had predicted. He'd foreseen housing estates. As it turned out, there was only one shock. At the corner of the moor we called Tadpole Place, a brand new house is being built. Where's the stream? Where's the pool where we caught the wriggly little creatures? I cannot believe the sacrilege! How could it be allowed? In fact, the new house has probably been squeezed onto ground that was a field rather than moorland, and so – with some deft handling – given planning permission.

The Barn, brought up to date by Chris Buchan, was frequently used – apart from providing a large room for Peter's studio. The rest of the building became the temporary home of Tim and Jane Courtenay and their indefatigable young terrier. In 2002 they'd sold Whitehall Manor and were overseeing major renovations to the farmhouse they'd bought on the opposite side of the valley. Their names regularly crop up in the pages of the diaries, less so in recent years as we all lead quieter lives due to age, and even more so now due to Covid. Other temporary Barn dwellers were the Listers, Sally and Richard, in 2002. The Listers were friends from Kentisbeare days. When we

lived in Goodiford Mill, Kentisbeare, I'd learnt that someone called Richard Lister was farming in Broadhembury, close to our friends John and Jo Allen.

Lister? Could he have anything to do with the Listers I'd known in Tavistock? It turned out that he was the older brother of Barbara, Jane's friend, and Joey, my friend. I discovered that their mother was living in Taunton, and I went to see her. Cicely Lister was a very sweet woman and it was lovely to be linked back to childhood through her. I remember being hugely impressed by the size of their refrigerator when I visited them in Plymouth. Richard and Sally became friends of ours later when we met through Sally Donnithorne. Sally and I were in the same year at the R.S. When we moved to Kentisbeare, Sally and her husband John were farming nearby, in a wonderful spot in the Blackdown Hills. We used to take Sophie and Ben to swim in their pool. John died young. Sitting in his armchair to rest after a day's sailing, his heart stopped beating. Sally has been a widow for very many years without ever seeming to be lonely; apart from many friends, her daughters are close. She gives large lunch parties. Another ex R.S. girl I re-met in these years was Celia Pridham. Her husband, Michael Adams, was a journalist for the Guardian with a famous scoop to his name. He was first with the news that Nasser had seized control of the Suez Canal. Through Michael and Celia we met Glencairn and Jenny Balfour Paul. So the ball of friendship rolls, gathering more names as it goes.

While the Listers were in the Barn, Joey needed a place to park his campervan. He and his wife came to lunch, leaving the van in the yard behind the Barn for a month or two. It reminded me of the time he drove to London to park his van outside my Edge Street bedsitting room. Here he slept for a few nights, hoping (I think) I was still unattached. He became a vicar, a very kind and understanding one, I'm sure.

Life between 128 and 125 million years ago

Life 128 million years ago

Writing an account of a lifetime is like Fair Isle knitting. Someone you met when you were young and then later meet again is like a strand of knitting wool that gets left behind for a while, to be taken up when you need that colour again. The back of your knitting is a network of different coloured strands, some appearing more frequently than others. I have feelings of guilt about people who were part of my life, important for a period before disappearing. But why take on the responsibility for keeping in touch – there is no need. It's a mutual business. And there are limits to the number of people anyone can hold in close friendship.

Pete Rose kept in touch, even though he married an Australian, and lived the rest of his life in Brisbane. He'd met June on his journey from London to stay with us on Amorgos. Peter reminds me that he borrowed a suit from Francis Wilkinson for the wedding. It had been run up in a few hours in shiny blue fabric by a Hong Kong tailor. The Roses stayed with us in Montolieu Gardens the night before flying to Australia, Pete to emigrate. June bequeathed me her dressing gown. It was quilted and warm, with a pattern of white balloons on a pink background. I can hear her saying *"That'll do me for a kangaroo."* This was much quoted by John Burge, after a trip to Regent's Park zoo where the Burges, Roses and Barretts had been eyeing wallabies. June had insisted they were kangaroos and an argument had ensued.

Pete and June had two daughters who were still young when June died of cancer. A few years later, Pete also got cancer. He came back to England twice, the second time was clearly his farewell visit. I can see him sitting with a mug of coffee at the garden table at the foot of Luggs' vegetable garden. We must have known how far advanced his cancer was, but I don't recall us feeling maudlin. That was down to Pete's steadiness. The only effect the death sentence had on our behaviour was the way we took turns in having Pete to ourselves. Peter needed to pick up an etching press from somewhere on Exmoor, so he took Pete with him. Then, on yet another perfect summer's day, Pete and I walked the coast path from the Gara Rock hotel near East Portlemouth while Peter drove to East Prawle to meet us for a pub lunch. The thrift was flowering on the cliffs, adding drifts of lilac-pink to the blue of the sky and the blue of the sea. I couldn't have wanted a more perfect English day and scenery to give our old friend as a last present.

Other uses of the Barn included meetings of the newly formed Blackdown Hills Business Association. Somehow, I'd got myself involved in writing a leaflet or doing something secretarial for them, as well as providing a venue. I soon retreated from this involvement, only to fall for another. I was persuaded, by our friend Richard Carman, to become a governor of Hemyock School. I managed to continue in the role for a year, attending meetings religiously as governor in charge of the arts. My year was transformed when I had the chance to put the school in for a county-wide project. A few schools would be selected to perform in an Exeter theatre a play written by Roger McGough especially for the event. I worked hard at Hemyock Primary School's submission and we were selected as one of the schools to take part. This was a major undertaking. I had lots of help with casting. We held rehearsals in the Barn. The play was called *My Dad's a Fireman* and Mark was one of the firemen. They tended to forget what they were meant to be doing and would wander off to scuffle on the sidelines until I had the brainwave of giving them a length of rope to hold. *This is the firemen's water hose,* I told them. It worked. They held on, sometimes using it as the rope in a tug of war. A gifted dancing friend came to help with the movements of the little girls who tripped on and off stage at certain moments. I can't remember what they represented. In Exeter for the performance, I had a lot of support from the parents. It was hugely exciting for all of us. I can't remember whether there were winners and losers or no competition at all among the schools performing. The main thing was the chance to perform.

About this time, I was indulging my own unfulfilled acting ambitions. I'd joined a drama group in Exeter. At school I'd harboured thoughts of going to drama school. (Art school, architecture and becoming a Wren were in there, too). My first cousin, Richard Easton who was well into his acting career, inspired me. I'm wearing on the little finger of my left hand a small signet ring with a purplish-blue stone. This was one of seven sent to me after Dickie's death last December and the finalisation of his estate this summer by his legatee, Jonathan Walker, a New York friend living in the same apartment block. The rings may have belonged to our mutual grandmother, Louisa Withington, or to Dickie's Easton grandmother. There's no knowing. I wear this signet ring for its connection with Dickie who was my missing hero-brother, being my (and Jane's) only first cousin. I wouldn't have become as good an actor as Dickie but I had a whale of a time in the Exeter group. The first play I was in was a silly farce in which I had to faint when someone came down a chimney. The next was a play based on Jane Austen's Pride and Prejudice. I played Lady Catherine de Burgh. *"Be nastier,"* urged the director. *"I'm trying to be,"* was my answer, *"but I can't."* I recall Laurence Oliver's response to some method actor, "Try *acting*, dear boy."

I stopped being a member of the drama group when the lease on the Stepcote Theatre, which had real lighting, stage and curtains, came to an end. Drama would not be the same in a village hall.

The Barn kitchen-dining room was the setting for Peter's 70th birthday party in 2005. A number of old friends stayed the night. Vicky Wilkinson came with Tim who she later married, Diny from New York was with her English literature tutor Ira (Francis had died when they moved from California to Atlanta); Christine brought Bob, her friend at the time; Kath wrote in the Visitors' Book *How they managed the Normandy landings without Susie I can't think – Magnificent!'* Virginia wrote beneath this *Yes, that's just the right word. It was! Old friends and new people – the noise level indicated that this was a real success. And Peter looked so happy!'* Sophie's 40th party was the following year when she and I cooked quantities of beef stew, which I mentioned a few pages back.

Were the 2000s the fullest decade? We were taking short breaks in European capitals, making up for all the time we'd spent further afield. Twice, we took Mark and Olivia with us. We had a wonderful time introducing them, first to Paris, then to Venice. Food interested Mark more than fine art. Olivia was willing to enter galleries and churches. We didn't insist, so long as they got something out of the experience. New ways with pizza, mainly. Also in the 2000s Amorgos came back into our lives.

Ever since our first children's book was published, we've looked for opportunities to work together. In the wake of Peter's enormous work on Evolution we had the idea of making a very small dinosaur the hero of a book for children.

Above, one of the illustrations for 'Mei Long'.

To the right and below, dinosaurs for the 'Illustrated Encyclopedia of Dinosaurs' by Dougal Dixon, Lorenz Books

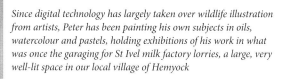

Since digital technology has largely taken over wildlife illustration from artists, Peter has been painting his own subjects in oils, watercolour and pastels, holding exhibitions of his work in what was once the garaging for St Ivel milk factory lorries, a large, very well-lit space in our local village of Hemyock

130

Kris Bushley came to stay with us briefly in Devon. We'd got to know the Bushleys when they built a basic two-room house on the knoll beyond the promontory where we used to moor the caique. She now told us that we could use it whenever we liked. It would be good to have it opened and aired, as they couldn't spend much time there. It was a glorious summer holiday home on its isolated knoll with no neighbours and a steep path down to the beach. In 2003 Sophie, Dean, Mark and Olivia came with us, a time we all remember as being very special. They stayed in Katapola and we were in the Bushleys' house.

After this holiday, Sophie and Dean began drifting apart. The idea of sharing Luggs with us was dropped. After one particular crisis Dean moved out and never moved back in. That was on New Year's Eve 2007. They divorced in 2008. Ben was on his own, too. He and Miriam had parted company when Don's scheme was collapsing. I'd become worried about money, realising we needed to rationalise our finances and our lives. I was tired of all the work Luggs and the Barn required inside and out. The more we owned, the more we had to do or find people to do it for us when we were away. I'd been looking for smaller properties and had seen several. Jennie Tierney often came to stay when we were away, to look after the place and Sam, our springer spaniel. She looked at one particular cottage I had my eye on. "*You'd be crazy,*" she said. It was tiny and wedged between other, bigger houses in the centre of a village. Of course, she was right.

I became enamoured of a house that was being built outside a small village not far away in Somerset. Modern! Brand new! Not much garden! We placed an offer with the builder and put Luggs on the market. After some months, potential buyers for Luggs made a reasonable offer. The very next day the builder of the modern house sold it to someone else. We didn't want to lose our buyers, so we gave ourselves a week to find something else. Lower Willand House in Churchstanton was for sale and that's the house we moved to in July 2007.

In 2008 Ben came to England for my 70th birthday party, bringing with him his new partner: Julia. The party was on board a Thames river boat. On the afternoon of June 20th 78 friends and family gathered at Westminster pier in quite a state of excitement. Many had met before at various Barrett parties. A few knew no-one else. It must have been a daunting occasion for Julia but she didn't seem daunted in the least. That doesn't mean she was overconfident or someone who makes her presence felt at once. On the contrary, Julia is quiet and steady in her own shoes. There she was, at Ben's side, her long hair blowing in the wind. We have lots of photographs taken during the trip, recording who was there and what they looked like at the time. It was a grey day, not ideal weather, but we could be on deck or inside the cabin. Christine had brought Malcolm Gluck, a writer whose subject was wine. Whenever Christine came to stay she brought bottles of wine that clinked promisingly in her suitcase on arrival; good quality wine recommended by Malcolm. Nowadays he's my liaison and information

centre for background news of Christine. He phones her regularly. He took the brunt of the overseeing care in London when she began to be incapacitated by her drinking. That was about five years ago now, when she kept falling down. We had no idea she was suffering from drink. We thought she was having small strokes.

A small group gathered in a corner of the deck with Malcolm as the nucleus. Where was the wine? Their impatience just penetrated my awareness and I urged on the bottle opening. The photographs aid my memory of who was on board. In the photographs I see Douglas Palmer and his wife from Evolution days, Virgil who we just caught before his death six months or so later. William and Jill Fell; Jane and her eldest son Michael, his wife Kathy and their sons; Virginia, Kath, Di, Karen, Jennie Tierney, Jenny Balfour Paul, Rachel Sidery with Mark who is now her husband, Sue Sidery, Tania the owner of Finn, my good friend the labrador I was looking after at the time; Alex and Virginia Richmond Scott (Alex had come down Luggs drive following the sign we'd put up about an exhibition in the Barn, and become a friend) – and, of course, Tony and Lucy, Hilary and Julian. Names of family and friends will mean little or nothing to readers but I include them otherwise this memoir would be puzzlingly unpeopled.

We and the family were staying at the Tower hotel, which was another cause for excitement, the buffet breakfast being a particular thrill. Sophie was on her own, after her divorce with Dean and before she met Nick. Mark and Olivia were in their teens, well before gaining partners. Ben and Julia were at the beginning of their relationship. That doesn't mean there were no explosions. In fact, there was one we witnessed very soon. After the birthday cruise, we took them to Cornwall for a few days. Jenny Balfour Paul lent us her flat in Port Isaac. Something happened to spark an eruption. Who knows what the trigger was. We never do know. We were in a car park by the ferry across the estuary to Padstow. Ben stormed off. Julia stayed admirably calm. He'll find his way back, she said. Her calm was infectious. We went off to have a cup of tea at the Victorian Gardens, halfway between Rock and Port Isaac. When we got back to the flat, Ben was waiting for us.

How sad it is that Ben's troubles were too much even for Julia, even though she managed life with him for a good number of years – in fact, until she developed bowel cancer. But in the late 2000s we were still full of hope. In 2009 we were back in New Zealand and we spent Christmas Day with Julia's parents in New Plymouth before crossing from west to east coast. We stayed with Ben and Julia in the Bay of Plenty where they were living on an orchid farm. Julia, a plant expert, was in charge of the hothouses. Ben was doing his best to pick up work. But strains and stresses were evident. The diary tells me that on two days, January 5th and 13th, there were explosions. The one I particularly remember is when Ben crashed his fist down on a glass table, breaking the glass and narrowly missing a vein.

Despite Julia's good influence, nothing much had changed. We flew home from Auckland on the 14th January 2010.

THE 2010s

I've reached the last decade in this memoir. How I view these final pages is tied up with the way I view the ending of my life. I feel apprehensive. I very much hope that the whole memoir will hang together and read well. I also hope that these last pages will not be my life's last page, nor that they will be Peter's. At the moment, that would be far too soon for both of us. Peter continues to paint, I to write. I'm already thinking of a new novel. Will

we get to do the things we hope to do? Only one thing is certain and that's
something that's been made clear while writing this account of our lives:
nothing is ever certain. We've lost many friends; the ones who have died and
the ones who haven't died but have lost their minds, which is perhaps worse.
I will make sure that on the very last page I will talk about the lives that are
just beginning. Brinley and Davinia will be our bright sparks.

*Looking westwards over the Bristol Channel from a headland at the foot of the
Quantock hills, one of our many favourite places for walks and cream teas*

My computer which I think dates from about 2007 went blank last week. I was in the 2000s writing away happily, when the screen and the computer's lights faded into silent darkness. When I tried it again some hours later, it worked. In my excitement I feverishly backed up what I'd been working on. Too feverishly, it so happened. I couldn't find the 1990s file. I'd printed that decade out, so I typed up a new file, fighting against despair and fury. When the computer did the same trick yesterday, I took it to Dave at 1-to-1 computers. He knew the answer. Poor computer! It can't cope with all the updates that keep coming at it from all angles. It's too old and slow. It needs to be switched off regularly to have time to catch up. Or so I understand it. I know the feeling; it has my heartfelt sympathy. I'm going to park it in a corner of my study where it can be the reservoir of years of work, while I continue on a spanking new machine which Dave will put together for me. Oh joy! Oh rapture! as I think Mole cried in The Wind in the Willows.

Our move from Luggs to Lower Willand House got short shrift in the previous decade to this one, as I was so anxious to get the 2000s buttoned up before the computer went blank again. And I don't want my mind to go blank before I finish this work. Is it all a matter of electricity? This morning (17th October 2020) I made sure that the plug into my computer was well and truly pushed in, after a night's rest. It's working. So am I.

I have witnessed the moment of death several times: it's as though the person's light has gone out. We become unplugged. Perhaps we get plugged in to another electrical circuit. We become part of Jung's collective unconscious where we all float around, being aware but not on an individual level. What do you think happens after death, I've been asked – by Di, in her last weeks, and by Sue last week. It's a question we all ask in our different ways, with different beliefs if we have any belief at all. I hold it to be all a matter of electricity. Ben's explosions are the result of overcharge. Our universe began with a big bang. The most complex things have simple causes.

I am having to take my blood pressure for a week, as I have done often in the past on monitors borrowed from the surgery. I see from the diaries that the doctor, John Davies at the Churchinford surgery, was on my case trying to bring my blood pressure down. That was 10 years ago when we lived at Lower Willand House, Churchstanton. It's still the same story but now I have my own monitor. My present doctor, Tom Winter at Hemyock, tells me to sit quietly for 20 minutes before taking my pressure, and then record the best of three. I may succeed in registering reasonable figures – yet this morning Ben rang just as I was sitting down quietly. Not a good recipe for a low figure. The lowest I managed was 187 over 87. I sometimes wish I lived in an age when they couldn't measure hypertension. If you can't measure something, it doesn't exist?

Churchstanton is the second line of the address of Lower Willand House. It has a church and a school yet if you set out to find the village, you won't. It doesn't really exist. There are just acres of fields in between the church and the school. There are three farms near the school: Higher Willand, Middle Willand and Lower Willand, which are sometimes confused with a real village called Willand a good 15 miles away. That Willand is where several friends live, ones first met when we lived in Kentisbeare: Sally Donnithorne (ex-RS), Catherine Heath whose husband Michael grew incensed over Margaret Thatcher's election as leader of his party – a woman! – and Mary Tancock, our neighbour at Goodiford Mill. That Willand is a proper village with a bus service to Cullompton and Exeter, popular with the retired. The Willand of the Churchstanton farms is much less real. It's as though a map-maker has set out to create a mystery. Many years ago, long before we moved to LWH, I got completely lost driving around the lanes at this point in the Blackdown Hills. I came across a charming rural scene. On a generous bend in the lane, having climbed a steep hill and passed the small school, I noticed to my right a triangle of mown grass with willow trees bending their necks over a narrow stream. There were hens and ducks. I vowed to come back another day. I'd locate it on the map and discover its name. But I never could find it again. Not, that is, until we moved there.

Lower Willand House was a stopgap purchase. We didn't want to lose our Luggs buyers who had appeared just as we lost the newly-built house we'd been hoping to buy. For such a speedy purchase, it proved to be a far more pleasant place to live than we'd imagined. It was a four-square, stone building with large double-glazed windows, converted from a barn on Lower Willand Farm for the married daughter of the farmer to live in. Its modernity was an attraction after low-ceilinged, small-windowed, beam and cobweb-rich Luggs. It gave us as much or more living space, yet it was easier to look after. It had a lovely large kitchen warmed by an Aga with plenty of room for our large dining table and a sofa. It had four large upstairs rooms, one of which was fitted out with a length of desk top, cupboards, drawers and a built-in filing cabinet, with plenty of floor space left over for two armchairs and a sofa bed. Peter – after weeks of workmen – had a marvellous studio in half a large barn which had housed pigs; the other half being a garage with storage in the four ex-pig stalls, and an automatic up-and-over garage door. There was a large flat field, with a further triangle which had been orchard and which held a tumble-down stone shelter which we rebuilt. The large garden at the back of the house had a pond which we freshened up, apple and plum trees which we pruned, and an area at the far end where we planted a group of carefully chosen trees. We put a summerhouse in the garden, solar panels on the garage roof and created a shrubbery alongside a new path to lead to the studio and garage. We improved the terrace at the back of the house, increased the herbaceous flowers and flowering shrubs on the banks above and below the terrace and eventually we could sit down and entertain our friends at the big garden table with its parasol, bought from Jan, the previous owner. We also bought from her the sit-on mower. Sudden ease of lawn-care, besides being fun for Mark.

What was wrong with Lower Willand House? The one thing that had made us hesitate on first sighting was the thing that prompted us to move away. That was the proximity of the farmhouse. From the kitchen window one could almost touch the corner of the house that now belonged, not to the parents of Jan, but to a middle-aged couple with a daughter and a couple of Jack Russell dogs. Mark and Kate were good and helpful neighbours. Their free range hens laid brown eggs with bright, yellow yolks. Their dogs were cheerful and friendly. But they were not our hens and dogs although

*Peter has always loved sitting on hillsides sketching in watercolour. Here are
some scenes which attracted him in Greece, New Zealand and France*

we seemed to be living with them, hearing their owners' radio as well as the usual household comings and goings. They also owned a wreck of a barn at the end of our shared drive which they let to a cider-making enterprise. None of this was as disturbing as it sounds in this paragraph, but it did impinge on my daily life in the house, and took up space in my mind. Peter was not concerned, being almost 100 yards away in the studio. It was I who responded most eagerly when Di rang to suggest we buy a bungalow near her called Little Penn. We knew the bungalow she meant. Little Penn sits on a lane that runs along the brow of one of the hills that hold Hemyock in their embrace. When we lived at Luggs it was part of our view to the east. The six houses spaced along Pencross lane were a familiar sight, even though the lane itself was not part of our route anywhere. Martin Pring, wood craftsman, builder and funeral director, had bought Little Penn with the aim of transforming it into a house which he would sell on as a beautiful modern property with a stupendous view down the Culm Valley. Our immediate idea

was to approach Martin, who we knew in any case – first met when Brian Sidery died, he was the funeral director – and see if he would sell us the bungalow in its present state, for a price that would cover the profit he would have made. That very morning, we had gone to the Spar shop in Hemyock for the Sunday paper. Christine was with us for the weekend. There was Martin coming out of the shop as we were about to go in. We broached the subject of the bungalow. Would we like to look at it now? he asked. We drove in convoy up the hill, turned left at Pencross Lane and, after a couple of hundred yards, turned right up Little Penn's drive.

It took some months to find a buyer for Lower Willand House but Rob and Tamara Paul turned up within the time limit Martin had agreed with us, February 2013. Now Peter has drawn the stupendous view from our bungalow for the Introduction to this memoir.

Three years before this, in June 2010, we celebrated our Golden Wedding at Lower Willand House. It was a perfect setting for a hog roast,

135

with rugs and cushions scattered on the lawn, the garage set up with food, plates, glasses, drink, and parking organised in the field. It would be impossible to hold such a party for 60 friends and family in our present home. The only element missing – and this became increasingly clear as we grew hungrier and hungrier – was the hog. Sophie urged me to phone the supplier which I eventually did, having been too relaxed about its non-appearance for far too long. It transpired that the driver's SatNav had taken him up a no-through lane some miles away and the trailer bearing the hog on its spit had got stuck in a ditch. It needed rescuing. Nick and Mark were despatched with volunteers Gareth and Alison Weekes. *I knew we were getting near the right place,* said Mark. *I could smell pork.* Our golden wedding is remembered for this event. It featured in an Observer piece by Kath. I wrote a piece of doggerel to send later to our guests. Here's an excerpt.

> *But – god! – what has happened to the HOG?*
> *There is no fog, there is no bog.*
> *We do not even have a dog*
> *Which might have eaten up our hog.*
>
> *We need Hog now at Willand House!*
> *We do not want our guests to grouse.*
> *They came to feast on hog and crackling.*
> *But hog and crackling's, dammit, lackling.*
> *… and so on.*

We didn't even have a dog, for the first time in many years. Peter grew up with cocker spaniels. The first was Sally in Wales. Peter remembers the horror of seeing his father carrying Sally back to the house in a blanket. She'd been killed on the railway line. Then came Raq, after the war at Burbage Road. A pastel Peter drew of Raq hung in the hall, so I felt as though I'd almost known this gentle dog. I grew up with Labradors; first, Sam, a black lab that drowned in Mr. Collum's frozen pond, an image which haunted me and still does. My mother wrote to us at school in Bath with the news. Letters were handed out at mid-morning break with the half-pint bottle of milk which we drank through a straw during the walk around The Run. The milk tasted of the cardboard disc on the top of the bottle, pierced to hold the straw. I found it hard to bear the thought that there was no Sam waiting for me at home in Markham. A happier association derives from Father Christmas's shoes which Jane recognised as belonging to Mr. Collum. *Shush, don't tell Sue,* hissed mother.

Sam was replaced by yellow Labradors. Copper was so named because he came from Colonel Harold Golden, the Chief Constable of Wiltshire, an old ex-Army friend of my parents. Copper was joined by Whisky, a paler lab also from the Goldens. Then, up the hill from the town, trembling uncontrollably, trotted a low-slung, broad-chested, hairy mongrel who wouldn't go home *Shoo,* said mother, but Bowey, named for his bow-legs, stayed. He was the sweetest and most devoted animal, probably with Yorkshire terrier forbears. Talking of the afterlife and different beliefs as I was a few pages back, this is a good moment to remember my mother's conviction. Dick, the man she married aged eighteen, would be waiting for her at the pearly gates with

Bowey at his heels. How comforting that must have been for her. The dogs were with my father when he died on the golf course.

As a family of four Barretts we chose a Lassie collie as our first dog. This was when we had moved to Goodiford Mill in 1974, at the beginning of our smallholding life. Pepper was soon joined by a black and white collie and-springer spaniel cross, inherited from a couple who couldn't handle a dog as well as a failing marriage. He came to us as Bryher, named after the Scilly island, but Sophie renamed him Charlie. He was definitely a Charlie; a bright, amusing dog who always knew what was going on and what benefit there might be in it for him. Pepper never worked out how to get from Luggs drive into the lane. He'd wait patiently for the side gate by the cattle-grid to be opened. Meanwhile Charlie had taken a flying leap over the grid, or swerved between the grid and the gate post, or gambolled over the hedge to the side of the entrance and shot off up the lane to the wood.

In the wood Charlie would bound away excitedly, hoping to rouse a deer, while Pepper looked down his long nose at his friend's silly, but possibly endearing, antics. We rarely had to put the dogs on leads. They would come to heel when necessary. And it was seldom necessary. In those days there were few cars, walkers and dogs. The countryside was more of a workplace than a leisure park. Nowadays people of our age gather in groups, armed with sticks like ski poles, and tramp off as though on a trek to the Himalayas. But they do walk – unlike wretched SB who avoids it, ever since a bad move at Tai Chi.

When Charlie and Pepper were no more, we were dog-less for a while, which saved the search for someone to look after the dogs as well as the vegetables, the garden, the sheep, and whatever animals we were still smallholding in the Papingo years. But before we left Luggs for Lower Willand House, I decided I needed to own a dog again. I fell for a brown and white springer spaniel puppy. Mark and Olivia helped me choose his name: Sam. We'd had a series of almost pet pheasants we called Sam. It was a species-free name. Sam the dog was not unlike Charlie in character, but less robust. I'm sad to relate that he died very young. He was barely two when he suffered a series of strokes. Luggs was going on the market at the time. A photograph in the sales brochure shows Sam cowering under an armchair in the dining room, taking refuge from the estate agent and photographer.

After Sam we didn't own another dog. But I needed the companionship for the daily walks I was keen on in the wood. I had made what I called rat-runs over the years, secret paths off the main track to check on badger setts and generally keep in touch with the life of the wood. I answered an advertisement, asking for a dog walker. This is how I met Tania and Fin, both equally dear to me. Tania, always struggling with too much going on in her life, moved away from Hemyock some years ago now, taking Fin too, of course, but before then Fin spent his days with me and we were excellent friends. He was replaced in my life, to a lesser degree, by Bramley, a dog who was a kindred spirit of Sam's but, fortunately for his family, calmer, hardier and healthier. Bramley and I kept the secret paths open in the wood but he was well exercised by his owners, so it was more a case of my borrowing Bramley than looking after him. The last dog I took on as a job was Saffy, a golden retriever, belonging to the mother of our tenant at the Wellington house we bought after selling Luggs. Saffy's owner ran a care home and would drop off Saffy at Lower Willand House on her way to work in Taunton. There was nothing at all wrong with Saffy but I never fell for her in the way I had done with the previous dogs. Saffie's owner tried to teach me how to use ski poles for walking. We strode up and down the garden, sticking our poles into the grass. That maybe had something to do with my lack of enthusiasm for her dog. We were different animals.

Lower Willand House had the best walks from the back door of any of our Devon houses. There was a long list of possible circuits to follow, each with its distinctive attraction. Down through the woods below the school, then around and back up the lane. Past Middle Willand Farm and up the bridle track to turn either left or right, each way leading to markedly different terrain, way over by the church or, in the opposite direction, by the newly opened farm shop. There were walks in the woods beyond the church, too, for longer hikes into foreign land. Had not Little Penn been so clearly the ideal post-Luggs property, we would have stayed happily enough at LWH. But we'd moved from Luggs to realise capital and to rationalise our life, and with Lower Willand we'd taken on almost as much and spent too much on improvements that we didn't really need to make. We view it as the necessary stepping stone between Luggs and Little Penn.

This corner of Devon has been our home for 46 years. A surprising setting, perhaps, for Peter who had preferred the more exciting landscapes of, say, Wales, Greece and California. The Blackdown Hills are by no means spectacular. They are not even, strictly speaking, hills. It's an area of steep valleys scored into a plateau that rises from the surrounding plains. The main routes for holiday-makers from the north and the east pass either side of the plateau, like a river flowing either side of a boulder. The town-dwellers on the plains view the Hills as undesirable territory, cold, wet and fog-bound. In fact, we are often in the sun when fog covers the plain. That's our secret. I think the area has always attracted people who want to hide from the business of the world. You cannot hurry in the Blackdown Hills. The jigsaw shapes of the small, hedged fields make the lanes twist and turn through the valleys. Only on the flat tops do the lanes straighten out, like the runways of the aerodromes created in world war two. When it was designated an Area of Outstanding Natural Beauty with a centre for information in Hemyock, it became more of a 'place' to be branded for tourism.

Peter has been painting the wildlife seen in the Blackdown Hills since we made our home in England for the children's schooling. Oils, pastels and watercolours of local subjects have been his preoccupation, alongside all the commissioned work he has done over the years. He has held exhibitions in Luggs Barn and, latterly, in Hemyock. I was at an exercise class in the village when I looked around at the hall and realised it would make a fantastic setting for an exhibition. Known as The Garages, it had housed the fleet of lorries that served the St Ivel milk factory, the source of employment for many Hemyockians, including Sophie's Dean, his parents, uncle and other

Our woodland has been a source of pleasure and refreshment since we bought it in 1983

in-laws. When the factory closed, Dean and all the other employees were out of a job, a great worry at the time. The Garages was now an exceedingly large, empty sports hall filled with natural light. Peter was able to hang an average of 120 pictures in four exhibitions over the last ten years. With no commission to pay, the paintings could be sold at half the price they would be in a gallery.

Other exhibitions he held in Devon were in public galleries. In the 1990s he undertook a project for the Devon Wildlife Trust. Over a year he visited and recorded whatever wildlife he saw in a habitat called Culm grassland. This "Culm" is unrelated to our local river. It's the term for a particular kind of boggy marsh, conserved in various parts of mid and north-west Devon and home to endangered species of insect, bird and flower. As it turned out, Peter was disappointed by the lack of visible wildlife. Although his pictures brought out its subtle attraction, it was a monotonous landscape. Monotonous, that is, save for two strange sights. He was squelching his way through marsh when he came across a man attacking a thorny hedge with a chainsaw. It would have been unremarkable if the man had been clothed. He wasn't. The chainsaw-wielder was entirely naked.

I was with Peter for Strange Sight Number Two. With boots firmly stuck in treacly mud, I was contemplating the view as I plotted my next move. There, on a hill the far side of a couple of boggy fields, I saw a tiger. A *what?* I looked again. However, I tried to argue with my eyes, my eyes insisted.

A tiger had paused in its pacing to gaze across the intervening fields at the intruder in his landscape – me. I called Peter to corroborate the sight. He did. He reassured me that the tiger was caged. In my memory's vision, I see no bars though perhaps there was some flimsy green netting? I wasn't keen to tarry and got Peter to haul me and my boots out of the mud. I went on ahead to the car.

What on earth was a tiger doing there? It was the subject of discussion for weeks, with lots of suggestions but no answer. Mid-Devon is a stranger place than the Blackdown Hills. You can almost see the mud when you recite the names of the places Peter sketched and painted: Meshaw, Rackenford, Vealand, Volehouse, Dunsdon, Knowstone, Stapleton Mire, Week, Quoditch.

The Devon Wildlife Trust paid Peter for the year's work. The paintings themselves were exhibited in three venues – Barnstaple Museum, Exeter Museum, and Otterton Mill – and the proceeds of the sales went to the Trust. Another similar project presented itself in 2016. We'd gone with Sue's Terry on a bird-watching boat trip off the North Somerset coast. Another member of the trip was Terry's Nether Stowey neighbour, Nigel Phillips. Conversation led to the idea that Peter would contribute paintings to an exhibition of local artists' work being held within a few weeks in Porlock. Through this, Peter became interested in the look of the coast, particularly in the patterns made by mud in Bridgwater Bay and the birds that gathered on the mud banks: mainly avocets, lapwings, redshanks, shelducks and dunlins. He exhibited the resulting paintings at The Garages. A couple from London were enthusiastic about a watercolour of a weatherbeaten groyle at Porlock Weir. They would buy it. Next day, we learnt from friends, they'd come to the conclusion it was too cheap. Therefore, it couldn't be any good. They didn't want it.

That was an instance of the strange phenomenon: many people do not trust their own aesthetic judgement. They need to be told something is good. It then becomes good in their eyes. This is why so much bad work fetches large sums of money. All it needs is enough publicity, which means those who can generate and pay for lots of publicity or by schmoozing in the right circles or by charging high prices can sell their work, while genuinely good work may not sell. Stating the case makes me feel like a niggardly sourpuss. But it is the way it works.

I have a difficult passage to bring in, one that is directly personal. It's a follow-on to something touched on near the beginning of this. Let's see how it goes.

We were staying in the Bushleys' house on Amorgos in the summer of 2013. Christine was with us. We were sharing books. Christine had brought a novel called *Middlesex* by Jeffrey Eugenides. Peter read it first. I froze when he told me what it was about. He said it contained a character that I might identify with. I read the novel and that began my panic stricken hunt for answers that I'd shelved for a lifetime. I have a file of information from that autumn. The easiest course for me is to include here the email I wrote on October 3rd 2013 to Diny and Christine. It must have been a follow-on to one that raised the subject in the first place.

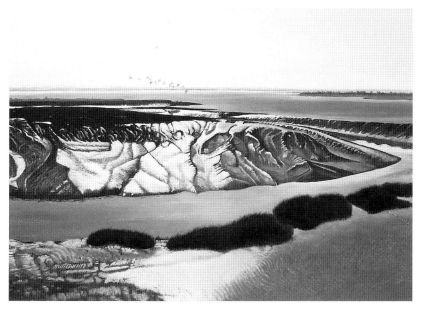

Peter painted some lesser known spots on the Somerset coast, fascinated by its rock formations, the shapes formed by mud banks, and the flocks of birds that gather in Bridgwater Bay

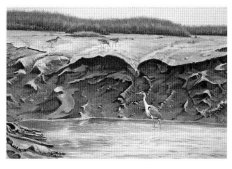

3/10/13

I have spent sixty-three years not wanting to learn why I'm like what I am, and what the hell am I like? This is a strangely ostrich-like attitude for someone who is always intensely interested in everything around me.

Then I read Middlesex. Sleeping dragons raise their heads and snarl. These dragons were born when I, aged 12 or thereabouts, was shut out of the bathroom while my mother had "a little talk with Jane." Why on earth? What would Jane be told that I wouldn't? It didn't sound like a surprise birthday present. I felt left out for no reason I could fathom. Later on, at the RS, I realised that something was going on that I didn't know about, didn't understand. It took some years of strange allusions – "you may be a bit late, but it'll happen to you too" – watching the queue outside Nurse's dispensay next door to the dining room grow with everyone else but never me. Then I began to learn the word: monthly periods, the curse, tampons. I realised blood was involved which I didn't like the sound of at all. Somehow or other I absorbed hazy knowledge.

My mother got our friendly local doctor in to chat. I think I may have been in the room, too. I remember the consensus between them was that I wasn't all that unusual. Some girls were very late. So that was all right, then. I was just late. Meanwhile, I knew I was lucky: never "off games", always okay, always feeling fine.

Possibly aged 16, 17 (it's hard to remember thoughts and feelings from so far back) I became a little apprehensive about the future. If I didn't ever have a period, would I be able to have children? I shoved that little dragon back in its box.

… When I would meet the man to marry, then I'd look into my lack of periods. … We agreed it was good to have a few years of freedom before having children, and we look into the matter when the time came.

As far as I remember, it was during our first summer on Sifnos that I, we, began to think I should investigate my innards. How old was I then? 1963 minus 1938 – 25. Back in London I began that exploration. First – for some strange reason, possibly through Peter Owtram's foster parents' connections – I went to an examination at the Royal Homeopathic Hospital. I remember waiting naked but for a green overall in something like a locker room in a grey dank building out of Dickens. The result of that was a bald statement: your vagina is a cul-de-sac, there's nothing we can do. Time passed. The next attempt to find out was through newspaper articles about fertilisation treatment at the Queen Elizabeth Hospital, Birmingham. This was a key event. After the examination, the surgeon told me that he could cut me open to see exactly what was inside but in his opinion it would be better to leave well alone; I was lucky to have a beautiful body and we could adopt a child. After this, I went into the loo and had a bit of a cry. Cried again with Peter, and then again with Peter's mother (who was brilliant all through this side of things).

And so, onwards to adoption – first, Sophie, then Ben. With Sophie I have felt a useless mother, not being able to guide her at all about periods, nor about birth control or childbirth. That's the dragon that snarls "You're not a good mother, you're not a proper woman." This can morph into a whole team of dragons, all chorusing the same message. I've been adept at banishing them. I have strong boxes to shut them in …

… until Peter read Middlesex and tells me I may not like it. What? What's it about? Dread fills me. I read it at the rate of knots, beguiled as a writer by an extremely clever writer, but at the same time hot on the trail of my own identity, with dragons breathing down my neck. Are you really a man? they ask, at their worst. Have you got hidden testes? Have you got a sneaky penis that will suddenly pop up? Freak out! Finally I reach the chapter where Eugenides uses a voyeur type of tank to display all the gradations of hermaphrodites. (I don't like that word at all! Half man, half woman? No, I won't belong there). Then I read about the character called Zora. I'm Zora, I say to Peter. Yes, he says, in a most matter-of-fact way. Christine doesn't seem to understand how I can be worried. Both assure me that I'm one of the most feminine women they know.

It may be that I boxed my dragons in so securely that no-one, including myself, has realised my lifelong horror that I might turn out to be a man. Even to write that needs all my writerly distance not to run shrieking out of the house.

But now – now I feel differently. Sitting next to Diny in the Moroccan restaurant in Bath was – well, what was it? A colossal turning point. Whatever we said together, Diny (and did the others round the table listen in? No, they were far too busy with their own conversations surely), has smoothed out what was a very crumpled bit of life cloth. Peter, Diny, Christine, clearly have never worried about me, never not accepted me for what I am, whatever that may be. Diny's knowledge of me from school days and talk of chromosomes, endocrinology, made me brave enough to ask my own questions. I went onto the Internet and dared google all kinds of – to me – frightening words. And with a calm head and heart I can now announce to anyone interested, even to the Gundenham Dairy milkman who delivers milk in glass bottles to our doorstep, that I am someone with CAIS. Yes, that's us, the ones in twenty thousand who has Complete Androgen Insensitivity Syndrome. Let's celebrate! We're okay. We're lucky.

I'm certainly lucky in having around me such special people.

BUT HOLD ON! That's not me at all! I went on to ask my doctor for help and she referred me to the Clinical Genetics department of the hospital. Result? I am 100% female. I have normal female chromosomes, 46 XX. Hear me celebrating! The syndrome has the initials MRKH (Mayer Rokitansky Kasler Hauser) and is a congenital abnormality, characterised by the absence of a cervix and uterus, which affects one in every 5,000 women. Anyone who has never had reason to question their sexual identity is unlikely to understand the relief of having the sense of personal gender confirmed. All this makes me extremely sympathetic to anyone who is struggling to pinpoint their identity, wherever it may lie on the continuum between male and female, and have it accepted.

My mother once, in a hesitant aside, said she was sorry she hadn't done a better job of making me. Of course, she couldn't help it! I was touched. In fact, to be born without a womb is congenital. These organs are developing when a foetus is around six weeks old. Something untoward happening to the mother at the time can interfere with the process. I was being made in the autumn of 1937, growing within a womb whose owner was wreathed in smoke with a strong gin and tonic to hand. Even if drink and nicotine were not the cause of my peculiarity, today's mothers can take more care, and have more care taken of them.

I was explaining this to Robin and Sue Hicks who'd come to lunch around the time I was excited by my discoveries. "But I do have a vagina," I told them. Robin exploded like a delighted hand grenade at this remark. He embarrasses me and Sue by remembering it with glee whenever we meet. Well, I think that's a very sensible way to react, so long as we're not in public!

Robin helped us put up the shed in the woods. That was in 2001 before they left to look for a house in Spain. They ended up in France, in two different places and we visited them in both. They are now back in England. They chose a Bristol flat with big windows looking over the floating harbour. It suits them, especially since Robin developed prostate cancer. He seems to be doing well. Robin's desire for country living (he was once a farmer) is fed by looking after people's houses and gardens and animals when the owners are away. We played croquet with them when they were house-sitting near Taunton. We each remembered different rules, except Sue who resolutely remained outside the lively discussions, schooled in such a strategy by brothers in childhood.

When they were living in the Madford valley where we first met them, thanks to Derek Robinson, Robin created an avenue of lime trees. In the house they moved to near Pezenas in France, he dug a channel across the lawn to fill with water from the river at the end of the garden, possibly with Alhambra in mind. He also made a cricket pitch in a field for the local ex-patriates. Sue was given the freedom of the town of Pezenas (or something of this laudable, medieval nature) for her activities in integrating the local English with the French. After one of our visits to France we went on to the south of Spain, having a flabbergasted look at Cambrils on the way, the fishing village of 1961 now a large modern city. In the countryside beyond Ronda we stayed with Martin Young, the friend made in Athens in 1962. He'd given up Greece for Spain, where he'd carved out of the arid landscape a wonderful garden while continuing to delve into the common origin of some, if not all, languages. How we spend our time, beyond the needs of sheer survival, is a visible demonstration of our personality. Turning the spotlight on ourselves, I see that Peter and I draw a very thin line between work and leisure. I get low if I haven't a piece of writing to ponder about or a troubled counselling client to work with. I will read or watch television for the sake of contemplating other's people's lives and narratives. Peter is always seeking the natural world. With our house moves and travels we are after new material for our work.

The Camargue appealed to us. We visited after staying with the Hicks, having first gone there after meeting Marcus Campbell. Marcus was one of the writers who sent his novel, *A Blue Forest*, for me to publish as an ebook on Writers Readers Direct; whereupon we fell into a correspondence which still continues. At that time, he was the resident caretaker in the second (or third?) home of an absent English baron. I think of carefully trimmed lavender bushes as I write and acres of vines to be pruned. Marcus, a good gardener, pruned a forsythia when he stayed with us here at Little Penn. This paragraph could shoot off in several directions. Towards the flamingos

of the Camargue which would lead us to Frances Mellersh and a large oil painting she liked of the pink-tinged birds standing on their painfully thin, knitting needle legs in shining, grey water. Or to the lettuces which Peter painted for the cover of the most recent book Marcus has produced with the title *"God is Weeding The Lettuces."* It's a book of notes by a novice, answering the questions of the visiting public. Marcus very nearly became an Orthodox monk and got as far as selecting a monastery on Mount Athos. He's written an account of that journey. The novel I put on WRD as an ebook was set in New Zealand and the background appealed to me, though the novel's structure was uneasy. Marcus's strength, and length, is in short stories. He also makes sculptures out of junk – *objet trouvees* in the language of galleries. His work is shown and sold in Paris.

I find myself well on the way into another digression. I'm now thinking of my pleasure in being asked to consider other people's conundrums in life and/or in writing. Yesterday a friend came for help in getting his book onto Amazon. Patrick Nicholls and his wife Bridget live in Whitehall Manor, where our friend the Courtenays lived in the past. Every Christmas period for the last 20 years or so a date has been earmarked in the diary for the Nicholls' drinks party. So they are old friends from the point of view of parties, but new ones in this Covid year. We've met on their sunny terrace. Patrick wanted to tell me how much he'd enjoyed *Elfrida* which, of course. pleased me enormously. I am taking Bridget out on Thursday for a short escape from the ordinary; her leg has been in a brace boot for weeks to allow a ligament to mend. They are in the throes of selling Whitehall Manor and buying something smaller. But the housing market is fragile in these Covid times.

Returning my mind to France, we also visited Peter and Jill Daniel, in several different places: in Provence, the Alps, and somewhere in the south west of France with a very, very distant view of the Pyrenees. Before this, they'd invited us to their home on St Lucia. They were generous hosts who moved houses and countries even more frequently than we did. Their last home, before Peter died, was in Wales. Jill visited us here, at the very beginning of Covid. She was on her way to old friends in Cornwall where they were living when we owned the Port Isaac house. Jill celebrated her 60th birthday in the Cornish house, a party which their daughter Louise organised. Louise died a few years later of breast cancer. As did the daughter of Desna of Otterton Mill.

We don't realise on what thin ice we skate in life, until reminded by these early deaths. Covid, too, reminds us of this and the way people need people.

I shall turn on this prompt to Olivia, our granddaughter who is so precious to us in her quiet way. She never demands attention. At least, this is our experience of her – she may well appear differently to others, to her friends, to Sophie her mother, to her partner Bertie. She and Bertie have just become engaged which is a cause for celebrating – if only we could all get together as we used to do for a meal – at Sophie's or here or in a restaurant somewhere in Devon. I'm thinking of a particular occasion when we shared the present that Sophie gave us: a spa afternoon in an Exeter hotel. Liv's birthday is July 13th, mine June 24th – so we're both Cancerians. Are we alike? I'd like to think so. As a possible proof, she and I went together to choose fabric to recover a chair I'd given her. I'd inherited the chair from my mother's family. I think it might have come originally from Holloway Hill House. It's an upholstered *prie-Dieu*, a Victorian low seated chair for kneeling on to pray. You'd place your arms on the top of its tall back. We went into three shops and sped through fat books of samples, easily agreeing on which to dismiss, which to return to. In the upholsterer's workshop we looked at more samples and homed in – in perfect unison – on two fabrics which Olivia photographed to take home to Bertie. We think they both have excellent taste. Of course, that's what anyone thinks when they find themselves in agreement with anyone else. The little chair, covered in a silvery, oyster-coloured brocade, is sitting by the restored fireplace in their Victorian artisan cottage which lies in a cobbled street that leads steeply down to Exeter's ancient city walls. The colours they chose for decoration are muted greys, silvers, slate blue. On the wall they have a Peter Barrett oil painting of a mudbank in Bridgwater Bay gleaming under a dark sky as though on a moonlit night.

Liv has spent lots of time with us over her life and it's always been a sheer pleasure. We've had the best of grandparenthood, and all on our doorstep. When she and Mark were with us on the weekdays Sophie was working, we had a long list of things we liked doing: painting, drawing, cooking, dancing, making up stories, taking the dog for a walk, obstacle races round the garden and playing Lions at the Zoo. That involved climbing onto the rocking chair – the car – and driving to the zoo to see the lion in his cage – Mark on the double bed in the spare room. Inevitably, the lion would burst out of his cage and rampage around, roaring and bouncing on the bed. Telephones and ambulances were involved, and a great deal of excited shrieking. We had a good time.

When Liv was between school and a job, she came to sit beside me and the computer in my study and we drew up whatever was needed at the time: personal statements, applications, and so on. She had thought of nursing but in the end got into Northampton university to train as a dental assistant. Before this she'd worked in two care homes. I can't think of anyone I'd rather have beside me in a care home than Olivia. Now she helps a dentist in an Exeter practice, handing him evil-looking instruments while she soothes patients' fears. To carry out her work these days, she's wearing a mask and PPE.

Personal Protective Equipment! What a number of new terms and activities we've learnt: Zoom, the R factor, lockdown, social distancing among them. It's now quite a shock to see people hobnobbing close together on television repeats. Individuals in Perspex boxes are the usual sight, or arranged like stamps on a Zoom screen.

Although both Liv and Bertie work full-time (Bert as a plasterer), they are in line for a dachshund puppy, '*a companion for Rufus*,' says Liv, in justification, Rufus being their first dachsund. They've chosen a rough-haired dachshund bitch which will be collected when she is six weeks' old. Liv could always be trusted to look after Sam. We used to talk of sharing a dog when she grew up. But that's not to be. I'm no good at walking, and we don't live near each other. I'm content to have Rufus visit us.

Over the years Di often encouraged me to join her on whatever activity had attracted her interest. I didn't always follow her lead. I didn't like to disappoint her but I put work first. If no-one is waiting for the result of your labours, it's hard to stay disciplined. Luckily, Peter's devotion to his working routine spills over onto me. I don't know what I would have produced, without him. And without Di, I might never have done a number of things which I enjoyed; cooking for local feasts and celebrations, sewing the Millennium screen, setting up yoga sessions in Luggs barn and going regularly over a period to a Tai Chi class in Tiverton. That was our most recent activity together. She loved losing herself in the movements, without ever learning the exact movements or the sequence. It removed her mind from worrying about Graham. He'd been drifting away from engagement with the world and into dementia for a long time. Tai Chi, for Di, was a rest. She moved gracefully, dreamily, in her own world. For me, it was something new to learn and perfect. I spent hours at home studying the routine, practising the movements and memorising the whole thing. I knew I wasn't being very Tao about it. I was devoting my energy to learning the way rather than losing myself in it. It was a conundrum for me: how can you follow the path if you haven't learnt how to follow the path? Di and I were at opposite ends of the spectrum. I am a natural Westerner – in this at least – an Easterner. Not that she would think in those terms.

I twisted my knee while doing Tai Chi. No doubt I'd been too rigidly Western in my determination to do it right. I'm still paying for that stupidity. It's not as painful as it was but I still feel the damage which was initially acute. We were visiting New York at the time, to see Dickie in the city and then go north on the train from Grand Central to Poughkeepsie to stay with Diny in Woodstock. This was a brilliant trip. Dickie took us for lunch to his favourite restaurant, the Red Eye Grill, around the corner from his apartment on east 54th Street. He led us there, walking well with a Zimmer frame. Although he'd suffered a stroke on stage a few years before, he seemed to be in a good enough state with no signs of dementia. The waiters knew him, particularly perhaps as a New York-based Tony winning actor, and hastened to look after him. Dickie had oysters and we had a sea food platter of enormous dimensions. I type this wearing the blue-stoned signet ring on my little finger in his memory. He died in December 2019. There was an obituary in the New York Times.

This trip to the States was important, not just to see Dickie for what turned out to be the last time but to catch up with Diny and her family. I'm feeling grateful that she and I have maintained our friendship since our RS days, despite geographical distance during a great proportion of those 70 years. I have the Visitors Book open beside me with a letter she wrote in October 1998 pasted in. This was after her visit to us and to Appledore to find her 1940s home. Instead of the place she remembered, she saw "a funny, little, naked house," She enclosed an old photo of the attractive, two-storey, creeper-clad house. Memory and climbing plants can play havoc with reality. We were with her and saw the house. Yes, it was naked, but neither funny nor little. I could imagine Diny, pre-R.S., living there with the woman she called Prawn, a stand-in for her London-based mother who was never as adequate a mother as Prawn turned out to be during her entire lifetime.

Diny ends that letter with this. "*It was wonderful seeing you all. Funny that 2 people who love their privacy have created a place everyone wants to come to!*" Well, yes. The Visitors Book is packed with grateful and excited voices, poems and drawings. Many names appear again and again. Virginia sent drawings which I pasted in. I have one of those drawings unfolded from a page which I've just scanned. On that page is a note that Jennie Tierney, Finch, Amber and Lyon stayed in April 1984. Jenny's visits over the years were sometimes for the pleasure of catching up and at other times to help us by looking after the place and animals. Vicky Burge, too, stayed in the Barn with her boyfriend as caretaker, besides being with us for a midsummer party. Ruth Sidery and her chap Paul occupied the Barn at one point.

I gave up keeping a Visitors Book when we moved to Lower Willand House. If I'd kept it going, Christine's name would have appeared even more frequently. It astonishes us to see, as we comb the diaries, how often she came to stay; perhaps, once every 6 weeks. It was not a two-way arrangement in that she could only have us to stay in her London flat if she moved out of her bedroom and slept on her sofa. We only needed to let her do this for us twice. We had a number of London friends with spare bedrooms. Most often, we stayed with the Lyalls in Hampstead and Polly and Theo, off Brick Lane. In Putney there were Joan and Terry Dalley, who would put us up for a night and, on the Heath, Elizabeth after Uncle Dicky went into a home. We stayed with the Fells in Wimbledon, and that brings me to the triptych Peter

painted for William to present to Skinners Hall. William was appointed chief Skinner – I'm sorry, I forget what the official title is – and invited us to his inauguration dinner at the Hall in October 2012. It was, for us, a most unusual and glittering occasion given an extra piquancy by its origin: a chance meeting in Greece's Vikos gorge. It was also one of the rare occasions in our lives that present a challenge to Peter's wardrobe of four levels of denim shirt and jeans (newest for occasions, then shopping, work and, lowest level, gardening). We went to Moss Bros, Taunton, to hire the kit. We should have had a dress rehearsal at home before meeting the Fells in the flat of the Master (yes, that's what William was) at the top of the Hall. Jill and I were getting into our finery in one room; William and Peter in the other. There was much to-ing and fro-ing, helping each other with zips and poppers, buttons and bows. Neither Jill nor I take on, at all easily, the appearance of businessmen's wives nor even high-powered women in their own right. We were pressed for time, too. I became aware of puffing and panting coming from the room next door, and anxious voices. Then Peter appeared in the doorway with a bright red face. He was being strangled by his shirt. *I can't breathe*, he gasped. William came up with the solution. There was a gentleman's outfitter just around the corner. Peter could buy a shirt there. He did – at a brisk run.

Oil paintings exhibited locally

After this dinner, William broached the subject of the gift a retiring Master traditionally presents to the guild. Perhaps Peter could paint a picture. From this, the discussion developed. William invited us to his 65th birthday celebration at the Hall, another fun occasion and, fortunately, less glittery. Peter came up with roughs of a triptych of fur-producing animals he could paint: a sable marten, a leopard and a lynx. The final framed painting, a kind of glowing, modern-medieval, three-part icon, was presented by William on June 30th 2013.

We stayed two nights with Kath. That's seven years ago now. She might have been showing signs of dementia by then. I know she did on the last occasions when we stayed. There was the time when the red wine from an opened bottle was undrinkable. Kath thought Peter was being a fussy wine buff wanting wine from the right side of the hill. No; it had become vinegar through an age spent in an open bottle in a hot room. The last time we stayed, I took over warming up our supper in the micro-wave. I wasn't certain what was wrong with her until she went straight to the matter in hand; *I think I'm losing my mind,* she said. If part of us could stay alert and aside from ourselves, Kath would have made a wonderfully sane guide for people with dementia and those close to them. What a loss she is. This autumn, 2020, her desk was being sold at auction in aid of people suffering from dementia. Bernard let us know. Also there was a piece in the Observer with a photograph of her standing beside the desk, and another of the desk itself. I never knew what a good piece of modern furniture it was. Lorry-loads of paper always covered it.

Christine's state of forgetfulness doesn't seem like dementia at all. Yet it is just as sad. We feel we've lost her, too.

Then there's the loss of Frances Mellersh. Although not related in any way beyond being the widow of my mother's second cousin, Frances had become a close friend and a stand-in for all the people in our parents' generation no longer living. I think we were equally important to her. She had very loving step-grandchildren and their families who cared for her but at a distance. She had two very good friends of much longer standing than ourselves who saw her frequently. Like them, we were on hand and willing. The diaries are full of mentions of Frances, and the meals we had with her in favourite places like Budleigh, Beer, Exmouth and Dartmoor. Latterly there were meals I'd cooked and taken to Topsham to warm up in her oven. She was frustrated at not being able to cook for us. The last time she managed this – her ritual Twelfth Night party with her old friends, still couples at the time before the wives became widows – she roasted a goose. When we arrived, we found her friend Sheila on her knees in the kitchen with a bucket and a sponge. The goose had slipped from the roasting tin. Soon after this, Frances gave up cooking.

This week I have an appointment to see if my macular degeneration has degenerated further in the last three months. Frances will be my role model in fortitude, should I lose most of my sight as she did. She was a stalwart character. In October 2019 she was deciding it was time to die. It's a difficult thing to die if you have a strong constitution. She'd been talking around the subject for a year or so. She wanted the doctor's help. But, we said, it's against the law. They are not allowed to help. In the end, Frances realised she had to do it on her own. She gave up eating and retired to bed. Then she wouldn't drink water. It took some weeks. She was awfully cross and pushed away the hands that wanted to hold hers.

I remembered sitting beside Cousin Beryl, another of my mother's cousins, as she lay immobile and unconscious after a stroke. I talked about Christmases spent together. I talked of a letter I'd written to her in which I spelt bicycle as bickle, for ever afterwards the name for a bike. A tear rolled down Beryl's cheek. Sweet nostalgia.

From that moment, it was proved to me what people say about hearing being the last sense to go. So I talked to Frances of a particular poem she'd recited from memory on the last occasion she'd been sitting in her chair. In bed, she'd been thrashing about, angry at the attention the carer at her bedside wanted to give her. Now she went quiet. I didn't realise how significant the poem was for her until I read it aloud at her funeral. Here are the last two verses of the 12-versed poem, *He Fell Among Thieves* by Sir Henry Newbolt.

Light on the Laspur hills was broadening fast
The blood-red snow peaks chill'd to a dazzling white.
He turned and saw the golden circle at last
Cut by the Eastern height.
"O glorious Life, Who dwellest in earth and sun
I have lived, I praise and adore Thee."
A sword swept.
Over the pass the voices one by one
Faded and the hill slept.

Elenora's falcons over a cliff on Amorgos

Frances was not religious and agreed with Peter that on death it's a matter of dust to dust, with no continuing awareness. I imagine her reciting this in her mind in her last moments and being glad when the sword swept for her on the night of her 101st birthday, December 17th 2019.

Earlier last year, Di had died. This was a death that was against all expectation and acceptability. We'd been in Scotland, on a wonderful drive around places unknown to me though a few of them Peter had visited during his national service in the Navy. Scotland, like Ireland and Wales was slowly replacing Greece and New Zealand for us. While we were away Di had been diagnosed with bowel cancer. She'd been warned by her doctor that she might not have long to live. This was unacceptable news that had to be acted on fast. As ever, she had a long list of things to get done. With the help of friends we went through the list, tackling most of them head-on while others fell by the wayside. The shade of her bedside table lamp was never a finished creation. We got Graham into a care home, where he still is. She spent time in our spare room, finding it restful to be out of her own house. She loved the view from the window; a close view of the steep bank up to the summerhouse, framed by trees and bushes, a hidden landscape that appealed to her, unlike the open view from the terrace which didn't. It crossed our minds how fortuitous it was that she had been instrumental in getting us to Little Penn, four miles closer than we were at Churchstanton. I was constantly on call during these last few months. I wrote her two poems during her dying days.

I was not a bit surprised to be so affected by her death but I was surprised to be affected by the death of Peter's sister Jennifer in the summer of 2018. It amazed me, too. that I'd found myself sad at losing Bill who we'd known since he'd replaced her husband Ian in the 1960s. Ian I barely remember except as someone I had nothing in common with. But Bill made a deep impression from the start. I had never before been in frequent company with anyone so completely boring. I tried to avoid sitting next to him at Sophie's dining table. However, when he went into hospital, and then a care home, I began to warm towards him. It's beginning to look as though I'm only happy to be with someone ill or dying. Can you see my half-rueful, half-ironical smile at this? Certainly, I had never appreciated Jennifer so much as when I slept on her sofa while she died slowly of mesothelioma. She was extraordinarily courageous and patient while having terrible trouble in breathing in the oxygen being piped into her nostrils. I admired her enormously and remembered many good times we'd had together. She was even-tempered with a detached attitude to most things while enjoying a laugh at absurdities. I worried that I hadn't thanked her adequately for making my wedding dress – which no doubt was a concentrated sample of all the feelings of guilt I had about not including her enough in our lives. Maybe she didn't mind at all. Now that's a thought.

It's easy to feel guilty about things done and things not done, especially while recollecting the events over such a long period. Perhaps I should have taken more care of the children's health. I passed on to them my attitude that there's no point in consulting a doctor. If something's going to mend, it will mend in due course, without intervention. Or if it's not mendable, you must live with it. It could be a result of growing up with a mother with such an outlook that Sophie developed into someone who will find out what can be done and see that it is done at once. If Sophie had been Ben's mother – here's a weird thought – she'd have consulted a doctor about his behaviour when he was a primary school child. I didn't do this. He's spent his life unable to control his anger. It has cost him dearly. It cost him, lost him, Julia. He is now living alone on a boat in the Bay of Islands. If only Julia had been able to stay with him …

They met at a party in Taranaki, their mutual friends having thought they were ideally suited and should be introduced. A short while after the party, Julia went to see Ben working on a mural and the friendship grew into a partnership. They moved to the area where Ben had been living. This was in the Bay of Plenty. He'd changed his trailer-dinghy for a small yacht that had been carved out of a single kauri tree trunk many years previously. *Merlin* was a beautiful yacht. So many "if only's" come to mind. If only Julia hadn't developed bowel cancer (I must quickly say she's alive and well) … If only Ben had been up to caring for her, earning a living, nursing her through it … If only he hadn't sold *Merlin* and bought *Reremoana*, a yacht so large, so difficult, in such need of repair … Alternatively, if only Julia and he had still been together and able to sail to the South Seas as Ben still dreams of doing. But how could he or anyone manage that and make a living, particularly in these Covid times?

Another unanswerable question. How would it have turned out, if we had followed through with the plan that so excited us in 2010? This was to divide our year between England and New Zealand, sharing with Ben and Julia there and perhaps Sophie here?

The thing about being Ben's parents is the way it's so easy to forget the bad times when we're having the good times with him. In his Julia years we had many really good times. I'm remembering a wonderful trip on Merlin, sailing out to an offshore island. We returned the same day as the wind had got up and heavy rollers were coming in from the east. On one particularly heaving roll, Major was flung out of his half-bunk by the companionway, Instinctively, my arms shot forward to catch him, as they used to do on sudden stops in the car, to save a child in the passenger seat, pre safety belts. I recall the astonished look in his eyes as I held him, a massive bull terrier, in my arms. *What ARE you doing*, he seemed to be saying, *seizing me from my bed like this*?

Our visit to New Zealand in 2010 was so good (despite the glass-shattering explosion talked about earlier in these pages) that we became enamoured of a house on a hillside in the Bay of Plenty which could be split in half. We were saved from making a severe mistake by a sudden hike in the Exchange Rate which put it out of the question. We'd been going to sell our letting property in Wellington to pay for it. We had the plan mapped out. It might have worked in practice as well as in theory, but we now know we could never have managed the twice yearly journeys there and back at our present ages. Just the *thought* of airports and long-haul flights makes us quail. We were saved from ourselves once again.

As for explosions, they still happened, even with the benefit of Julia's patient companionship. A memorable one occurred at Lower Willand House. In the midst of a calm, domestic scene, I was stirring something at the Aga and musing about nothing at all important – as I recall, it was the idea that every generation's new born are more advanced than the one before. Without warning, I heard a bang on the table and the shriek of a chair's legs on the tiled floor. Ben flung himself out of the room, shouting something unintelligible. Our expressions were probably not unlike Major's on the boat. What *had* happened to Ben? I had a go at unpicking the puzzle over the next days, but not with Ben. He had stormed out into the night, barefoot until the gravel on the path sent him back for his boots. Julia had thrown their things into a backpack and followed him out. We heard nothing for four days. Then he contacted, wanting to come back. He and Julia had walked to Sophie's in Hemyock and after a night or two gone on to his old school friend Grant and Grant's partner Tam.

On another visit to us in England there was a horrid explosion in a car park in Cornwall. Have I described that one? The one I know I haven't written about happened the last time we saw Ben. It was in 2018. On our third day with him in the flat in School Road, Paihia, which Julia had shared and paid rent for until her cancer diagnosis, he was hoping to persuade Peter with a video that evolution was a lie. Peter, carefully and quietly, objected. Ben exploded and raged out of the flat. We heard his motor bike roar away. We'd agreed before coming out to New Zealand that we would leave at the first explosion. We hadn't imagined it would happen so soon. Without a word to each other, we bundled our things into our bag, left the flat and got into the van we'd hired. We were about to drive away when Ben returned. We didn't wait. We weren't going to talk and return to the years-long pattern of forgiveness and continuation. We felt too old for that. I can see Ben's expression as we drove away. Disbelief and distress, all in one. We drove to the next large town where we went into a travel agent and changed our flight. Next day we were on the plane from Auckland to Hong Kong. During the three-hour wait in the transit lounge I rang Ben. He'd driven to the nearest camp site, thinking he'd find us there. It was a tremendous shock for him to learn we had left. Such a dramatic change in our response to his behaviour might have made a lasting difference, if he had greater command of his emotions.

We haven't seen Ben since, though he phones us regularly and we phone him. He is living on *Reremoana* in the Bay of Islands, slowly making her seaworthy. Lonely and eccentric? Turn this picture around and you see a contented yacht-owner, moored like other such solitary yacht-owners in a delightful setting, dreaming of sailing to the South Seas. Ben also has the amazing ability to paint *trompe d'oeil* murals on walls of restaurants and hotels. During our latest phone conversation, he sounded cheerful. He said he no longer gets so angry when things go wrong. He's finished the huge mural he was doing of Waitangi. He accepted, without demur, that we won't be able to send such generous injections of cash any longer. Perhaps, like a teenager growing out of spots, he's growing out of the disorder I described earlier. How marvellous that would be.

As for Sophie, all is well. Nick appeared on the scene when we were at Lower Willand House. I can see him sitting on the sofa wearing his beanie. He got used to us quite fast, and we to him. When Sophie announced that they were going to get married and she wanted a white wedding with all the works, we were pleased – but with reservations. All the works? We'd done a very special wedding for her, in Papingo. Another white wedding? Really? Splashing out on something quite so expensive went against our frugal, wartime upbringing. In the end, we got caught up in the excitement of the occasion. It was a glorious day and there are lots of professional wedding photographs to prove it.

The next really happy occasion was our holiday with Sophie and Nick, Mark and Rio, Olivia and Bertie in Cefallonia. Sophie arranged to rent a villa in Lourdas and invited us to join them. We found a room that suited us right behind the beach. It was all very pleasant and easy. There were loungers on the beach and many tavernas and restaurants for evening meals. It was a million miles from the Greece we used to know and love, but still very enjoyable, most especially as we were having time with the family. Also, there was an added bonus. By now we had picked up our friendship with Yannis and Vaso Angelopoulos, who we'd first met in Athens in 1962. During that first year in Greece, we'd spent many weekend days together in the countryside and seaside around Athens. Now in the summer of 2017 Yannis and Vaso had come to see us in Cefallonia. Yannis took a video of Peter painting a little hut in an allotment near our apartment. On its gate hung a notice which said in Greek that this was the garden of the grandfather. I had a brainwave in the night. This would be the title of the book we were thinking about; a collection of the best of the photographs we took in our first ten years in Greece. This – as I've written earlier – came out in 2018. I made a slide show presentation and put together a talk we could give to launch the book. The first talk took place at the Blackdown Healthy Living Centre in Hemyock. I nearly had a total breakdown when I couldn't connect up my laptop to the centre's projector and screen, despite having succeeded at a trial. The centre's manager who'd been busy elsewhere appeared at the last minute and rescued me from utter despair. We had a launch at Brendon Books, Taunton; one at the Anglo-Greek Society in Bristol; one at Tony Anderson's lecture club *Ebeneezer* in a hall called the Seed Factory in Langford, Somerset, all of these being well-enough attended with satisfactory book sales. But the best of all the launches took place in Athens, thanks to the British Ambassador – and that was thanks to an introduction by William Fell. The presentation took place in the Katakouzenas family apartment, opposite the Zappeion. It had seen many famous people gather there in the 20th century, Freud among them. Bernadine Demos came to see us perform and took us back to their house in Kapandriti, far to the north of Athens for the night before we flew home. A fantastic trip, just one of very many over the years.

Before I run out of pages, I want to simply list some magical times in our lives:

Taking teenaged Mark and Olivia to Paris one year, to Venice another

Watching cousin Dickie act, at Stratford, at the Old Vic, in Bath and Taunton, and in the TV series my mother loved, "*The Brothers*"

Meeting Ben in Paihia outside the library where he was holding an exhibition

Going to galleries in London, Amsterdam, Venice, Italy and museums in Athens

A new departure for Peter was a series of paintings focusing on the natural life of human beings in West Country coastal towns during the off-season

Listening to live classical music, particularly work by Schubert, Mozart, Beethoven, Tchaikovsky

Seeing and hearing Rigoletto performed by Welsh National Opera in Plymouth

Family Christmases, nowadays given by Sophie

The sea crashing on the cliffs at Hartland Quay, Devon, and lapping at night in Port Isaac harbour, Cornwall

The thrush singing in May from its perch on the dead elm at the bottom of our garden

Thunder at the moment lightning flashes across the night sky

Seeing the flamingos in the Camargue and on Lake Naivasha, Kenya

Following a kiwi on Stewart Island, New Zealand

Watching fox cub and young badger greet each other in our wood

Dolphins in the Aegean; groupers underwater; the golden eagle swooping over our heads on the slopes of Astraka; elephants lumbering past the terrace of a Kenyan hotel …

Choosing a few moments like these shows even more clearly the impossibility of catching something so full and complex as a lifetime. This book is our attempt in words and pictures to capture a flavour of ours. It's a particular and personal account which is representative, too, of the universal human tasks of leading a life, from childhood, through adulthood to old age. How anyone else navigates their journey is always of interest to me, however ordinary or extraordinary their life. If there is more than one reader of this, I hope it's of interest to them, too. I end with the lines I wrote in response to Peter's picture of our life together which he painted for our diamond wedding anniversary and which is reproduced on the cover of this book.

Life. Like. Love.
Is it only in English they link,
These four-letter words that mean so much?
You paint. I write. We met.
McCanns in Fetter Lane.our common ground.
Who's he? Who's she?
Could it be we'd found our mate?
Do we like, do we love – for life?
I think so, I said.
(I still need time to think)
You're painting now our life
In tiny oils, sixty years of it.
Can I write in sixty words
A picture of it
Making our life
A single illuminated manuscript?
I would need to choose each word with utmost care
Make sure each glowed in jewelled colours, threaded
One behind the other,
diamond-beaded,
In a chain of days, linking our lives together.

Rain, sun, sand, sea, rock.
A blue door in a white wall.
Potatoes sizzling in a Sifnos pot
Over a driftwood fire.
Long afternoons.
Brown bodies clad in the sea's silken coat,
Holding ready a harpoon gun.
Fish weave around us, rainbow wrasse.
Cave-deep groupers with spaniel eyes
Watch you glide close. Then
A jack-knife dive and, later, soup.
(Sixty words and I've only just begun).

Hunter and prey. Food from sea to table
Or grilled on a beach.
Journeys by van. By boat. By plane and car.
Africa, America, Bermuda
London, Greece and Devon.
Books and art. We followed our stars.
Success came to each with ease.
Failure and sadness too. You were so good
Never to mind I was unable
To produce our own-created life.
Just books. And homes and family,
Together we created the places
Where we could create.
Endless ideas and inspiration.
And crisis, too. We combined
The best of you and the best of me
With the worst of you and the worst of me.
We did not break. We healed and carried on
With sheep and cows and hens and dogs
Amassed, then shed. A natural rhythm,
Learning how to live and like and love
Through sixty years of life, pictured now
In the only way we can –
Your painted timeline, my sixty lines.
Here are the years we've spent
Liking. Loving. Living

Devon, December 2020

In appreciation of our family and all the friends we've made over the years with particular thanks to Jennie Tierney and Alex Hill who read the typescript with eagle eyes. We also want to thank Short Run Press, especially Paul Luffman, for their care and attention in translating Peter's design into the production of this book.

BIOGRAPHIES

Peter Barrett, born in India in 1935, was educated at Dulwich College, London. He attended St. Martins, Chelsea and Camberwell Art Schools on day release and for evening classes while working in design groups and advertising agencies in London, later in Canada and Athens. While living on the islands of Sifnos and Amorgos, he was able to return to painting. He had four one-man exhibitions of abstract paintings at the Drian Galleries, London. A couple of paintings, large abstracts in oils, were accepted for the Royal Academy Summer Show.

From 1970 onwards he developed his talent for wildlife illustrations in watercolours. His many clients included Mitchell Beazley, Reader's Digest, the Sunday Times and the Observer. He has illustrated books by David Attenborough, Desmond Morris, Gerald Durrell and James Herriot among others – altogether over 40 books on wildlife as well as children's books. His most recent major work of illustration was *Evolution* with text by Douglas Palmer, published by Mitchell Beazley, the Natural History Museum and the University of California Press. He now devotes his time to painting wildlife subjects of his own choosing in oils and watercolours. His work has been exhibited in many galleries in London, Devon, Greece and USA.

Susan Barrett (nee Withington) was born in 1938 in Plymouth, Devon, and educated at The Royal School, Bath. Her early career was spent as a copywriter in various London advertising agencies. Her first novel was published by Michael Joseph in 1969. Film rights were sold and renewed over several years. She went on to write six more novels which were published with mainstream publishers in hardback and paperback in UK and USA. She provided the text for several natural history and children's books illustrated by Peter. Her one and only play for television was produced and shown on London Weekend Television in 1978.

In the 1990s Susan trained in humanistic counselling and gestalt psychotherapy and practised as a counsellor for many years. She continues to write fiction and nonfiction. Her latest novels, *Making a Difference, White Lies, A Home from Home* and *Elfrida Next Door* are available on Amazon.

Peter and Susan married in 1960. *So Far, So Good* is the third in an unintended trilogy of memoirs. The first was *Travels with a Wildlife Artist, the Living Landscape of Greece*, commissioned and published by Harrap Columbus, and Gerstenberg in Germany in 1986. This was followed in 2018 by *The Garden of the Grandfather, Life in Greece in the 1960s*. The present book is a covid-delayed celebration of their diamond wedding anniversary, a uniquely personal story that reflects universal themes.